THE MODERN LIBRARY

OF THE WORLD'S BEST BOOKS

I can get it for you wholesale

The publishers will be pleased to send, upon request, an illustrated folder setting forth the purpose and scope of THE MODERN LIBRARY, *and listing each volume in the series. Every reader of books will find titles he has been looking for, handsomely printed, in definitive editions, and at an unusually low price.*

I
can get
it
for you
wholesale

Jerome Weidman

THE MODERN LIBRARY *New York*

RANDOM HOUSE *is the Publisher of* THE MODERN LIBRARY
BENNETT CERF · DONALD S. KLOPFER
Manufactured in the United States of America by H. Wolff

I can get it for you wholesale

I

About nine-thirty a girl came puffing up Lexington and turned into Twenty-Fifth. I'd never seen her before, but I knew she belonged. She wasn't wearing a hat and she was built like a battleship in the rear. Somehow all those radicals look alike. When she came to the stoop she stopped and turned and ran up the stairs. A couple of minutes later the light went on in the top floor window.

I smiled to myself and lit another cigarette. I shifted the lamppost into a more comfortable position between my shoulder blades and set a ten-minute maximum.

I was off by almost eight minutes. Before I even had the cigarette going good, I saw him coming up Lexington. If he would have been moving slowly, I might have had some doubts. But when I saw he was hurrying, I knew I was right.

I crossed the gutter slowly, to meet him, and just as he started to turn the corner, we came face to face.

"Hello, there, Tootsie," I said, grinning at him.

He jumped back a little, and stared at me with his mouth open. It didn't make him look any better.

"Bogen!"

I bowed from the waist, like an actor.

"Tootsie Maltz, I presume?"

His mouth closed slowly, and he smiled a little.

"What the hell are *you* doing around here?"

"I'll bet I don't have to ask what *you're* doing," I said and winked.

"Why, what do you mean?" he said.

He drew himself up and tried to look outraged.

"It's all right, Tootsie," I said. "You can let your hair down in front of me."

"I don't know what you're talking about, Bogen," he said sharply. He was still trying to look like he was a count or a duke and he'd just been accused of cheating at cards. Which

3

was pretty funny. He was short and fat and had an innocent-looking moon-shaped face. On top of that he wasn't wearing a hat or a coat; he needed a haircut and had been needing it for a couple of weeks already; and his shirt looked like it had seen the laundry last about the time he stopped wearing knee pants. It was all I could do to keep myself from laughing in his face.

"Come on there, Tootsie," I said. "Don't give me any of that bull, will you?"

"Listen, Bogen," he said. "I don't know what you're talking about."

Oh, no? Well, I didn't want to get him sore, but I had to let him know I wasn't a rummy either.

"So you don't know what I'm talking about, eh?" I put my hand on his arm. "This isn't Wednesday, is it? And it wouldn't happen that Wednesday is an off night for the Club, and nobody shows up, would it? Which wouldn't mean that the coast was clear for a little fancy yentzing, would it? And from what you know about me, you'd say my memory was so crummy that I didn't remember any of this, just because I've been away for a while, wouldn't you?"

He looked up at me from under his thick eyebrows like a kid that's being bawled out. His face melted into a sort of half-grin.

"Aah, well," he said, shaking his head.

"And all of a sudden I'm getting blind," I said, "and I didn't just see a dame with a can like an elephant go up the stoop to the Club, not more than five minutes ago."

By this time we were both smiling at each other.

"Same old Harry," he said.

I slapped him on the shoulder.

"You mean same old Tootsie," I said.

"All right, then, Mr. Wise Guy," he said. The grin on his face was a mile wide. "If you're so smart, and you know where I'm headed for, then what's the idea holding me up?"

"I've got something important to tell you," I said.

"Don't kid me, Bogen, will you? What's more important than cuzzy?"

"I'll give you one guess," I said.

That stopped him.

"Aah, I don't know, Bogen," he said, looking past me toward the stoop. "You know how those things are."

"Sure I know," I said. "But what the hell, in a time like this?"

He scratched his head and looked from me to the stoop and back again.

"I don't know," he said slowly.

I felt so good that I wanted to tell him to go ahead and meet me later. I knew how he felt, and how it can drive everything else out of your mind. But I couldn't afford to let him have his way in anything, even a small thing. Right from the start I had to impress on him who was boss.

"There's jack in this, Tootsie," I said, "heavy jack."

He stood there, undecided, chewing his lip.

I put my hand on his shoulder.

"Come on," I said, "put it on ice for a while. It'll keep."

He looked at me, smiling a little, and sighed.

"I don't know, Bogen," he said, "I don't know what it is you've got."

"You won't be sorry," I said. I took his arm and steered him toward Lexington Avenue. "And anyway," I added, "she didn't look so hot from the back."

"Yeah?" he said. "That's what *you* know!"

But he turned away!

From then on I knew I was home. When you can talk a guy out of *that,* then you know you're good.

At Lexington we turned right and started to walk uptown. I took out my pack of cigarettes and offered it to him. He took one. I knew he would. Those radicals are the biggest chiselers in the world. We walked and smoked in silence for a while. I knew he was burning up to know what it was all about, but I let him wait. I figured it would do him good.

"Well, what's up, Bogen?"

I looked at the lamppost we were passing. Twenty-Eighth Street. That meant that three blocks was his limit. Which wasn't bad. Most people couldn't have kept quiet that long.

"Plenty," I said, inspecting the ash on my cigarette closely, like it was the first time I'd ever seen anything like it.

"Ah, gee whiz, Bogen, why don't you cut it out?"

"What's all the hurry?"

"You're asking me?" he said. "You were the guy that was in a hurry. Five minutes ago you were in such a hurry that you wouldn't even let me take time out to get boffed. And now you ask what's my hurry."

I laughed and put my hand on his shoulder.

"Okay, Tootsie," I said, "come on."

"Well, aren't you going to tell me?"

He was primed all right.

"In a little while," I said. "Let's get something to eat first."

I didn't expect any objections to that and I didn't get any.

"Where'll it be?" I asked.

"I don't know," he said, then stopped and jerked his thumb over his shoulder. "Stewarts is back this way, on Twenty-Third. We're going in the wrong direction."

I took his arm and pulled him along with me.

"Oh, no we're not," I said. "We're going in the right direction. When you eat with me you don't eat in cafeterias."

He shrugged.

"It's okay with me."

As though I didn't know that.

"And you can paste this into your hat right now, Tootsie," I said. "As long as you string along with me, your cafeteria days are over."

He didn't say anything.

"That is," I added, looking at him out of the corner of my eye, "unless you're too busy with the revolution to find time for some easy dough."

He looked at me and grinned.

"The revolution can wait," he said.

Could I pick them?

"All right, then," I said. "Now we eat."

At Thirty-Fourth we turned left. I knew a little Hungarian place between Lexington and Fourth where they had regular tablecloths and a couple of waiters. For Tootsie that would be good enough. After cafeterias this would look like the real big time to him.

I waited until he went through the chopped liver and the soup and the goulash. I wasn't particularly hungry myself, but I can always eat. From the way Tootsie dug in I couldn't make up my mind which he needed most, the meal or a haircut. I was willing to buy him the meal, but if I had anything to say about it, he wouldn't take a haircut for at least another month. He suited me perfectly the way he was, dirty, ragged, unshaved. That was the way I needed him. And that was the way he'd stay. Not that he was such an odd-looking specimen. You can pick dozens like him off Seventh Avenue any day in the week, except Sunday, with your eyes closed. But of all those you can find, show me one that had his point of view. The rest of them are just a bunch of dopes who would consider it an honor and a pleasure to die for dear old Stalin. The only person Tootsie would ever die for is Tootsie Maltz, and even then he'd find a way to wiggle out of it. Which showed that he wasn't so dumb.

After a while he pulled his mush away from the plate and sighed.

"How was it?" I asked.

He rolled his eyes and smacked his lips.

"Boy!" he said.

"I guess you wouldn't have much objection to eating like that every day, would you?"

"What do *you* think?" he said.

He'd probably drop dead if I told him.

"Well, maybe I can arrange it for you," I said.

"Yeah? How?"

"Well, if you're a good little boy, and you pay close attention to what Papa says, and you don't get snotty, and you answer all questions correctly the first time, and you don't interrupt—"

"So? So?"

"So listen."

I took a fresh pack of cigarettes from my pocket, ripped the top off, and put them on the table in front of him.

"Help yourself," I said, pointing to them. "Every time you open your yap to say something, take a cigarette instead. Don't interrupt me. Just listen and answer when you're asked. The rest of the time, smoke."

"Okay," he said with a grin and reached for one. I lit one myself and settled back to look at him.

"You working now?" I asked finally.

"No," he said, then: "Say, you're not going to all this trouble just to offer me a job, are you? Because if—"

"Smoke," I said.

"My mistake," he said, laughing, and drew on his cigarette.

"Ever been around Seventh Avenue? The garment district?"

"Once in a while."

"You never worked there?"

"Nope."

"That means you don't know much about it, doesn't it?" He nodded.

"All right, then, Tootsie," I said. "Hold on to your hat. Besides a good meal, you're going to get a little education to-night. And personally, I don't think it'll hurt you. Just remember to keep your ears open."

He lit a fresh cigarette. He should worry. They were free.

"Now, then, Tootsie, we'll get down to facts and figures. I don't know how strong you are between the ears," I said, "but even if you were a real mental heavyweight, I wouldn't bother you with too much detail. You know how it is, Tootsie. I want you to save your energy. You probably need a lot of it for those wrestling matches of yours with those red elephants."

He started to open his mouth, but I held up my hand for silence. He grinned and I blew smoke in his eyes. We both laughed.

"All right, then," I said. "On those few square blocks between Thirty-Fourth Street and Times Square on Seventh Avenue, there are over six thousand firms that manufacture dresses. *Exactly* how many there are doesn't matter. Just take my word for it that it runs into the thousands. All right. Now, every one of these firms employs at least one shipping clerk. You know what a shipping clerk is, Tootsie?"

He shook his head and waved the cigarette to show me why he wasn't talking. He was all right. He was catching on.

"Maybe I better explain it to you," I said. "After all, a gentleman of leisure like you, you know, how would you ever know what a shipping clerk is? See what I mean? Well, Tootsie, a shipping clerk is a kind of two-legged animal, without a hell of a lot of brains, that never sleeps and hardly ever eats. It's always on the go, chasing over to the contractor with a bundle of cut work, trying to make the post office with a special before the parcel-post division closes, running from one piece-goods house to another to match a swatch that some crazy buyer has brought in, or lugging half the sample line to some buying office on Thirty-First Street so some dizzy broad that must have been a snappy number about the time Dewey sailed into Manila Bay can make one more selection before her train leaves for Cleveland or Chicago or God alone knows where. The reason I know all this, Tootsie, my boy, is that at one time I was just about the world's champion shipping clerk. Anybody who could hold down a job with Toney Frocks, Inc., the joint I worked for, under the heel that ran it, a certain gent by the name of Schmul, would have to be the world's champ. If you don't think that makes me an authority, just go out on Seventh Avenue some day and ask. In the meantime, though, just take my word for it. By the way, Tootsie," I added, "if this is beginning to bore you, just say the word. I'm only mentioning these things to keep the record straight."

He nodded, still grinning.

"So anyway," I said, "we've gotten to the point where every firm on Seventh Avenue has at least one shipping clerk. A lot of them have more than one. But that doesn't matter. The only thing to remember is that no matter how dumb a guy is, he can still see that there must be thousands of shipping clerks on Seventh Avenue. *You* see it, don't you?"

Again he nodded. It doesn't take me long to get them hypnotized.

"Now, it happens, Tootsie, that the average salary for a shipping clerk is fifteen bucks a week. They even paid *me* that." His grin widened a little. "Here's where I want you to strain yourself a little, Tootsie. Do this bit of mental arithmetic with me. Fifteen times several thousand, I don't know how many exactly, but several thousand, fifteen times that— gives you what?"

He opened his mouth, but I put up my hand.

"Right," I said. "Right. All those thousands of dollars are paid out every week on Seventh Avenue to shipping clerks."

I leaned back in my chair and grinned at him.

"Now, of course, Tootsie, I don't know how many steam yachts and butlers they had in *your* family." The grin returned to his face. "But me, Tootsie, I'm Grade A presidential timber. I was born on Goereck Street and my old man never made more than fifteen bucks a week in his life, except during the War, when he made twenty, which was no break for me, because all it did was raise the standard of living in the family so damn high that when the old man dropped back to fifteen bucks a week I had to go out and peddle papers after school so the old lady shouldn't have to sell her ermine wraps."

I lit a cigarette and blew smoke in his eyes until he blinked.

"Ever since then, Tootsie, I've hated people who make fifteen bucks a week. Which means that I don't like shipping clerks, see? But if my reasons don't suit you, then, just to make you feel better, Tootsie, let's say I don't like the way they part their hair, or that most of them come from the Bronx, or anything you want. Anyway, I don't like them. And it makes me twice as sore to think that they're getting all that money every week. So what have I done? I've figured out a way to turn most of that money into my pockets. And, at the same time"—I dropped my voice a shade to make sure he'd understand this was for his benefit—"into the pockets of my partner, whoever he may be."

He perked up a little at that. My theory is that a shot in the arm every once in a while keeps the patient interested. I guess I should have studied medicine. I had the right bedside manner.

"Now, I know what you're going to ask," I said. "You're going to ask 'How?' And that's just what I'm going to tell you."

I lit another cigarette and leaned across the table toward him. As I talked, his own cigarette went dead, and his mouth opened. Once or twice he started to say something, but I shut him up quick. Finally he couldn't hold it any longer. It popped right out of him.

"But Bogen, where do *I* come in?"

Did you ever walk along the street, thinking of nothing in particular and feeling pretty good, when smacko, you stub your toe or you bunk into somebody, and it brings you up cold, right out of that pleasant state of mind? That's how I felt right then. Here I'd been talking away, sailing through the thing like a dose of salts, with him sitting across the table from me, smoking and nodding his head and looking intelligent. Then, when I hit the climax, he comes out with that crack. Maybe I'd given him credit for more brains than he had. I guess being a radical does things to a person. It had certainly done things to Tootsie Maltz. He was a lot quicker on the uptake when I first knew him.

"What do you mean, where do you come in?"

"Just that," he said, looking like he'd just come out of a table. *"This* is where you come in."

"Right here, you dumb baloney," I said, smacking the table. *"This* is where you come in."

He looked at me and scratched his head. Well, I guess there was nothing for me to do but roll up my sleeves and sail in.

"Listen, Tootsie," I said, trying to keep my voice even and low. "Did you ever take a good look at yourself in the mirror?"

"What the hell is that got to do with it?"

"Nothing," I said, "except that if you ever did, and you saw what a homely puss you had, you'd realize that your chances of winning beauty contests were pretty slim."

"So what? I still don't get it."

"Then listen for a change, and you will," I said. "If you could only see what you look like, you'd realize that I didn't need you for a front. Unless I was going into the circus business and was trying to get a menagerie together," I added. If anybody would've talked to me like that, I'd've rapped him in the puss. But he just sat and listened. "But I'm not getting together a menagerie. I'm trying to make some dough, and if I come to you, you can be pretty sure I need you for a special reason. Understand?"

He shook his head.

"I *still* don't get it," he said.

Can you imagine anybody as dumb as all that?

I hitched my chair a little closer to the table and leaned forward on it with my elbows, putting my face as close to him as I could get it.

"Listen, dope," I said.

2

The thing was set for eight-thirty. Which meant that it probably wouldn't start before nine. But I was there at eight. I wanted to give everything a last once-over. Not that I was worried about there being a hitch or anything like that. It was just that I had nothing else to do. For the time being my end was clear. And anyway, I got a kick out of it. My brains had thought the thing out. My dough was paying for it. It gave me a feeling of power to stand there and watch and see the whole thing take shape under my nose.

Across the front of the building, right over the doorway and under the sign that spelled out Pythian Temple in electric lights, was the big sheet of oilcloth lettered in red and black:

8:30!   MASS MEETING TO-NIGHT!   8:30!
SHIPPING CLERKS
OF THE GARMENT DISTRICT
MATTERS OF IMPORTANCE TO YOU
WILL BE DISCUSSED
ADMISSION FREE
8:30 TO-NIGHT

That sign had set me back five bucks. At first I couldn't make up my mind whether it was necessary. The circulars that Tootsie had been distributing for over a week had been clear enough. They had Pythian Temple spread all over them. It would take an awfully dumb guy not to be able to find it if he wanted to get there. But you don't know how dumb shipping clerks can be. With those rummies you couldn't be too careful. So it would cost me an extra five bucks, so what? After all the dough I'd spent already, it would be stupid to take a chance on spoiling the whole thing because of a little thing like that. So I ordered the sign. It looked good, anyway. It gave the thing a final, business-like touch. Let those mockies see that this thing was being run by people who meant business.

I looked at my watch. A quarter after eight. And nobody in sight. I was beginning to feel nervous. Suppose nobody showed up? Or suppose only a few of them came? Which would be just as bad. What then? I shook off the feeling of worry and lit a cigarette. What was I getting excited about? It was still early. And anyway, only small-time heels worried before anything happened.

I crossed the gutter and leaned against the doorway of a building that faced the entrance of the Temple. It certainly was a swell sight. It ought to be. It had cost me plenty. How much? Well, let's see. First there was the rent for the hall. Fifty bucks. Then five for the sign made it fifty-five. And ten, fifteen, twenty, twenty-three for mimeographing circulars made it—fifty-five plus twenty-three—made it seventy-eight. Then add all the extras, feeding Tootsie and a couple of other things, and it came pretty close to a hundred. Whew!

That was a lot of money in any man's country, especially when you're drawing on your capital. At that rate I wouldn't be able to hold out for very long.

All right, then, I'd just have to make it short and sweet. The faster you work, the better chance you have of succeeding. It doesn't give those that might have a brain or two a chance to start figuring things out.

Two or three fellows turned the corner and began to drift up the block. I noticed them immediately. You can tell a shipping clerk a mile away. Three days after pay day every one of them quits eating lunches and borrows carfare. But that doesn't stop them from trying to dress like the Meadowbrook polo crowd. Every nickel they can beg or borrow is on their backs.

The ones coming up the block toward me had one other distinguishing characteristic, besides the regulation shipping clerk's uniform of suede shoes, peg-top pants in a loud check, and Tyrol hat. They walked slowly, as though they were ashamed of what they were doing.

When they came near the Temple they stopped. One of them pointed to the oilcloth sign.

"This must be it," he said. "Look at the sign there."

I guess that sign wasn't such a bad investment after all.

"Yeah, I guess so," another one said.

Just a couple of bright boys.

"Let's go in."

They went inside and I breathed easier. I knew it would work. It had to. I had planned everything too carefully. At first I wanted to rent a hall up in the Bronx, because that's where most of them live anyway. But then I figured I'd be losing out both ways. First of all, I'd be losing all those that lived in Brooklyn and down on the East Side or any other place but the Bronx. And then the next thing was that if I called the meeting in the Bronx, they'd have a chance to go home and eat first. Once they had a chance to eat and wash up and get comfortable, maybe they wouldn't feel so hot about the idea of getting dressed and going to a meeting. But like this, by hiring a hall right here in Manhattan, not far from the garment district, those that wanted to come would have to stay downtown.

And judging from the way they began to arrive now, it looked like there were plenty of those that wanted to come.

Those circulars Tootsie had been distributing all over Seventh Avenue were honeys. I'd written them myself. Me and Lenin. Shipping clerks attention! Step-children of the garment industry! Come out and fight for your rights! Organize against your exploiters! No more seventy-hour weeks for fifteen dollars! Demand higher wages and fewer hours! And get it, too! Come to the mass meeting at Pythian Temple and learn how!

And a lot more of the same. But that's enough to give you the general idea. I could rattle it off for you by the hour, but how do I know you've got a strong stomach? My insides aren't exactly what you'd call delicate, but two and a half minutes of that baloney is enough to make me puke.

By now they were coming down the block in droves. I hadn't realized myself that they might be as interested as all this. Maybe conditions were even worse for them than I'd thought? After all, I'd been away from the Avenue for nearly a year. Watching them pour into the Temple, I got a feeling of the power that was there, if they only knew how to use it. Well, here was one guy who knew what that power was, and who knew how to use it, too.

My watch said twenty to nine. Time to start. As I looked up I saw Tootsie climbing the steps into the Temple with a dame on either side of him. I couldn't see their faces, but I recognized the one on his right immediately. Or rather, I recognized her can. My bet was that there were only half a dozen like it in captivity. It was big enough to play a game of two-handed pinochle on. Once you see something with those dimensions, you don't forget it. It began to look like this Tootsie wasn't such a dope after all. Near the top of my list of things to do, I jotted down a note to look into the situation as soon as I had a little time.

The crowd in the street had thinned out. I crossed the gutter and entered with the stragglers. The large auditorium was just off a small foyer. I went in and took a seat in the rear. It was the only place where you could get a seat. The rest of the room was jammed. At the front, on a small raised platform, sat Tootsie and the two dames, their heads bent together, reading something spread on the table in front of them. I looked around the room.

The manager had told me there were six hundred seats in the place. But there were more than six hundred shipping clerks there already and the door kept opening and closing as new ones arrived. They were doubling up on the chairs, and plenty of them were standing. I tried to count them, but it was too much of a job. I made a rough estimate. Close to a thousand. Not bad.

The air was heavy with smoke and there was a steady hum of low voices. But there was no shouting or pushing or laughing. And it wasn't only that they were quiet because they seemed to be afraid of something. It was just that they'd never before been brought together in a mob where they could take a good look at themselves. Alone, in their shipping rooms, wearing their fancy clothes, they knew they were heels, but they could still feel superior. But here, jammed up together in a crowd, they could look at themselves multiplied by a thousand. It was a little too much shipping clerk. Even for me. I felt slightly embarrassed myself.

Suddenly Tootsie stood up and rapped on the table with a ruler. The noise stopped immediately, as though it had been coming from another room and a heavy door had been closed suddenly to shut it out.

"Fellows," he said, looking around the room with a quiet smile, "before we go into the serious business of the evening, I want to congratulate you on your showing. I don't mind admitting that we didn't expect such a big turnout. If we had, we would have arranged for a larger place." The hell we would! "But we'll come to the point without wasting time and settle our business quickly. So please bear with us."

He was better than I expected. There was something about his fat face and long hair and serious-sounding voice that made him look the part. I couldn't have done better myself.

"I guess it's no secret to you," he said, "why we've assembled here to-night. Every one of you has, at some time during the last week, read one of the circulars that we have been distributing. Or, if you haven't read it, you've been told about it. And what we have said on those circulars has interested you. Otherwise, you wouldn't be here."

One of the pots that sat at the table on the platform was writing away with a pencil, her head bent down over her work. The other one was just sitting there, listening. That was a good idea of Tootsie's, having the dames along. It made the thing seem real. I'd noticed that a long time ago. A secretary adds importance to whatever you're doing, no matter how stupid it may be.

"I don't think I'm overstating the case," Tootsie said, "when I say that the shipping clerks of Seventh Avenue are probably the hardest-worked and poorest-paid class of workers in the country. I know, because I was a shipping clerk myself once." Oh yes, he was! "And when the season rushes come along, I'd say they were the poorest-paid workers in the whole world. Now, there's no reason for that. There's nothing about the dress business that makes it impossible for shipping clerks to make a decent living wage. The operators and finishers and pressers have succeeded in getting minimum-wage and maximum-hour concessions from the employers' groups. When that five-o'clock bell rings, those factory workers are on their way home. And when their envelopes come around on Wednesday, there's something more in it than just plain cigarette money. But when the five-o'clock bell rings, where are the shipping clerks? They're still chasing all over the damn city with bundles, or sweating blood wrapping packages, or doing the thousand and one jobs the shipping clerk is called on to do. And what does he get for it? I'll bet if I called for a show of hands of all those here who were making over fifteen dollars a week, there wouldn't be an even dozen. But I'll bet, too, that if I called for all those who averaged more than sixty or seventy hours a week, there isn't a man here who wouldn't put up his hand."

From the quiet way they sat and took it in, you'd think they were listening to a choice bawling out from the boss. It was a good speech. I've never written a bad one yet.

"Why should there be such a great difference between a shipping clerk and an operator? Why should the shipping clerks be the step-children of the garment industry?" He paused. "There's only one answer." He leaned far across the table and pointed at the middle of the crowd. "Because the shipping clerks aren't organized!"

He stopped and straightened up. The crowd began to move restlessly.

"Oh, I know what you're thinking," Tootsie said, holding up his hand like a traffic cop. "The minute I use the word organize, you right away begin to think of unions. And the minute you think of unions, you think of a bunch of dumb greasers, like finishers and operators and pressers. You guys are all Americans! You don't want to have anything to do with unions! Why, that stuff is only for grease balls!" He leaned across the little table and leered at them. And when a guy with a squash like Tootsie Maltz's leers at you, it's something to see. I'd like to have some statistics on how many of those dopes woke up for months afterward from dreams of that puss. "Well, clever boys, those grease balls have thirty-five- and forty-hour weeks, and they've got minimum-wage scales that make your maximums look sick."

He straightened up and slapped the table. He was even getting the gestures right. And I'd only rehearsed him a couple of times. Maybe I could forget about being an actor as well as about being a doctor. It looked like I had a good future as a director.

"But don't worry. I'm not here to talk you guys into a union or anything like that. I'm here for just one purpose. The bosses have you guys where they want you." He shot out his arm and grabbed a fistful of air. "They've got a strangle hold on you. And I'm here to show you guys how to break it."

"Yeah? How?"

Louis the wise guy. There's one in every crowd. But

they're nothing to worry about. You just have to provide for them in advance. And I had.

"Listen, and I'll tell you," Tootsie said. "Most of you are so groggy from working seventy hours a week and more, that you don't even realize how important a part of garment industry you are. The bosses themselves don't know how important you are. They're so used to having you around at fifteen bucks a week that they take you for granted. But if all of a sudden the whole bunch of you were to disappear, they'd realize quick enough how important you are. You guys are the lifeblood of Seventh Avenue. You're the main artery. You're the grease that keeps the works from squeaking, the gasoline that keeps the motor running, or whatever the hell you want to call yourselves. Just take that away for a while, and see what happens. I know what you're going to say. They can hire shipping clerks overnight. They can replace the whole bunch of you in twenty-four hours. Sure they can! But if something was to prevent them, if after you guys all disappeared they *couldn't* replace you, then they'd realize how important you were, wouldn't they?"

Even the wise guy was quiet now. They were all listening. Tootsie leered at them again. I should have warned him against overdoing it. We powers behind the throne have to think of everything!

"If the whole bunch of you walked out some day, and they couldn't get anybody to replace you, they'd listen to reason then, wouldn't they? They wouldn't be so snotty about putting a few more dollars into those pay envelopes and cutting down those seventy-hour weeks, would they?"

He stood back and grinned at them for a moment. Then, quickly, his face became serious again.

"And you want to know how?" he said quietly.

No answer.

I was a little surprised myself at how quiet they were. Shipping clerks are pretty well used to listening. But I didn't expect such close attention. They didn't move. They just sat there, under that haze of smoke, staring up at him.

"Did — you — guys — ever — hear — the — word —

strike?" he said, spacing the words out slowly, the way I'd taught him, like he was driving nails. "Strike!"

That broke the spell. The chairs began to creak as they moved about in their seats and the hum of voices began to rise. He bent down and went into a huddle with the two dames. The rest of them buzzed away, talking excitedly to each other, lighting cigarettes, arguing. I'd told him to let them have two or three minutes of this. When the time was up he rapped for order.

"Remember," he said in loud, clear tones, "I'm not talking union to you guys. Later on, if you want a union, you can have one. It's none of my business. Right now, the only thing that interests us is that one word—*strike!* Nothing else matters. The future can take care of itself. All we're organizing now is something that'll knock their eyes out with a single blow. We're going to paralyze them, like *that*." He snapped his fingers. "It's the only way. They're not expecting it. The fall season is coming on. We'll catch them with their pants down."

I don't think Tootsie realized himself the importance of convincing them that we weren't trying to unionize them. But I had impressed on him that he had to make that point clear. That was all I cared about. A fat lot I was going to worry about whether he understood what he was doing or not.

"What do you say? Are you willing to fight for a little of what's yours by right? It won't take long. A week at the most. They won't be able to stand it for longer. All it means is a week's pay. That's not much to give up, is it? All you lose is a week's pay. And think of what you get! A decent salary! Hours like a white man, not a nigger. What do you say? Is it a strike?"

The excitement in his voice was getting them. They moved about restlessly. I watched the faces near me. They weren't just staring at him blankly any more. They began to look alive. Their eyes were blinking. Their lips were working. They were beginning to smile.

A single voice rose above the rest. "How are we—" was all I could make out before it was drowned out.

Tootsie rapped heavily on the table.

"Somebody back there have a question?" he asked.

"Yeah!"

A big guy without a chin and with a mouthful of teeth stood up. I knew what he was going to ask even before he opened his mouth. So did Tootsie. I had told him.

"What is it?"

"What's gonna stop them from hiring new shipping clerks when we go on strike?" the guy with the teeth asked.

They quieted down immediately. All heads turned to Tootsie. But I just sat back and smiled to myself. It was almost like looking at a newsreel for the second time. You know just which horse is going to win the race and what Senator Whozis is going to say about the child labor amendment.

Tootsie leaned forward and grinned like a wise guy. I shut my eyes. That much fake even *I* can't stand.

"What are you gonna do with those muscles you developed from schlepping bundles and pushing trucks all these years?" Tootsie said. "Leave them behind in the shipping room when you walk out?"

The crowd broke into a laugh that must've been heard in Brooklyn. The guy with the teeth sat down.

"Any more questions?" Tootsie cried.

Just then the door in the back opened and a Western Union boy came down the aisle, headed for the platform. The laughter began to die down as the boy made his way through the room. When he handed the telegram to Tootsie, the room was quiet. Tootsie ripped the envelope open and read the telegram to himself. Then he turned to the crowd with a smile.

"Listen to this, fellows," he said, waving the yellow sheet. He began to read: *"Have just learned of your planned militant protest against unbearable conditions in garment industry. Stop. High time steps were taken. Stop. As soon as feasible will call out elevator operators' union and truck drivers' union in garment center in sympathy strike. Stop. Wish you luck and speedy success. Stop. Assure you that American Federation of Labor is behind your strike one hundred per cent. Signed, William Green, President."* He paused and looked up from the telegram. "What do you say, fellows, do we strike?"

The cheer that went up almost split my eardrums. For a few minutes I watched them yelling and screaming and pounding each other's backs. Then I took a look at Tootsie, standing on the platform, holding the telegram and smiling down at them like he'd just done something big. For the first time since I knew him, he seemed to be happy. He'd been carried along by his own enthusiasm to the point where he was no longer acting. He couldn't have made a slip now if he wanted to.

I stood up and made for the door. I held it open for a few moments, watching. I waited just long enough to see Tootsie quiet them down a little and begin the election. As soon as he was elected chairman of the Strike Committee, with one of the pots as secretary, I closed the door behind me. No sense in killing any more time. I'd give Mama a break and come home early for a change. The other offices were only dummies and could be filled from the ranks. Tootsie had his orders.

Out in the street, I took a deep breath of air and gave myself a final pat on the back. I could have made it a straight telegram. But what would I have gained? A night letter costs half the price and you can say twice as much. And anyway, when it's read aloud from a platform, who knows the difference?

3

As long as he was eating, he was all right. But the minute he opened his mouth, and there was no food to shove into it, he started to talk. So I'd figured out a little system. I kept my eye on his plate, and as soon as I saw he was getting close to bottom, I called the waiter.

"Nathan!"

He came across the small room on the run. On the run? Well, sure, like a prisoner on his way to be executed. The service you get in some of these dumps is a joke. But just the same there's one big advantage in coming back to the same place over and over again. You get so you can call the waiter by his first name. For myself I don't care. Make the food good and let there be plenty of it and it doesn't make any difference to me if the waiters walk on their hands. But when you're with people, especially people who don't know their way around so well, being able to call the waiter by his first name means something. It makes an impression. Add up all the impressions and they'll spell anything, from dough to pussy.

"You want something?"

"Yeah," I said, pointing to Tootsie's plate. "Get the gentleman another plate of blintzes."

"Aah, no!" Tootsie said quickly. "I had enough."

"What? Three plates of blintzes, and you say it's enough? You call that a lunch? What are you, sick or something?" I turned to the pot with the big can. "Can you imagine that? All he had was three portions, and he's through!"

She laughed and gave my hand a shove.

"Go on, quit kidding him," she said. "He's had enough. If he eats any more he won't be able to even talk this afternoon."

"Yeah," I said. "He won't be able to talk! I got a picture of Tootsie Maltz not being able to talk!"

She laughed again. Say, she wasn't so bad! The only thing wrong with her was her can. And she was sitting on that. Everything you could see of her, the part that was above the table, was all right. And on second thought, what's wrong with a big can?

"I don't think they're so good for his stomach, anyway," she said. "I mean, to eat so much of that stuff, I don't think it's so—"

"Do me a favor," I said. "Don't watch his stomach. One person on that job is plenty. He's doing all right for himself as is. No, Tootsie?"

He didn't answer.

"I don't see *you* eating so many of them," she said.

Look, she was beginning to notice things!

"I know," I said. "But I can't help it. I only like them the way my mother makes them." I rolled my eyes. "Boy, could I go a plate of them now!"

She began to giggle. I looked at her in astonishment.

"Did I say something clever?" I said.

She almost doubled up, giggling harder.

"You—you," she began, but she was laughing so hard she couldn't talk. I just looked at her and smiled pleasantly. One thing was sure, there were no medals on her when it came to brains. But what's the sense of complaining? Just as she was, she was right up my alley.

"Listen, Harry. For the last time." It was Tootsie. He'd finally gotten his mouth empty. "Will you be a little reasonable?"

"And for the last time," I said, imitating his voice, "will you stop making a pyoick out of yourself?"

"Kidding aside, Harry. This is no joke."

"Did I say it was a joke?" I turned to the pot. "Did you hear me say it was a joke? Did I laugh or something? Look at me. Look how serious I am. And he tells me it's no joke!"

She giggled and shoved my hand again. This was going to be a pushover.

Tootsie slapped the table and pointed to the clock on the wall.

"Look at the time," he said. "It's two o'clock already and I gotta be there at three and you keep on—"

"Maybe you better scram, then," I said. "You don't want to be late for the meeting of the one and only Associated Dress Manufacturers of New York, Inc., and don't forget that I. N. C."

"But Harry—"

Okay, pal, you asked for it.

"But my ear," I said, talking tough. "Three-quarters of an hour ago it looked like this was going to be a pretty pleasant lunch. The food's good, the company's all right, and we had plenty of time. But you've been working like a nigger to spoil it. Every second that your mouth's been free from food, you've been yapping away like you were getting a dime a word for it. I don't know about Regina, here"—I nodded my head toward the dame—"but I'm getting pretty sick of it."

He pulled in his lips and half closed his eyes and began to shake his head.

"I can't help it, Harry," he said. "You don't understand these things." This was pretty good. I didn't understand these things, but Tootsie Maltz did! "The way things stand now, it looks too raw, Harry. What I'm gonna tell them there this afternoon, why, they'll just laugh at me. Who ever heard of a shipping clerk getting twenty-five dollars a week? For a forty-hour week yet, too! And you gotta throw in a two-weeks' vacation on top of it! They'll just laugh at me. You gotta be *rea*sonable, Harry. Let's not make is so steep. Let's say we want an eighteen-dollar minimum, or maybe a twenty. But something reasonable. Not twenty-five dollars! And yeah, you want time and a half for overtime, too! For God's sakes, Harry, at least let's give them a break on the hours. Those shipping clerks are working seventy now, so if we demand a minimum of fifty they ought to be satisfied. And it'll look better, too, when I put it before them this afternoon. Like this, the way we got it now, they'll just laugh at me. They'll say I'm crazy. If we come down a little in our demands, it won't look so bad. After all, everybody knows you can't expect to grab everything at once. Let's make it a little reasonable, so they'll at least listen to me. Like this they won't even do that. They'll just laugh at me. I'm telling you, Harry, if I put it before them the way we got it now, it'll look too raw. They'll just laugh at me."

Brother, you said a mouthful. This shining light of the revolution didn't know it, but he'd stated the case perfectly. That's what I wanted them to do—laugh at him.

"Listen, Tootsie," I said. Listen was right. I was going to

make a speech. I hoped she'd keep her ears open. "The trouble with you is you haven't got any nerve. You're not thinking about those poor kids that lug bundles around in the heat and snow and rain for seventy hours a week and more at fifteen bucks each. All you're thinking about is what those pot-bellied bosses are going to say to you at that conference this afternoon. Just because they're gonna kick like steers when you put the Strike Committee's demands before them, you want to reduce them. You're willing to take those few bucks out of those poor kids' envelopes just so you should have it easier for an hour or two at a conference. Stop thinking about yourself so much. Think of those poor kids." This was getting a little thick. A couple more sentences of that bull and my stomach would do a double flip. "Go in there and tell those kikes what we want. Twenty-five dollars a week minimum. Forty hours. Time and a half for overtime. Two-weeks' vacation. The whole works, or else."

Applause.

"Aah, gee, Harry I tell you we—"

"Tootsie, dear," I said slowly, "You're going to be late."

He opened his mouth and then closed it. Then he shrugged and got up.

"Okay, Harry," he said, "but remember—I told you."

That was one for the books. Tootsie Maltz told me!

"You remember." I said. "You give your report on the conference at the general meeting to-night. We'll see you then."

He stood there, hesitating.

"What's the matter," I said. "Forget something?"

"You coming with me, Regina?" he said.

Before she could say anything, I stood up and put my hand on his shoulder.

"What's wrong, Tootsie?" I said. "You scared or something?"

"Who *me?* What's there to be scared about?"

"I don't know," I said, grinning. "But maybe *you* do. What do you want Regina for, to carry you when you get weak?" I was willing to bet she could do it, too.

"Nah, I just thought—"

"You just run along then," I said, slapping him on the shoulder, "and give them the works. Remember," I added as he turned away, "eight o'clock to-night. Pythian Temple. Don't be late."

I waited until his fat figure went through the door and turned up the block before I sat down again.

She didn't talk, just sat facing me across the table, shoving the salt shaker around in little circles. I pretended that I was looking at the menu, but I kept watching her with my eyes half closed. There were other people in the restaurant, talking and moving around, and outside trucks and streetcars kept going by. But I could still hear the way she breathed, in short gasps, with her mouth open, as though she were holding herself back and trying to make it sound natural. Through my elbows on the table I could feel how tense she was. I had a feeling she was going to break the spell with some crack about Tootsie, but she didn't.

"How about having something else?" I said, rustling the menu.

She jumped a little and then smiled and shook her head quickly.

"Oh, no. I've had enough, thanks. Anyway, I'm eating too much." She giggled. "I've got to watch my figure, you know."

Baby, I thought, you don't know the half of it. Watching her figure was a job for the police force, working in double shifts.

"What's the matter with your figure?" I said, although I could have answered that question myself in a short little lecture of twenty minutes or so. "It looks all right to me," I said, giving her the once-over in a way that wouldn't leave any doubts in her mind.

She giggled crazily and moved her can into a more comfortable position on the chair.

"You're a funny one, all right," she said.

"Who *me?* Why, I'm the most serious guy you ever met."

"Yeah, you're serious! You're all the time kidding and jok-

ing and things like that. What do you do for a living, anyway?"

So *that's* how she got the short nose. She must've worn a
couple of inches off it by sticking it into other people's business.

"Me? Why me," I said, "I'm a poet."

"A what?"

"A poet. You know, one of these guys with long hair that
goes around making up poems."

"Ah, come on. Cut it out. There you go kidding again."

"Honest, I mean it. I'm a poet."

"Yeah, a poet!"

"Sure. I even made up a poem about you."

"About me?"

Well, if this baby wasn't a case of arrested development,
then she was Sarah Bernhardt.

"Sure, about you. You want to hear it?"

"Yeah! Yeah!"

Well, I figured, here I go.

> *There was a young girl from Alaska,*
> *Who would put anyone that would ask her.*
> *But then she—*

Suddenly she hid her face in her hands and began to giggle
so hard that I had to stop reciting and grab the table to keep
it from going over.

"Nathan!" I called to the waiter. "Check!"

From now on every minute I spent in preparation was just
so much time wasted. I was in.

4

When we reached the Pythian Temple the crowd was all
settled. But Tootsie hadn't begun to speak yet. He was sitting at the table on the platform, thumbing through a small
batch of papers. There were no more seats, so we found a
small cleared space against the rear wall, near the door, and

leaned against it. I was a little surprised at the turnout. It wasn't quite eight yet, and the meeting had been called for eight sharp. They seemed a little more interested than they had been a week ago.

Promptly at eight Tootsie stood up. There was very little noise, and that stopped at once.

"The purpose of tonight's meeting, fellows," he said, "is to hear the report of your Strike Committee's conference with the Dress Manufacturers' Association which was held this afternoon." He talked slowly and carefully, as though he wanted them to understand that what he said was very important. "You know what our demands were, and you know what the alternative is that we threatened them with if they refused us." He moved forward a few inches on the platform. "Well, I'm not going to waste any more time or keep you in suspense." I knew what the answer would be, but even I found myself leaning forward a little anxiously. "They said no," Tootsie said, and paused.

I leaned back against the wall, relieved. So *that* was all right.

"They turned us down flat," he said. "They laughed at me."

Could you blame them?

The crowd began to shift about a little, and you could hear the chairs squeaking and the shoes scratching as they moved a few inches on the floor.

"I told them what we'd do if they turned us down," he said, "but they didn't care. They just laughed at me." His voice rose a little. "They said go ahead!"

He hoisted a part of his behind onto the small table and sat like that, swinging one leg.

"As far as the Committee is concerned," he said, "there's only one thing left to do. And that's to set the date for the strike." He looked at one of the papers in his hand. "We've decided to show these guys that we mean business. No crapping around. We told them what we wanted and what we'd do if they said no. Well, they said no. All right, then, we're gonna let them have it right between the eyes. The Committee has set the date for the day after to-morrow. Any objections?" He looked around the large room. They all looked at each other. Nobody spoke. "What do you say, then? Is the day after to-morrow okay?"

"Okay!" they yelled suddenly and went into an uproar. They climbed out of their seats and pounded each other on the back and shoved chairs around and threw wads of paper into the air and cursed at the top of their voices until it began to be positively dangerous to stand still.

The pot got nervous and grabbed my arm.

"Gee," she said, "maybe we better get out of here."

"Don't worry," I said. "True-Blue Harry is at your side to protect you."

"I'm not kidding," she said. "They'll begin to throw chairs in a minute."

"Okay," I said, "let's edge our way to the door. We can wait for Tootsie outside."

If I could have used that can of hers like a snow plow, we could have broken our way through a mountain in thirty seconds flat. But after what happened that afternoon, that wouldn't have been polite. So I led the way slowly to the door and in a few minutes we were outside. I took her to the doorway across the street, facing the entrance to the Temple, and said, "We'll wait for Tootsie here. It won't take long."

She looked disappointed.

"What do we have to wait for him for?" she said.

"I just want to ask him if he thinks the Giants'll win the pennant next year," I said.

She giggled, but her heart wasn't in it. I knew where her heart was.

"I mean, what's the sense of standing around like this, doing nothing. We could, well, we could meet Tootsie later."

"Yeah?" I said. "Where?"

"Oh—I don't know," she said slowly, biting her lip. "But I guess we could meet him later."

If it was ice cream, she'd eat it.

"Nah," I said, "we'll wait for Tootsie."

It took even less time than I thought it would. In less than a half hour they came pouring out, still excited, and spread out in all directions in small groups. Tootsie came out with the last batch, and we crossed over to meet him.

"How was it?" I asked.

"Okay," he said, "but what happened to you?"

"They got so wild in there, it wasn't safe where we were standing, so we came outside to wait for you. Everything all right?"

"Swell," he said. "It's all set for the day after to-morrow. I told them where to report for their picket signs and we split them up according to the buildings they work in. The only thing that worries me is what the cops'll do about the mass picketing."

"That's all right," I said. "They can't do a thing. It's not really mass picketing. There's a couple dozen firms in each building, and if they got the names of their firm on their picket signs, there may be a couple dozen guys picketing each building, but it's really only one guy for each firm. See what I mean?"

"Oh, yeah. That's right."

Well, I'd sleep better that night. Tootsie had said it was right.

"So all right, then," I said, putting my hands on their arms, "I've gotta run along now." I turned to Tootsie. "I'll see you to-morrow at the restaurant? Say about nine or so? There's a coupla little things I'd still like to talk over."

"Okay, Harry," he said, "I'll see you to-morrow at nine."

"No, wait a minute," I said. "Better make it ten. I'm a little tired. And sometimes my mother, you know, she doesn't wake me up on time or something like that. Better be on the safe side, and make it ten. Ten all right?"

"Sure," he said. "To-morrow at ten."

"You mean you're leaving?" she cried.

There was a brain for you. Einstein's only rival.

"Yeah," I said. "I've got a coupla things to take care of."

"Oh," she said, disappointed.

I knew what I was passing up. But I was still saying good night.

First of all, this was no time to get Tootsie sore at me. And then, too, I really felt sorry for him. He'd suffered enough for one night.

And secondly, it would have been against my principles *not* to say good night. I never go back to the same pump too often. As long as I had my health and was in my right mind, nothing that wore skirts was going to tie a string to me.

"There's only one thing worries me," Tootsie said. "I hope they don't forget all about the strike by the day after to-morrow."

"Just you leave that to me," I said. "They won't forget."

5

When we came out of the restaurant I said to Tootsie, "You wait for me here. I'll be back in ten minutes."

"Where you going?"

"To get my nose picked. Just wait, will you? I'll be back in ten minutes."

The garage was right around the corner, on Fourth Avenue. The driver was standing in front of it, waiting for me.

"Everything set?" I said.

"Everything set," he said.

I followed him inside and up to a long, closed truck, with smooth black sides. Along the edge of the truck at the top, on both sides, was a long, thin cylinder, with a piece of rope hanging from the middle, like a window shade. I pulled the long sheets of oilcloth down and let them snap up again. I did it a few times, on both sides, to make sure they were working.

"They're both okay," the driver said, leaning out of the caboose up front.

"Yeah, I know," I said, "but I just wanted to make sure." I opened the door in the back and climbed inside. He watched me over his shoulder through the little window over the front seat.

"How's the mike?" I asked.

"Okay," he said. "You can test it if you want to."

I flicked my fingernail against the nickel rim of the mouthpiece and a short, sharp bellow came out of the loudspeaker in the roof of the truck.

"I told you it was okay," he said.

"Yeah," I said, "I know."

I climbed out and closed the door in the back carefully. Then I walked up front and got in on the seat beside him.

"Turn into Thirty-Fourth," I said. "I want to pick somebody up near the corner."

"Okay," he said.

"Wait a minute," I said. I dug into my pocket and brought out my wallet. I took out a five and gave it to him. "Don't get tough with the cops and let me do all the talking." I didn't like his attitude and I didn't want everything spoiled because he might get temperamental or something. At this stage of the game another five or so made no difference. "I paid your boss already," I said, "so that's for you. And if you don't scrape your fenders there'll be a little more for you later."

"Okay," he said and grinned.

We drove out of the garage and up to Thirty-Fourth. Then we turned and drew up in front of the restaurant. Tootsie's chin dropped another three inches when he saw me get out of the truck.

"What the hell is that?"

I turned around to take a good look at it.

"Maybe I'm wrong," I said, "but it looks like a truck to me."

"Sure it's a truck. What do you think, I'm dumb or something?" Well, he certainly wasn't something. "But what the hell is it for?"

"Well, you're looking a little peaked, and I thought a little ride in the fresh air would do you good, so I just went out and rented me a truck, and so here we—"

"But no kidding, what's it for?"

"This, my boy," I said, tapping the fender, "is the latest way of running a strike that has yet been invented."

"What the hell, am I nuts or are you?"

"Well, Tootsie, *I* feel perfectly okay."

"But what the hell is it for?"

"Jesus Christ on a raft!" I said. "What did you do, make a record of that? Don't you know any other songs?"

"Yeah, but what the?—"

"Ah, nuts," I said, grabbing his arm. "Here, you're gonna ride up front here, with the driver. I'm gonna be inside, on the floor, so nobody can see me." I handed him a piece of paper. "That's the route we're gonna follow. You keep reading it to the driver, to make sure we stay on it, and keep your eyes open. If anything starts to happen, anybody starts to get tough, maybe the cops or somebody, you let me know. Understand?"

"Sure, but—"

"But my eye," I said. "Look at this."

I grabbed the piece of rope on the side of the truck and pulled down the wide sheet of oilcloth and fastened the piece of rope to a nail at the bottom. The sheet of oilcloth that came down like a window shade was a sign. It said: SHIPPING CLERKS ATTENTION! DON'T FORGET THE GENERAL STRIKE! TO-MORROW AT 8:00 A.M.!

"Gee," Tootsie said.

"Yeah, *gee!*" I said, pulling him after me around to the other side of the truck. I hauled down the other sign and fastened it at the bottom. By now a small crowd was beginning to collect, so I pushed him into the truck next to the driver and climbed into the back myself. I parked myself on the mattress on the floor and motioned to the driver.

"Get going," I said.

"Where to?"

"What time is it?"

"Ten after twelve."

"That's just right. Go right up Thirty-Fourth till you hit Broadway, then turn right and go up Broadway slowly, about ten or fifteen miles an hour, till you hit Forty-Second. Then turn left twice and go down Seventh Avenue, till you hit Thirty-Fourth. After that follow the route on the paper I gave him." I pointed to Tootsie. "Understand?"

"Okay," the driver said, and we began to move.

Through the crack between the doors in the back of the truck I could see a little of the street. In a couple of minutes I could see the "L" pillars on Sixth Avenue and hear a train going by above me. We turned right, into Broadway, and slowed down for the traffic in front of Macy's.

"What time is it?"

"A quarter after twelve," Tootsie said.

That was just about right. Most of them would be out on the street. I waited until the truck began to move forward slowly. Then I leaned over to the mike and began to speak.

"Shipping—clerks—attention," I said slowly, and heard the words come booming out above me louder than all the noises of the street. "Shipping—clerks—attention," I said again. I almost laughed out loud at the look on Tootsie's face as he looked all around him and then back into the truck at me. "All—out—for—the—general—strike—to-morrow. All—out—for—the—general—strike—to-morrow. Shipping —clerks—attention. General—strike—to-morrow—morning —at—eight. General—strike—to-morrow—morning—at— eight. Shipping—clerks—attention."

Through the crack between the doors I could see the crowds milling around the truck, moving along with it, laughing and yelling.

I repeated it slowly and clearly, spacing out the words so that they would be understood. Then I paused for a few seconds and started again. Sometimes I varied it a little, adding a crack to keep them interested.

"Shipping—clerks—attention. Step-children—of—the— garment—industry. Fight—for—your—rights. Turn—out— for—general—strike—to-morrow—morning—at—eight. Shipping—clerks—attention."

The crowd loved it. They ate it up. They laughed and

shoved and followed the truck. They couldn't seem to get enough of it, but they certainly didn't have to walk along with the truck to hear me. The amplifier carried my voice for blocks. Once in a while I caught a glimpse of the side of a building through the little window over the driver's seat. People were hanging out of all the windows, watching the street below, laughing and pointing to the truck as it moved up toward Times Square.

"Shipping—clerks—attention. General—strike—to-morrow—morning—at—eight. Shipping—clerks—attention."

Strikes on Seventh Avenue are no novelty. They've got a new one every Monday and Thursday. The garment district is usually as full of pickets as the rotogravure section of the *New York Times* on Sunday is full of brassiere and corset ads. But they go just as quickly and easily as they come. They have no novelty, no zip. People just take them for granted. Any rummy can call a strike. But who ever hears of them? What happens to them? Well, this was one that they'd hear about! Not only would those dopes remember that they were supposed to go out on strike the next day, but the rest of the garment district would remember it too. When I do something, I do it right.

"Shipping—clerks—attention. General—strike—to-morrow."

At Times Square the truck turned left and then, quickly, left again, and we were on Seventh Avenue.

I began all over again, rolling the words off my tongue and listening to it come roaring out. Suddenly the truck stopped. I knew what it was before the cop reached the truck. I was a little surprised that we hadn't been stopped before this.

"What the hell's going on here? Where d'you guys think y'are?"

Tootsie leaned in through the little window over the driver's seat.

"Harry, it's a cop."

"You mean it?" I said. "I thought for a minute it was Greta Garbo."

I pulled the permit out of my pocket and handed it to

Tootsie through the window. I didn't want anybody to see me, just in case some of those shipping clerks were around. As far as they were concerned, I had nothing to do with this strike.

"Show this to the law," I said.

Tootsie took it and leaned across the driver to give it to the cop. In a few seconds he handed it back in to me and we began to move forward again.

"It's a lucky thing you had that," Tootsie said through the window.

Luck nothing. You can do almost anything in this world. All you need is enough brains to plan everything in advance. Getting a permit in advance sounds simple. So does the idea of hiring a sound truck to remind a couple of thousand shipping clerks of their appointment to go out on strike the next day. But the guy who would get both these ideas is one in a million. Like me.

But I didn't have time to explain all that to Tootsie. I was too busy with the mike.

"Shipping—clerks—attention. General—strike—to-morrow. Fight—for—higher—wages—and—fewer—hours. Shipping—clerks—attention. General—strike—to-morrow."

We kept it up until half-past one, crisscrossing through every one of the streets between Thirty-Fourth and Forty-Second, from Sixth Avenue, across Broadway and Seventh Avenue, to Eighth Avenue, and then around the circuit we'd started with—the triangle that's formed by Times Square, Broadway and Thirty-Fourth, and Seventh Avenue and Thirty-Fourth.

We could have stopped at one, because there isn't a shipping clerk in the whole damn neighborhood who gets more than a half-hour for lunch, anyway, and most of them are plugging away again by one o'clock. But I was getting a kick out of it, the longer we kept it up the longer we'd be remembered, and anyway, I'd had to hire the truck for a full half-day, so keeping it in the neighborhood for another half-hour or so didn't cost anything extra.

"Shipping—clerks—attention. General—strike—to-mor-row."

Finally, though, I began to get hoarse. I had the driver stop the truck and I told Tootsie to hop out and release the signs. Then we drove back to the garage.

"Well, Tootsie," I said as we walked away, "how's that for a way to run a strike?"

"Oy! Swell," he said, "I only hope it works."

"Don't worry, stoop," I said, keeping my hand in my pocket to prevent it from poking him one. "It'll work."

6

It took me less than an hour to come down from the Bronx, and I'd left the house before eight, so I was on Seventh Avenue long before nine. But early as I was, the pickets were ahead of me. The first building I saw was 463, on the corner of Thirty-Fifth. About a dozen of them were parading up and down before the front entrance, their backs and bellies plastered with large signs. As soon as I got near enough, I saw another dozen, on Thirty-Fifth, covering the freight en-trance. They had the building bottled up. Nice work.

I went up Seventh Avenue quickly, spotting all the main buildings: 469, 498, 525, 530—they were all covered. I didn't have a chance to go through the side streets, but as I passed I glanced into them and I could see the marching pickets, with their red and white signs, and the crowds watch-ing them. Broadway was the same: 1359, 1375, 1385, 1400, 1410—they all had their quota of pickets. Tootsie was all right. He had done his work well. He was a little thick at times, and once in a while you had to talk your left lung off to make him see two inches in front of his schnob, but in the long run he was all right.

Now that the first survey was over, I breathed a little easier. I walked around more leisurely, watching the crowds. They didn't know what to make of it. It was a few minutes to nine, and they were rushing to get to their places on time, but the sight was too much for them. They had to stop and look. Shipping clerks on strike were enough of a novelty. But such a slew of them, covering every building—it was terrific.

Most of them were laughing. Shipping clerks on strike? Who ever heard of shipping clerks going out on strike? Operators and pressers and finishers—all right. But shipping clerks?

I stopped to watch a small parade of them as they went back and forth in front of 1410. A few others stopped, too, and in a minute we were a small group, watching and laughing.

"Looks like they mean business, hah?"

"Looks that way."

"I'll tell you the truth, honest, I never knew there were so many around."

"Well, it only goes to show you."

"I wonder what they're striking for?"

That one was a lulu. I had to turn around to get a good look at the big brain that dropped that one.

"What'd you say, mister?" I asked.

He looked a little scared, so I smiled and said, "I thought you said something to me."

"No," he said. "I only was wondering what they're striking for?"

"That's easy," I said. I couldn't help it. The opening was too wide. "They want to crap in the street, like horses," I said. "See, they do the work of horses, shoving trucks around and things like that, so they want to have the right to drop it in the street, just like horses."

I didn't wait to hear what he said, if anything. Can you imagine any one person being as dumb as all that? He wondered what they were striking for!

I moved on down Broadway, feeling good. And every time I passed another building, and saw the pickets parading back and forth in front of it, I felt better. By the time I hit Schrafft's I felt so good that I decided to go inside for a soda. Halfway through it I remembered the guy who wanted to know what they were striking for and what I had told him, and I began to laugh. But the edge was taken off because I knew there was nobody I could tell it to. That's the price you pay when you pal around with dopes.

After the soda I lit a cigarette and went outside. You don't find any shipping clerks standing in front of Schrafft's in the middle of the day. But you'll find plenty of dress salesmen. When I was a shipping clerk I used to envy these heels. Some day, I promised myself, I'd be standing there with them, punching the bag and taking time out every half-hour for a twenty-cent ice cream soda. Well, now I was doing it. I was through with being a shipping clerk. For that matter, I was through with working for other people. Nobody ever made any money that way. The way to make money is to get other people to work for you. You be the boss, not the other guy, even if it's only a peanut stand you're running.

Promptly at nine-fifteen Tootsie drifted by.

"Hello, Tootsie."

"Hello."

"Everything okay?"

"Looks like it to me. Did you take a look around?"

"Just for a few minutes," I said. "Everything looked all right."

"I checked on every building," he said. "They're all out."

"Side streets, too?" I asked.

"Everything."

"How many do you figure are out?"

"Well, we had over five hundred picket signs this morning, and there isn't a one left."

"That's fine," I said.

"Yeah, and plenty of them are picketing without signs."

"Any trouble yet?"

"A couple of wise guys tried to take a truckful of dresses out the Thirty-Ninth Street side of 1410, but we stopped them."

"What do you mean, you stopped them?"

"What do I mean? What do you mean, what do I mean? We stopped them, that's all."

"That's all nothing," I said. "Don't just stop anybody. What do you think you're doing, playing pisha-paysha? In case you don't know it, Tootsie, this is a strike."

"I know it is. So what's that got to do with it—?"

"All right. All right. Don't look so dumb," I said. "And don't start to cry on me, either. The only thing is, don't tell me any more you just stopped anybody. Anybody tries to come through with dresses or a truck or something, tell those pickets to sail into them. Let's have a couple of broken heads around here. Then they'll know we mean business. Understand?"

"Yeah, but what do we have to go around looking for trouble for? Isn't it enough we stop them? As long as they don't go in or out, that's enough, isn't it?"

"Listen, Tootsie," I said, "we haven't got all year for this thing. This strike is less than an hour old, so nothing's happened yet. But before it's an hour older the whole neighborhood'll be lousy with scabs. Maybe they don't understand English so well, but if they get a good swift kick in the pants or a rap in the snoot once in a while they'll understand all right. So just shake the lead out of your ass for a change and pass the word around that you want them to stop all scabs with force. Come on, now, shake your ankle."

"Okay, Harry, but—"

"Just let me handle the buts. You tell them to break some heads."

"Yeah, but gee whiz, Harry—"

"Gee whiz what?" I said, scowling at him. "You got any complaints maybe, or something?"

"Nothing," he said, biting his lip. "I was just—"

"Save it for later," I said sharply. "Get going."

"Okay," he said.

"And another thing," I said. "I'll try to stay put right here. You keep on circulating around and report here, say, every fifteen minutes or so. Anything comes up, something you don't know what to do, you can find me here. But first

of all, remember, we want them to kick the nuts off every
scab they get their hands on. Okay?"

"Okay," he said.

From where I stood I had my eye on about three buildings. I watched carefully, but nothing happened. The pickets
kept on marching in front of the entrances and the small
crowds gathered to watch them for a while and then dis-
persed. So far as I could see, no packages were going in or
coming out of the freight entrances.

But soon I began to notice a truckful of dresses passing me
in the street every once in a while. Where the hell were they
coming from? The couple of buildings I could see were water-
tight. Where was the leak?

By the time Tootsie reported, I was good and sore. But
I don't go around shooting off my mouth until I lay the
groundwork.

"How does it look?"

"Great," he said.

"Great, hah?"

"You bet. I went over the whole route again, and there
isn't a single building that we haven't got covered."

"So everything is covered, hah? You got the whole thing
in the palm of your hand, hah?"

"I sure have. You oughta see the way they've got those
entrances stopped."

"I ought to, hah? I knew I was missing something."

"You wanna come around with me? You wanna take a
look?"

"That'll be just dandy, won't it? That certainly is goddam
nice of you, Tootsie. I gotta say it. It certainly is nice of you."

"Say, what the hell is the matter with you, anyway? You
nuts or something? You sound like you dropped a load in
your pants."

I stopped smiling.

"You just worry a little less about me and my pants," I
said, "and do a little more worrying about this strike. Then
maybe we'll be better off."

"What's the matter now? Isn't everything okay?"

"Sure everything is okay. Everything is just one hundred per cent. One hundred per cent lousy, that's what it is."

"Listen, I'm no mind reader. If you got a kick or something, so tell me. But don't make me speeches without telling me what it's all about. What's the matter, anyway? I thought everything was okay?"

"Well, in the future you just let me do the thinking. And besides," I said, "what's okay by you, isn't exactly okay by me."

"Jesus Christ alive! Will you tell me already what you want? What the hell is the matter?"

Before I could tell him what I wanted to, I spotted one of those hand trucks coming up the Avenue, about a block down, with two guys pushing it.

I grabbed his arm and twisted him around to face the truck. Then I pointed to it.

"Take a good look," I said. "Ever see one of those before?"

"Where? What?"

Can you imagine a blind bastard like that?

"There. There! Right in front of you! What do you want me to do, carry you over in my arms? Can't you see straight any more?"

"You mean that hand truck?"

"No, the Washington monument! What the hell do you *think* I mean?"

"So what about it?"

Go give him answers in writing!

"Listen, you balloon-headed schmuck," I said, keeping my voice down, and talking quickly. "That's a dress truck, see? And those two baloneys that are pushing it aren't taking it to the Automat so they can get a bite to eat, see? And those canvas curtains they got hanging over the truck aren't put there to protect the wooden sides, either. They're there to protect dresses, see? And trucks full of dresses don't grow in the middle of Seventh Avenue like potatoes. If it's there so you can see it, it means it came from some place. And it also means it's going some place. And if it came from some

place then it means that some of those lousy pickets of yours
are blocking some of those buildings like with a sieve. And
if any more of those trucks start floating around you might
as well tell those pickets to go home and go to sleep, for all
the good they'll be doing around here. Because before you
know it the whole goddam strike won't be worth a fart. *Now*
do you understand?"

I stopped to get my breath, but I swear he didn't look
any more intelligent than he had looked before I started.

"So what am I supposed to do?" he said.

This was my first lieutenant, my right arm!

"I'll tell you what you're supposed to do," I said quietly.
What was the sense of getting excited? With dopes like
Tootsie Maltz there's only one rule. The easier you take
it, the longer you'll last. "I already told you what you're
supposed to do," I said, "but I'll tell you again."

"*When* did you tell me?"

He was getting excited!

"Keep your drawers on," I said. "Less than a half-hour
ago, that's when I told you. Didn't I tell you to pass the
word around that they should break a couple of heads?"

"Sure, but what—?"

"Then what the hell are you waiting for?"

He stood there, undecided, and suddenly the truck was
abreast of us and I could read the words that were painted
on the canvas sides. Don't try to guess, because you wouldn't
get it right in a thousand years. *Toney Frocks, Inc.!*

I grabbed his shoulder and shook him until his teeth
rattled.

"You get some of those pickets of yours and clean those
son of a bitches off the street right now," I yelled. I was
so excited that I forgot I was supposed to be one of those
cool, bored, well-dressed wise guys that have marked the
sidewalk in front of Schrafft's for their very own. "Come
on, you fat-head," I almost screamed, "get after them!"

For another second he hesitated. But I wouldn't even spare
him that. The truck was moving past us, and I was so afraid
I'd lose this chance to get even with that fat bastard Schmul

that I used to work for, that I almost ran after it myself. Almost, but not quite. Even when I'm so excited that I can't see straight, I've still got enough brains left to keep from pushing my puss into a jam.

I gave Tootsie a shove that sent him flying out into the gutter. The blow must have cleared the horse manure out of his head. Because he had sense enough not to slow down, but to keep running.

In a few seconds he was across the street and in the middle of the gang of pickets in front of 525. He didn't waste much time talking and they wasted even less listening. Before I recovered my balance from the shove I'd given him, they were speeding down the street after the truck. They reached it near the corner of Thirty-Sixth Street.

For half a minute or less I had a clear view. Four of them piled onto the scabs and layed them out in the gutter. The others pitched into the truck. They ripped off the canvas cover and sent the bright red and yellow dresses flying into the mud and dirt. They still had the scabs on the ground and were pasting hell out of them, and they were still making ribbons out of the dresses and toothpicks out of the truck when the crowd closed in around them and cut off my view.

But I wouldn't miss a second of this for all the pussy in Paris. I joined the mob that was rushing over to see the scrap and fought my way in until I had a ringside seat. What that truck and those dresses and those two slobs looked like was nobody's business. Maybe that fat louse Schmul didn't remember a certain kid named Bogen who had worked for him as a shipping clerk about a year before. But that certain kid named Bogen had remembered Mr. Schmul all right.

The two guys who had been shoving the truck were out cold, but those pickets were half-crazy. They kept pounding away at them.

"Kill the goddam scabs," they kept yelling, "kill the lousy jerks." And then they went ahead with the job of doing it.

They would have done it, too, if it wasn't for the cops. Two of them came running up, took a quick look around, and sailed in with their clubs. But those shipping clerks were too far gone to worry much about the color of a guy's coat or the fact that it was trimmed with brass buttons. And besides, they were about a dozen strong. They just took the cops in their stride.

But new ones began to arrive. And in a few minutes the sirens of the radio cars were screaming and coming closer. The mob cleared a path and the reinforcements took control. When the patrol wagon arrived it was all over. They piled the whole bunch of them in and drove away.

The crowd began to melt and the traffic that had been stopped for blocks around began to move.

I felt so good about the whole thing that I whistled as I walked back to Schrafft's. From my post on the sidewalk I gave the Avenue the once-over. Another dozen pickets had taken the place of the squad that had been arrested in front of 525. Everybody was talking about the strike, but this time they weren't laughing. Broken heads don't mean a thing on Seventh Avenue. But ripped-up dresses do. This was serious.

I watched the traffic that passed me very carefully, but I didn't see any dress trucks. For the time being, the strike was a success.

I was just going in to celebrate with a soda, when Tootsie came up on the run. I felt so good that I wanted to take him inside and treat him to a soda, but I changed my mind. Tootsie isn't the kind of guy you take into Schrafft's for a soda. He looks more natural in Max's Busy Bee with a hamburger in one hand and a mug of root beer in the other. Schrafft's is for people like me, not Tootsie.

"Listen, Harry," he said, "what'll we do about those kids?"

"What kids?"

"The ones that were arrested. What'll we do about them?"

"Nothing," I said.

He looked at me with his mouth open. I put my hand to his face, thumb on his chin and forefinger on his nose, and closed it.

"You mean you're gonna do nothing about them?"

"Stop, Tootsie," I said. "You're killing me. You mean to

say you actually understood something I said for the first time?"

"Gee whiz, Harry, this is no joking matter."

"That's true," I said. "I never thought of that, now that you mention it, though, I'm inclined to agree with you. Yes, sir, Tootsie. You're one hundred per cent right. This is no joking matter."

"But they arrested them!" he cried.

"And hot dogs taste better with mustard. So what?"

"What are you, crazy?"

"No, are you?"

"But they arrested them!"

"I think you said that before. Watch your script there, Tootsie. You're getting your cues all bollixed up."

"And they just arrested another bunch over on Broadway. That's what I came over to tell you. We gotta do something, Harry. I told them to stop every scab and every hand truck. There'll be fights by the dozen."

"Good," I said. "That's great. You say they just arrested some more of them over on Broadway?"

"Yeah, they saw some guys carrying—"

"That, my dear Tootsie, is the best news I've heard in three and a half minutes flat."

"But Harry, we gotta do something."

"Oh, no we don't," I said. "It's perfectly okay, Tootsie. It's good publicity." I patted him on the shoulder. "Now don't you worry your pretty little head over this," I said. "You just keep after your pickets and see that they break the back of any guy who tries to get through with a package or a truck or anything."

"But what about the guys they arrested?"

"That's all right," I said. "They're doing their part. Being in jail is the best thing they can do for us. It won't hurt them, because from the way things are going, it looks like this strike'll be over in no time. In their own way, by parking their cans in a cell, they're doing us more good than by wearing out their heels picketing. It's good publicity having them in jail."

"But Harry—"

"But Tootsie," I said, imitating his voice. I put my arm
through his and pulled him along with me. "Come on, I'll
take you in and buy you a soda to cool you off a little."
What the hell, let Schrafft's worry. "Only you've got to promise me one thing."

"What?"

"That you'll read the papers to-morrow. Just wait till you
see them. Oh, boy!"

7

"Is Mr. Pulvermacher in?"

It was a mouthful, but I managed to get it out without a
slip.

The broad at the switchboard behind the information window looked me over. Well, she could look until her eyes wore
out. I've never yet been ashamed of the way I dressed.

"Who wants to see him?"

I'm from J. P. Morgan's office. I've got three million dollars I don't know what to do with, so I came up to see Mr.
Pulvermacher, maybe he's got an idea of how I can get rid
of it. But this was no time for clowning, so I said:

"Well, he doesn't know me, but—"

"What's the name, please?"

Snappy, eh? So this was the way they handled people
who came up to see the great Pulvermacher of Pulvermacher,
Betschmann & Kalisch, Inc., manufacturers of Pulbetkal
Frocks, Gowns of Distinction, Street and Formal. Big-shot
stuff. Well, I guess the great man of Seventh Avenue had to
live up to his reputation.

"Bogen," I said. "Harry Bogen."

She closed the window in my face and pushed a plug into
the board. Her lips moved for a few seconds, then she opened
the window and turned to me again.

"What is it with reference to?"

Cross-examination, eh? Maybe I ought to begin worrying about an alibi.

"Tell him it's about getting his dresses delivered."

She gave me a dirty look.

"Say, you're not one of these men from the union, are you? Because if you are, then you can just—"

I laughed.

"Oh, no. Not me. Just tell him I've got a service that'll deliver his dresses for him, strike or no strike."

"Oh," she said and slammed the window in my face again.

Before I could begin to get sore, she had it open again.

"Go right into the showroom," she said. "Straight ahead Mr. P. said he'll be out in a minute."

So *that's* how they avoided breaking their teeth every time it came to saying his name.

"Thanks," I said, and went in.

Have you ever been in Grand Central Station? Well, put a purple carpet on the floor, cover the walls with mirrors, spill a dozen small white tables all over the place and twice as many soft chairs and sofas, finish it off with a handful of classy-looking paintings on the walls, and if you can tell the difference between it and the Pulvermacher showroom, then you're a better man than I am. If the money that that room cost couldn't pay off the national debt, then I'm Mahatma Gandhi. I took a mental snapshot of the whole place and filed it away for future reference. I'd seen showrooms before, but this one walked away with the onionskin medal. I was learning things.

A short, fat guy came out of a door in the far end of the room and walked toward me like his ass was made of cake and he was afraid to crack the icing. Except for two things he was such a dead ringer for my ex-boss Schmul of Toney Frocks, Inc. that I was getting all set to spit in his eye. But when I saw the glasses he was wearing with the black ribbon that went around his neck, and the white piping that showed up under the edges of his vest, I knew I was in the presence of a big shot himself. To wear those kind of glasses and white piping under your vest you've either got to have a lot of nerve or a lot of dough. And this guy looked like he never even crossed the street against the lights.

I walked across the showroom to meet him.

"Mr. Pulvermacher?"

"Yes, sir?"

"My name is Bogen."

"The girl told me." Ah, well, that eliminated *her* automatically. I don't like dames that talk. "What can I do for you?"

I decided to be a wise guy. Within limits, of course.

"I'm afraid it's the other way around, Mr. Pulvermacher," I said, giving him the old toothpaste grin. Joe Personality. You know. "I'm afraid *I'm* going to be the one that's going to do something for *you*."

What did I mean, I was afraid? Well, that's being a wise guy within limits, isn't it? So all right.

"So?" he said.

Yeah, *so,* fat boy!

"Shall we go some place where we can talk?" I said.

He waved his hands around the room.

"What's the matter with here?"

"Nothing," I said. "I only thought it would be better if we could go some place where we wouldn't be interrupted by buyers coming in and—"

"Don't worry about buyers," he said with a grin that must have hurt him, judging from the way it looked. "Since that damn strike began we haven't been able to move a dress out of the place. Cancellations we're getting, not orders. Don't worry about being interrupted by buyers. I haven't seen one in three days."

I'll bet the buyers weren't complaining.

"Well, that's just what I'm here to talk to you about," I said.

"Then you better talk quick, young man," he said, "because things can't keep up like this for long. If we don't get our dresses moved in another couple of days we'll have to meet the demands of the strikers, that's all. We can't afford to have things go on like this."

Jesus Christ and the gas company! It looked like I'd just come in under the wire.

"Oh, you don't want to do that, do you, Mr. Pulvermacher?"

He shrugged.

"Of course we don't. But what else can we do? We can't get even with them until the slack season sets in. Right now, we've got to move our dresses. We've got to fill our orders."

"Sure, but you'd rather do it without giving in to the strikers, wouldn't you? You don't want them to be able to say they won the strike, do you? And besides, I hear they're making some pretty high demands in wages and hours and things like that. You don't want to give in on all that, do you?"

"What are you doing, cracking jokes, Mr. Bogen?" Look, he remembered my name! "Of course we don't want to give in to them. But what can we do?"

"I'll tell you what to do, Mr. Pulvermacher." The hell with him. From now on I was going to leave it out. Why couldn't he get himself a handle that you didn't have to take a running start for? "That's what I came up to see you about. I've got a way to get your dresses delivered, cut your costs on it in half, and at the same time you won't have to give in to the strikers. Does that sound good to you?"

"It *sounds* good."

Little Pulvy, the skeptic!

"And it's even better than it sounds."

"Well, let's hear it."

I took his arm and pulled him over to a sofa.

"Let's sit down," I said.

He pulled out a couple of cigars and handed one to me. I took it, but I didn't light it. I can't smoke them. Every time I light a cigar, I have to sew up the bottom of my pants first.

"How many shipping clerks have you got, Mr. Pulvermacher?" There I go again! I just can't keep my resolutions.

"You mean how many *did* I have."

To all my other troubles, he has to turn out to be a wise guy. All right, dope, have it your way.

"That's right," I said. "How many *did* you have?"

"Let's see. Ten, twelve, and the two colored boys—fourteen. I had fourteen."

"And how much do you?—excuse me. How much *did* you pay them a week?"

"I paid them what they were worth. Nobody that works for us is underpaid. Our wage scale is one of the highest on Seventh Avenue. You can't expect us to pay a shipping clerk what we'd pay a—"

"I *know* they were well paid, Mr. Pulvermacher," I said. Yeah, I knew it. "I'm just interested in how much you paid them. I want to do a little calculating for you, Mr. Pulvermacher, that's all. I'm not in any way *crit*icizing you."

"Fifteen dollars a week, with fifty cents extra for supper every night they work late. And I'd like to see anybody on the Avenue say that's a bad salary for a shipping clerk, or that they pay more than—"

"Fifteen dollars a week for fourteen shipping clerks makes two hundred and ten dollars every week, doesn't it?"

"Two hundred and ten? Yeah, yeah. Two hundred and ten. So what?"

"Just a minute, Mr. Pulvermacher, please. Now, how many times a day would you say each of your shipping clerks goes out with a delivery? I mean, how many trips does each one make? Just roughly, now, just an estimate. I don't expect you to make it accurate or anything like that, but just an estimate."

He rubbed his hand over his bald dome and shrugged.

"I don't know," he said. "How should I know?"

"Well, I mean roughly, you can make an estimate, just a guess."

"Well, I don't know—three-four times, maybe five—I don't know. How should I know a thing like that? I don't sit there watching them."

"You'd be surprised how right you are, Mr. Pulvermacher. I know because I've made a study of these things. The average shipping clerk goes out four or five times a day. All right, then. You say five times. But for the sake of my figures, just to allow for everything, we shouldn't take any chances, you know, let's say six. Let's say six times. Let's say every shipping clerk goes out six times a day with a delivery."

"All right," he said.

"So what've we got? We've got fourteen shipping clerks going out six times each, means, let's see, six times ten is sixty, and six times four is twenty-four, twenty-four and sixty—makes eighty-four. That means your shipping clerks make eighty-four trips a day. Right?"

"If you say it's right, so it's right."

"But Mr. Pulvermacher, I want *you* should say it's right. There's nothing wrong with my arithmetic, is there? Six times fourteen is—"

"Yeah, yeah, yeah. It's right. It's right. So what?"

"Now just one more little bit of figuring, and we're through," I said. "You're open here six days a week, aren't you?"

He nodded.

"So we have eighty-four trips a day, times six days in the week, means—here, wait." I pulled out a pencil and a pad and did the multiplication so he could see it. "That makes five hundred and four trips a week. So it should be easier to talk about, let's say five hundred. Five hundred trips a week. Right?"

He nodded again. Strong silent stuff. Maurice Pulvermacher and Calvin Coolidge.

"So what've we got?" I said, leaning back. "We've got five hundred trips a week for which you're paying out two hundred and ten dollars." I pointed the cigar at him. "If I were to tell you, Mr. Pulvermacher, that I could make those five hundred trips for you for a hundred and twenty-five dollars —meaning you'd be saving eighty-five dollars every week, maybe even more, but at *least* eighty-five—if I told you that, would you be interested?"

He shrugged and said, "Well, why not?"

He was lukewarm, but I wanted him hot.

"And suppose I were to tell you further, Mr. Pulvermacher"—it wasn't so bad, once you got used to it—"that you wouldn't have any labor troubles, you wouldn't have any strikes, you wouldn't have to worry about hiring shipping clerks, or anything like that. *And,* on top of all that, besides saving you the money, when the slow seasons come around, and there aren't so many deliveries, instead of paying fourteen shipping clerks they should sit around on their behinds all day, instead of that you'd only be paying for the few deliveries a day that they made, and you'd save twice as much as during the busy season, suppose I were to tell you that, what would you say?"

He lit his cigar, hunching himself around it, before he spoke.

"You been doing a lot of talking, Mr. Bogen," he said, "and all I been doing is listening, but I still don't see what you're driving at. How are you going to save me all this money and cut out all my labor troubles and all the rest of this *shmei-drei* you been talking about? How are you going to do it?"

"That's easy. I represent the Needle Trades Delivery Service, Inc." This is a free country, isn't it? "We specialize in deliveries in the garment district." You'd never guess that from the name. "For twenty-five cents a package," I said, "we'll deliver as many packages, bundles, boxes, or what-have-you, that you ask us to, any place in the neighborhood. At twenty-five cents each we'll deliver those five hundred packages for you. It'll only cost you a hundred and twenty-five dollars, instead of the two hundred and ten you're paying now. There won't be any shipping clerks to go out on strike on you. When it gets slow, and you don't have five hundred deliveries a week, it'll cost you just that much less. You pay as you go, twenty-five cents a package, and we do all the worrying. How does that strike you?"

He took the cigar out of his mouth and began to pinch his lower lip. I put my cigar into my pocket and lit a cigarette.

"What firms do you do this kind of work for?" he asked.

The clever little son of a bitch!

"I'll be frank with you, Mr. Pulvermacher." To a baloney

bender this is what's known as making a virtue out of a necessity. To me it's just using your head for something else besides a brace to keep your ears apart. "We've just started our organization," I said. "You're the first one we've approached."

"And why me?"

Well, *now* he'd let himself in for it.

"Because not only are you the president of the biggest and most representative firm of dress manufacturers on Seventh Avenue, Mr. Pulvermacher, but you're also the president of the Associated Dress Manufacturers of New York. That's why."

He smiled a little and plugged his mouth with the cigar. But he should have seen me. Inside I was laughing out loud.

"What good will it do your organization if we sign up for your service, if we're the only ones you're working for?"

"Ah, Mr. Pulvermacher, that's where you're wrong. Once we get you on our books, the rest of them will follow like sheep. You know that as well as I do. You know they do anything you say, Mr. Pulvermacher."

Maybe he didn't know it, but all you had to do was take one look at his squash to see that he believed it.

"Oh, I don't know," he said, waving the cigar at me. "What makes you so sure?"

Fore!

"I'll tell you," I said, taking a deep breath. "I happen to know that there's going to be a meeting of the A.D.M. this afternoon. Am I right?"

"Never mind," he said. "So?"

"And I also happen to know that the purpose of the meeting is to discuss the demands of the strikers for the last time, and, if necessary, vote to meet them. Right?" He didn't say anything. "Now, Mr. Pulvermacher, if you were to drop a bombshell into that meeting. If you were to tell them that they don't have to meet the strikers' demands, that they don't have to give in, because you know a way to beat the strikers at their own game, if you could tell them that, Mr. Pulvermacher, what would happen? Don't tell me," I said,

although he seemed to be about as ready to do that as I was
to kiss him. "Let *me* tell *you*. Two things would happen. The
members of the A.D.M. would think you're about the smartest man between here and Three Oaks, Michigan, which, I
don't mind adding, they wouldn't be far wrong." Boy, could
I sling it! "And, incidentally, the Needle Trades Delivery
Service, Inc. would go over with a bang."

He patted his belly, smiled, bit off the soggy end of his
cigar, spit it out on the carpet, and kicked it under one of the
classy-looking sofas.

"Ohhhhh, I don't know," he said slowly, meaning he
knew damn well, "maybe you're, well, over*est*imating my,
well, my, my *power* over the members of the Associated.
Maybe you're gambling a little too heavily on my ability to
swing them over to you. After all, I'm only a human being,
you know."

That's what *he* said. I wouldn't put any money on it unless
I saw an affidavit.

"Mr. Pulvermacher," I said, in the tone of voice that that
yoineh Nathan Hale must've used when he made that crack
about dying for his country, "Mr. Pulvermacher, I'm willing
to take that chance. No matter what the odds, Mr. Pulvermacher, the Needle Trades Delivery Service still puts its
money on you."

He jumped up quickly.

"You wait here, Mr. Bogen," he said. "I'll be back in a
couple of minutes."

He hurried across the room toward the door through
which he had come and before I knew it, I was alone.

Well, he was interested. That was sure. I lit a cigarette
and settled myself to wait.

I thought of Tootsie Maltz and that bunch of radical
schmiggeggies he hangs around with and how strikes are supposed to be second nature to them. They run strikes as regularly as they sit on the toilet. But if they had as much luck in
the crapper as they had with their strikes, they must've been
good and constipated. It was a lucky thing I'd come along

with a plan that required the running of a successful strike as part of it. They must've needed a physic pretty badly.

I had to laugh at the way I can do so easily all the things those other guys have to sweat their eyeballs off trying to do.

The door at the end of the room opened and little Pulvy came hurrying toward me, still watching his ass like he was afraid of putting another crack into it.

"All right, Mr. Bogen," he said, just the teeniest-weeniest bit excited, "all right. I'll talk to the Associated Dress Manufacturers this afternoon. Now, then, one thing. How soon can you start delivering for us? I mean, I've got to be able to give them some facts and dates this afternoon. How soon can you start delivering?"

"Give me two days," I said quickly. "Is that too long? Two days?"

"Two days!" he said. I could tell he was surprised, because he forgot that he was supposed to be a Seventh Avenue big shot and, for a few seconds, he looked like an ordinary Avenue C pushcart peddler in a set of trick clothes that all of a sudden didn't fit. "You can start deliveries in two days?"

"Sure," I said, getting up. "Two days."

8

I grabbed Tootsie before he went inside.

"What the hell is the matter with you?" I said. "You look sick."

"I'm all right," he said, but he didn't sound like he meant it.

"Well, you better be," I said. "I don't want to have to hire this lousy hall any more. I'm no Rockefeller. Three times is enough, understand? This has to be the last time."

"Okay, Harry, okay," he said. "Only—"

"Only what?"

"Well, it's kind of a tough assignment, you know."

If that little yellow baloney laid down on me now—

"Sure it's tough, Tootsie." I put my hand on his shoulder. "I know that. But what the hell, it has to be done, that's all. Think of all the dough we're gonna make. You don't expect it to come climbing up into your lap, do you? You've gotta work for it. This just has to be done, that's all. Just think of it that way, that's all, and you'll be all right. Aah, come on," I gave him a shove, "what the hell are you worrying about?"

"I'm not worried."

Oh, no, he wasn't worried! The other times he'd started to cry he'd been doing it just for the exercise.

"Then why don't you look alive a little, instead of moping like a—"

"Okay," he said, grinning a little. "I'm all right. I only hope it works."

"Don't worry," I said. "It'll work."

"I mean, I only hope they believe me."

He was making things clearer for me. Tootsie Maltz was explaining things, so I would understand them!

"Don't worry," I said. "They'll believe you."

I waited while he went up the steps. I wanted to give him time to get in. I didn't want anybody to see us going in together. Then I went up after him and into the hall.

He was still walking down the center aisle toward the platform when I came in. All eyes were following him, so nobody paid any attention to me. I leaned against the back wall, near the door, with a lot of others that had been unable to find seats.

Tootsie went up onto the platform and turned to face them. He opened his mouth once or twice, hesitating, but did not begin to speak until the entire room was quiet.

"I'm afraid I've got bad news, fellows," he said in a low voice. He took out his handkerchief and wiped the corners of his mouth. "I hate like hell to have to tell you this, fellows," he said, "but I'm afraid I'll have to." He folded the handkerchief carefully, then crumpled it in his fist and shoved it into his hip pocket. "You guys've put up a tough fight these last few days. You've earned the right to be told you've won this strike. And I wish to hell I could be standing here now telling you that, fellows." He shook his head and began to fish for the handkerchief again. "But I'm afraid I can't," he said. "I've got to tell you I just come from a meeting of the Associated, this afternoon." He'd finally gotten the handkerchief out again, and he was rubbing his chin with it as he talked. "They're not going to meet our demands," he said slowly. Then, faster: "They laughed at me again. The way they did the first time, before we went out on strike. They just laughed at me." He shook his head. "I'm afraid it's all over, fellows," he said tragically.

My eyes opened a little as I watched him. He was better when he was scared and worried than when he felt all right. It gave the whole thing the right note, sincere and sad.

"Where do you get that stuff, it's all over?"

Tootsie almost jumped out of his skin. He stared at the big, tough-looking guy in the middle of the room, and everybody else did the same.

"Where do you get that it's-all-over stuff?" the tough guy said again, his voice hard, but not loud, because the large room was so quiet.

Tootsie recovered himself quickly.

"Will you please do me a favor and sit down, so we can go on with this meeting?" he said in the same low voice.

"I'll sit down when I get good and ready," Tough Guy said. "In the meantime I wanna know what's all this business about it's all over? Where did you ever get that idea, that's what I want to know?"

For the first time since the whole thing started I was really worried. No matter how smart you are, you can't provide for *everything*. This was a delicate situation. I was afraid Tootsie would piss it all up. I wished I was up there on the platform instead of him.

"I get that idea from the meeting of the Associated Dress Manufacturers that I attended this afternoon," Tootsie said, and I breathed a little more easily. "That's where. If you'd only sit down instead of standing there holding up the works I'd have a chance to explain the whole thing so everybody would understand what—"

"I'm not worried about explanations," Tough Guy said, waving his hand at Tootsie. "I know all you guys with your explanations. You guys are lousy with explanations. You can do all that later. I just wanna know one thing. You trying to tell us that this strike is over, that we lost it? Is that what you're trying to tell us?"

The whole room leaned forward for his answer.

"That's right," Tootsie said quietly, but with his face stuck forward a little, like he was sore at being questioned. "That's what I've been trying to tell you, only you've been so—"

"Then all I can tell you is you're a goddam lotta crap, that's all." Tough Guy turned to face the crowd. "You hear what he's trying to tell us? We lost the strike! Why, we got every damn building on Seventh Avenue sewed up, and he's trying to tell us we lost the strike! Why, there ain't a single garment been moved out of any dress house in the whole stinkin' neighborhood in a week, and he comes bullshittin' around here with that crap about we lost the strike!" He turned back to Tootsie. "What the hell you think you're talkin' to, a kindergarten? We wasn't born yesterday."

The second he paused the rest of them broke loose.

"Yeah, yeah, that's right!"

"How the hell can we lose, when we got—?"

"Something's frigged up around here!"

"If this isn't a doublecross, then I don't know what."

"How the hell can those son of a bitches say we're losing, when—?"

I was all set to begin edging toward the door, when I took a look at Tootsie's face. He was just standing there, watching them, with a sort of tolerant half-smile on his map, as though he were waiting for them to pipe down a little before he'd let them in on a little information that would show them what a bunch of dopes they all were. It was so different from the scared, worried look he'd gone in there with, that I knew he'd gotten over it. I decided to stick around and see what happened. I looked at my watch and did a little lightning calculation. If he could only stall them for a little while longer, everything would still be all right. And from the look on his face I had a funny feeling that he could do it, too. Before he even opened his yap, I felt so relieved that I could've kissed him. Well, no, not exactly that. That was asking too much. But anyway, Tootsie Maltz's stock went up a couple of points with me.

"Do you guys mind if I get a word in edgewise?" he said good and loud, as soon as there was a break in the yelling and the noise. They must've run out of gas by then, anyway, so they began to quiet down a little, and soon you could hear Tootsie clearly. "I don't blame you guys for feeling the way you do. I felt the same way when I went to that meeting this afternoon. I went in there all cocky, because I knew we had them up against the ropes. But the minute I opened my mouth to repeat our demands to them, they just laughed at me again. Naturally, I couldn't understand it." He was talking so smoothly and seriously, that they couldn't help listening. I was even listening myself. "We're winning this strike, I said, but they only laughed again. You mean you *think* you are, they said, and then it didn't take me long to find out what made them so snotty. You known what they've been doing?"

He looked around the room, from side to side, and now there wasn't a single disturbing noise.

"They've been making deliveries at night," he said. "After we all went home, late at night, after eleven, until three-four in the morning, they've been backing up trucks, loading up dresses, and carrying them away. Before I had a chance to tell them what we were gonna do about *that,* they told me they knew what I was thinking and I could save myself a lot of trouble. You know what those wise bastards did? They hired a squad of private police, a couple of hundred of them, regular cops with guns, and these guys keep watch on the trucks while they're being loaded. You guys can keep on striking till next Christmas, they told me, but it won't make any difference to us. The dough we used to pay you guys, they said, we're paying these cops. They admitted it was costing them a little more, but they said they didn't care about that. They said they were only interested in one thing, fellows; they said they were gonna beat this strike. And they said one more thing," he added dramatically, "and I believe them, too." His voice dropped a couple of notches, but in that room the only effect was to make it sound louder when he spoke. "They said these cops had orders to shoot, to shoot anybody that tried to stop those night deliveries." He straightened up and spoke in a simple, matter-of-fact tone. "That's what we're up against—guns. And we can't fight back. Not that way. That's why I say it's all over."

He stepped back, to rest his can on the edge of the table. The voices started slowly, just a low buzz, then they grew louder and soon they were yapping away as much as ever. They weren't as violent, as sore, as they'd been before. They were too stunned. After all, they were only kids. It's one thing to chase another kid down the street in broad daylight and kick his fanny in because he's pushing a hand truck full of dresses. But it's another thing to get tough with big bruisers in uniform in the middle of the night, guys with guns and itching trigger fingers. But the disappointment was too great for them to keep their pans shut. They had to let off steam some way. And talk is cheap and safe. Here and there you could still hear somebody yelling "double cross" and "frame-up," but it wasn't loud enough or general enough to make any difference, and I would have let it ride.

But not Tootsie! All of a sudden, now that he saw they were licked, he became tough. Ten minutes before, when it was important for him to open up and say something, he had such a stranglehold on his mouth that you'd think he was giving away a pint of blood with each word. And now, when the smartest thing to do was to keep quiet, he became a stinking spellbinder.

"What do you guys mean, frame-up?" he demanded, shoving his scowling puss so far across the platform that you could have hung a kettle on his chin. Even I was startled. They shut up at once. "That's a hell of a way to talk. Didn't we work night and day for you guys? Is it our fault that those lousy truck drivers are scabs and that those lousy bosses hire cops with guns? What do you think *we're* getting out of this, anyway? Did we ask you guys for any dues or any contributions or anything like that? We ran this strike on our own. Who do you think paid for all those circulars and picket signs and for renting this hall and that sound truck and all that stuff? What do you think we do, go around and pick those things up in the street? Those things cost money and plenty of money, too."

So far as I was concerned, he was ad-libbing. And it wasn't bad, either. When it came to money, he talked with feeling. But my heart was in my mouth and I had my fingers crossed for fear he'd run away with himself so far that he'd let the cat out of the bag. Besides trying to swallow my heart and keeping my fingers crossed, I was doing another thing too. I was watching that door and praying. But dear old Tootsie was still talking.

"We took all this money and spent it because we figured it was a good cause. We wanted you guys to win that strike. After you won, we figured there was time enough to ask you guys to kick in your share of the expenses. But in the meantime we laid out all that dough. And we're not getting a cent of it back either. This thing has cost us plenty. We'd be the last ones to admit failure, wouldn't we? Why, if *you* guys wanted to quit and we thought there was half a chance we wouldn't let you. We wanted you to win even more than *you* did. What the hell kind of talk is that, frame-up! Why we'd be the last ones in the world to—"

The door in the rear opened with a bang and I breathed such a sigh of relief that my knees knocked together. A blue-uniformed Postal Telegraph messenger was walking down the aisle to the platform. That was the artist in me. Once khaki and Western Union, next time blue and Postal Telegraph. The kid handed the envelope to Tootsie and walked back.

Tootsie read the telegram to himself and then turned to the crowd with a sarcastic smile.

"As though we haven't got enough," he said. "Listen to this. It's from William Green, president of the American Federation of Labor." He read: *"Regret exceedingly neces-*

*sity for cancelling contemplated sympathy strike of truck
drivers' and elevator operators' unions. Stop. Present conditions render such move impracticable. Stop. Trust you will
carry on undaunted. Stop."*

Stop was right. In more ways than one. That was the end
of their squawking. And that was the end of Tootsie's career
as an extemporaneous speaker.

There was more to the telegram, but I didn't stay to listen.
Repetitions bore me.

9

WANTED! SHIPPING CLERKS!
WANTED!

We want one hundred (yes, 100!) shipping clerks to
start work immediately. Applicants with experience in
garment center preferred. Apply Room 2706, 224
West 37th Street. Needle Trades Delivery Service, Inc.

I tore the corner of the page out of my copy of *Women's
Wear* and stuffed it into my pocket.

I went over to the news stand and bought a copy of the
Daily News Record and hunted through it. There it was, on
page nineteen. I tore that out too. What the hell, I'm senti-
mental about those things. I like to save a copy of everything
I write. What with those circulars I had written for Tootsie
to mimeograph and distribute, and the speeches I had written
for him, and now these ads, it was getting to be quite a collection.

I went into the building and waited for an elevator. When
it started to move up I said, "Twenty-seven," and almost
added, "please." But I caught myself in time. I don't say
please to boogies.

When I got out on the twenty-seventh floor I took one
look and thanked God I'd had enough sense to insist on their
cutting in a side entrance to the loft before I signed the lease.

The front door was open and jammed with what looked like every unemployed shipping clerk on Seventh Avenue. Across their heads I could see into the large room. It was so crowded that I couldn't even see Tootsie, but believe me, I could hear him.

"I don't know, fellows," he kept yelling, "I don't know any more about it than you do. I got a letter from this Mr. Bogen and he told me to come up here this morning, he wanted to see me. That's all I know, fellows. I don't know any more about it than you do."

Which was probably more truth than poetry, the dumb baloney!

I took another look at the mob and congratulated myself once more. It was getting to be my favorite indoor sport, but what could I do? The occasions for it were so many, that I just couldn't help myself.

Pulvermacher must have talked turkey to those Associated Dress Manufacturers. Judging from the mob clamoring around that door it looked like not a single shipping clerk had been rehired after the strike was called off.

I used my key on the side entrance and went into the little private office I'd had them partition off for me. I hung my hat and coat on the rack and straightened my tie in front of the mirror. Not bad. I looked a little young, but I didn't let that worry me. In fact, it made me seem a little more important, running a thing like this and looking so young. Maybe it wouldn't be a bad idea if I tried raising a mustache. I put my finger on my upper lip and looked at myself in the mirror. No, it didn't look right. Anyway, I don't like mustaches. Combing and shaving were enough of a nuisance without adding something else to take care of.

I gave my tie a final pat, adjusted the handkerchief in my outside breast pocket, and lit a cigarette. Then I opened the door between the private office and the rest of the loft. The noise stopped at once and everybody looked at me, including Tootsie.

I walked toward them, until I was up to the wooden rail-

ing that fenced off part of the loft for a couple of desks and
chairs.

"Is there a Mr. Maltz here?" I asked.

"Yes," Tootsie said, putting up his hand. "Here I am. I
got a letter and—"

"I'm Mr. Bogen," I said, reaching out my hand. He took
it and we shook hands solemnly.

"I don't quite know what to make of this, Mr. Bogen,"
he began, holding out the letter.

The dumb schmooh! I told him to say, "I don't know what
this is all about, Mr. Bogen," but he's got to add a couple of
his own decorations. He didn't quite know what to make of
it, eh? Well, this was the last time Tootsie Maltz would ever
have a chance to screw up the works for me. From this point
on I took the helm. And what a relief that was! I swear, I
could rattle off at least eleven million times in the last couple
of weeks when I'd nearly gotten heart failure because of the
dumb things that came out of that mouth of his when he
opened it.

"I don't blame you," I said. I turned to the rest of the
crowd. "Suppose I clear the whole matter up for everybody,
then." I waved toward the gang that was jammed up around
the door and flowed over into the hall. "Can you all hear
me back there?"

"Yeah, sure."

"We can hear."

"All right, then," I said, resting my hands on the rail.
"Here's the situation. This organization, the Needle Trades
Delivery Service, Inc., is in the business of delivering packages, bundles, hand trucks, anything at all, for the manufacturers of Seventh Avenue. In the last couple of days, for
reasons that I suppose you're pretty well aware of, we've
received a tremendous number of new clients. In fact, we've
almost been overwhelmed with new business. In order for us
to function, we need men to work for us, to carry these
bundles for us. Naturally, with this new crop of accounts, we
need a new crop of delivery men. Our old staff is in no posi-

tion to handle the overwhelming amount of business we now have, so we are ready to put on a large number of men."

I paused and turned to Tootsie.

"This, Mr. Maltz, is where you come in. We've always worked with a rather small staff, and I have always been able to handle the whole thing myself. But now, with the huge staff that we shall be forced to employ, it will become necessary for me to get an assistant." I turned back to the others. "I have been an interested observer of the recent strike in the garment industry, and I don't mind admitting that I saw at once where my new business was coming from. I asked some of my new clients point-blank why they were signing up for our service, and they said they were not going to re-hire their old shipping clerks. I thought it only fair, therefore, since most of my new staff would probably come from the shipping clerks who were out on strike, I thought it only fair to hire as my assistant the man who, I have been given to understand, led the strike so brilliantly." Phooey! "In this way I will be doing myself a service, since I'll be getting a competent assistant, and I'll be doing the right thing by my new staff, since they'll be under the supervision of a man they knew and know they can trust."

If there were any rummies in that crowd to whom it appeared to be a little strange that I should be making such a big public stink about hiring an assistant, they had enough sense not to talk about it. They were here for the purpose of trying to get a job, and they weren't taking any chance on losing out before they even started by opening their traps. Not that there was any great danger. Shipping clerks are used to spending three-quarters of their time listening.

"If you'll please come in, then, Mr. Maltz," I said, "we'll be able to get started."

I held the gate in the railing open and he came in.

"Now the first thing we'll do," I said, "is take the names and addresses of all those who wish to apply for jobs. I don't know exactly how many we will be able to use, but I should judge it'll be about a hundred. So what we'll do is start off by hiring one hundred men to-day, and then—"

The roar that went up drowned me out, and I knew what was wrong. There must've been over three hundred there.

"Wait a minute men," I called, holding up my hands. "Just a minute men." When they quieted down, I continued. "I know there are more than a hundred here, and so we're going to do this as fairly as possible. Here's what we'll do. Every man will fill out one of these cards with his name and address. Then we'll mix them in a hat and I'll pick out a hundred of them. That hundred men will go to work immediately, to-day. The others I will keep on file, and as soon as we need extra men I'll send for those who have made out cards here to-day. Let me add," I said, raising my voice to stop any murmuring, "let me add that new accounts are coming in so fast, that the chances are we'll need plenty more before many days go by. So please help us out by doing this quietly and quickly, so that we don't have to kill the whole day."

I gave Tootsie a pack of printed applications and let him hand them around. They filled them out and handed them back and Tootsie dumped them into an empty wastepaper basket that I put on one of the desks back of the rail. Then I put my hand inside, shoved them around a little, and drew out small batches of them. Tootsie read off the names, and put the cards aside, keeping careful count of the number. When he had ninety, I began to take them out one at a time, until we hit one hundred.

"All right, men," I said, holding up the one hundred cards. "Will all those whose names were called, whose cards I hold in my hand, remain here, and will the others please leave?"

They filed out slowly, talking and shoving a little. When they were all gone, I motioned toward the door.

"Somebody please close that, will you?"

After the huge mob that had just been there, the one hundred that were left made the room seem empty.

"The next question to take up," I said to the gang we had hired, "is that of compensation." I figured I might as well show them I had the words to go with the fancy suit. "You men will be on a piece-work basis. You'll get a dime for every package you deliver, and twenty cents for every hand truck."

The arrangement I had made with Pulvermacher, and which went for the rest of Seventh Avenue, was two bits for every package and fifty cents for every hand truck. That meant we made a profit of fifteen cents and thirty cents per delivery. But these mockies didn't have to know how much we were making.

"Things are still tentative," I said, taking a piece of paper out of my pocket and looking at it as I spoke, "but judging from the number of accounts we have on our books right now, I should say we can almost guarantee you men about three deliveries an hour, say two packages and one hand truck, which means your compensation will average about forty cents per hour. Of course," I added, "with the way accounts are rolling in, the chances are this amount will be increased very soon. But for the time being, I can almost guarantee, as I said, I can almost guarantee you forty cents an hour. And we work, I might add, from nine to six, with one hour off for lunch. This is not a dress house, and we don't keep dress-house hours. Eight working hours a day, five days a week. No working late nights and no work Sundays, or Saturdays, unless it's something special."

I turned to Tootsie and then, as though I had remembered something. I turned back to them.

"Oh, yes," I said, "there's just one more thing, before I forget." Before I forget was good. Any time you catch me forgetting anything like this, just let me know. "Each one of you will have to deliver your first ten packages free, to pay for this." I pulled a cap out of the drawer of one of the desks and held it up. I had designed it myself, and it was a beauty. Red flannel, with a yellow band running around the edge, a stiff, black patent-leather visor, and right above it, standing up straight, so that it could be read easily, a metal plate with the words NEEDLE TRADES DELIVERY SERVICE, INC. engraved on it. For a moment I was sorry I hadn't called it the "Harry Bogen Delivery Service, Inc." "This is the only item of uniform that you have to wear," I said, "and we let you have

them at cost price. They cost us one dollar and that's what
we let you have them for. The price will be deducted from
your first week's salary. Now, let's see, is there anything
else?"

I scratched my head and squinted at the ceiling, pursing
my lips at the same time, the way all executives do.

"Well, then, I guess there's nothing else. Remember, you
report here every morning at nine and get your assignments
from Mr. Maltz or myself. When you get through with your
assignments, you come back here for more. I might add, men,
that the success of our business, as well as the size of your
weekly pay check, depends upon the speed and efficiency
with which we do our work. The quicker you deliver the
packages you get, the better pleased the customer is going to
be and the sooner you're going to get another set of assignments, which means the more money you'll have at the end
of the week. Any questions?"

"Yeah."

A big guy, whose face I remembered seeing at one or two
of the meetings in the Pythian Temple, got up slowly.

"What is it?"

"You say we'll be making about forty cents an hour?"

"About that. Yes."

"And we work eight hours a day?"

"It looks that way now. From the amount of business we
have booked right now, it looks like you'll all be kept busy
about eight hours a day. Of course, you realize how those
things are. There's no telling what—"

"But about eight hours, no?"

I nodded.

"That means a little over three dollars a day, doesn't it?
Eight times forty is three-twenty. A little over three dollars
a day, right?"

I nodded again.

"And five days a week, means about fifteen dollars a
week, maybe a little more, maybe a little less, but about
fifteen, no?"

"That's right," I said.

Well, at least here was one that knew how to multiply.

"Well, gee whiz," he said, like Columbus discovering that he wasn't in India but somewhere south of the Bronx, "that means we're no better off than we were before we went out on strike. It's the same fifteen dollars."

It looked like somewhere, I don't know just where, but somewhere in the shuffle, this bright lad had gotten the impression that the Needle Trades Delivery Service, Inc. had been organized for the purpose of seeing to it that shipping clerks should receive more money. I toyed with the idea of breaking the news to him that he was wrong, but I decided against it.

"We can't help *that,*" I said.

The hell with them. If they didn't like being shipping clerks, then let them take a crack at something else. The way I did. I didn't see anybody walking around worrying about me, so why should I worry about the rest of the world? Maybe I'm getting a little cockeyed, but I don't seem to see anything in the papers any more about eccentric old millionaires running around snatching hard-working, deserving young men out of poverty and rewarding them with fortunes.

"We can't help *that,*" I said again, shrugging and playing with the heavy deck of application cards that the two hundred shipping clerks who had been turned away had left with us. Nothing too obvious, you know. I just bounced them back and forth in my hand so that they should all see them and know what I meant. "That's the best we can do," I said. "After all, you know, you don't *have* to work for us."

10

I stopped in at the bank and cashed a decent-sized check.

"Better give it to me in singles and fives," I said to the teller. I wanted the roll to look important.

Then I went into the subway and took a 180th Street-Bronx Park Express. It was only a little after four and the trains weren't crowded yet. I got a seat. At least that was *one* advantage of being your own boss. You could leave whenever you wanted to and avoid the mob.

I got off at the last stop and walked up 180th Street. I went into the bakery on the corner of Daly Avenue and bought a cheese cake and a *Stollen.* Then I walked up the remaining two blocks and turned into Honeywell Avenue.

I paused in front of the house and looked at it. A couple of the neighbors were leaning out of their front windows. But I didn't pay any attention to them. I was doing a little calculating, trying to figure how much longer it would be before I could afford to move her into a decent place.

"One more month," I said to myself finally, "and out you go."

Or maybe two months. But whenever it would be, she was first on the list.

I rang the bell and walked up the stairs. She was holding the door open for me when I reached it.

Her face began to light up as soon as she saw me, but she squeezed the smile out of her lips and looked stern.

"Hello, Mom," I said grinning.

"Hello, Big Business Man," she said sarcastically, holding the door wide for me to pass her.

"How's the girl?" I said, and stooped to kiss her cheek quickly as I went by.

"Go on," she said, ducking away and making a threatening gesture. But she couldn't hold the smile back any longer. It broke out and spread all over her face. "I thought maybe you forgot the way home already."

"Aah, you know I'd never forget *that,* Mom," I said over my shoulder as I walked ahead of her to the kitchen.

"Yeah," she said, "I know. Then why weren't you home last night?"

"Aah, now, Mom," I said, "didn't I tell you it was the last day of our first month? Didn't I tell you I wanted to be downtown early so's I could look through the checks that came in the mail? Didn't I?"

I set the packages down on the kitchen table and turned

toward her. She was trying to wipe her hands on her apron and tuck her loose hair back at the same time. I put my arms around her quickly and kissed her, lifting her off the ground a few inches. In public I could kill guys that did things like that.

"Heshie!" she said sharply, but she put her own arms around me and kissed me back.

"Come on, now, Ma," I said, kissing her again. "Didn't I say I wouldn't be home for the night?"

"Sure you said it," she said. "But just the same you weren't home, were you?"

I laughed and hugged her, lifting her off the ground again.

"Say, you want to watch your figure, there, Ma," I said. "Pretty soon I won't be able to lift you up any more."

"Never mind," she said. "Don't tell me any stories. I weighed myself only yesterday."

"Yeah?" I said. "How much?"

For answer she walked over to the table and began to undo the packages.

"Come on, now," I said. "How much?"

She looked at me and we both began to laugh.

"It's okay, Ma," I said, putting my arm around her. "You put on as much weight as you want. I'll like you just the same."

"I know, Heshie," she said. "But promise me you won't stay away no more. It gets lonesome at night and I start worrying and I don't know what happened."

I snapped my fingers.

"That reminds me," I said. "That's another thing we're getting. A telephone."

"Don't try to mix me up what I'm saying," she said. "At least you could call me up by Mrs. Hirsch, from downstairs. Even three o'clock in the morning she would call me to the telephone. Last night, for a nickel, you could—"

"What?" I said. "And have Mrs. Hirsch know that I called up my mother?"

"What's the matter? It's something to be ashamed of?"

"Of course not," I said, "but she don't have to know my business."

Letting Mrs. Hirsch know something was like buying fifteen minutes on WEAF.

"But Heshie—"

"Aah, you don't have to worry about me, Ma," I said.

"Sure I don't have to," she said. "But what am I going to do when it comes night—oh, Heshie!" She'd finally gotten the packages open and seen the cakes. "You didn't forget!"

"Me forget?" I said. "How could I forget a thing like that?"

She broke off a corner of the cheese cake and bit into it. "A taste?" she said, holding it out to me.

"Later," I said, going over to the gas range and lifting the cover of a pot. "What, no blintzes?" I said, turning back to her.

"Of course, no blintzes," she said. "If you let me know in advance when you're coming home, I'll make you blintzes. But like this, you don't come home two nights, you don't call me up, you come home five o'clock in the middle of the day, without telling me anything, how should I know to make them?"

"That's a fine how-do-you-do," I said, striking a pose like an actor. "A hard-working son like me, I nearly wear myself out and kill myself starting a delivery business, so my mother should have diamonds and furs, and when it comes to a little thing like blintzes, I can't get them!"

"Stop already with the fancy speeches," she said, laughing. "Somebody would think I was starving you. So you'll have them to-morrow. But tell me, Heshie, how did it go with the business? Everything is all right?"

For answer I pulled out the roll of bills and held it up.

"*I* think everything is all right," I said. "How does it look to you, Ma?"

"Oy, yoy-yoy, yoy-yoy," she said, shaking her head a little and holding her hand to her face. "I thought you said it was a delivery business? You didn't tell me it was also a bank!"

"I thought you'd know that," I said reprovingly. "Would

I go into any business, Ma, if it wasn't at least as good as a bank?"

"Let me *tokke* take a look," she said, reaching for the roll.

"One second, Ma," I said, dodging her skillfully. I peeled off six fives quickly and held them out to her. "This is for you for the house," I said. "You ought to be able to make plenty of blintzes on that. You be a good girl, Mom, and make them like I like them, and you can have that every week. All right?"

"I should say it's all right," she said, looking important. "Business is business." She folded the money and put it into her small purse carefully. Then her face became pleasantly sad. "*Ai,* Heshie," she said, shaking her head, "you're a good boy."

Well, that was one thing about my mother. I was sure she liked me.

"This is nothing, Ma," I said. "This is only the beginning." I snapped a rubber band around the rest of the roll and held it out to her.

"Now take a look at the rest of it, Ma," I said.

She took it and squeezed it a little and bounced it in the palm of her hand. Then she handed it back to me.

"That's a lot of money for a young boy like you to carry around, Heshie," she said. "Maybe it would be better if—"

"Don't worry about it, Ma," I said. "Any time you want any, no matter how much or what for, you just ask for it. Okay?"

"I know that, Heshie," she said. "I wasn't thinking about that." Maybe she wasn't. "I was just wondering—" Her face took on a worried look. She leaned toward me a little as she spoke. "You're making it in a nice way?" she asked.

"Sure," I said. "All I have to do is stand on Forty-Second Street and Broadway in a full-dress suit and a silk hat and people go by and hand me twenty-dollar bills. It's so nice, I don't even have to touch the money. I wear white gloves."

The worried look disappeared from her face and a smile took its place.

"Now you're joking with me," she said. "But maybe it's

better I shouldn't worry. I'm sure if it's your business, Heshie, it must be nice."

That was *one* way of looking at it.

"For the time being," I said, "it'll do."

"I'm only a little worried," she said. "I mean, now you're making so much, what are you gonna do with—?"

"Come on, and I'll show you," I said, taking her hand. I led her through the kitchen and the foyer to the living room and stopped in the doorway. "First of all," I said, "look at that sofa. How long've we had it?"

"How should I remember a thing like that?" she said. "What's the matter, you think I have nothing else to do but to figure out how old every piece of furniture in the house—"

"Okay, okay," I said, patting her shoulder. "Don't start with the speeches, Ma. I just asked how long we've had the damn thing." She opened her mouth to say something, but I stopped her with a hug. "Never mind, Ma. Whatever it is, we've had it long enough. Well, that's where part of this is going." I tapped the money in my pocket. "First of all, the first thing, I'm going to buy a new sofa."

If I really wanted to, I could have moved her right then. But it wouldn't have been to as nice a place as I was sure I would be able to afford before very long. When I'd do it, I'd do it right. And besides, I don't like to make too big a splash right at the start. All it means is that later, if something goes wrong, you look like twice as big a jackass.

"The next thing is this," I said. I led her over to the armchair and said, "Sit down, will you, Ma?"

She pretended she didn't know what I was up to.

"Heshie," she said, "I got things on the stove—"

"They won't run away," I said. "Come on, Ma." I took her arms and pushed her into the chair gently. "There. Now, how does it feel?"

"Go tell him how it feels!" she said. "How do you expect it should feel? Like an elephant? It feels like a chair!"

"That's what *you* say, Ma," I said, laughing. "To me it feels like a coal pile."

"Since when did you get such a soft behind?" she asked,

smiling up at me. "All these years it was good enough, it felt like a chair. For your father, he should rest in peace, it felt good enough. For me it felt good enough. For you, even, it felt good enough. But all of a sudden, from a clear sky—"

"All right, Ma," I said. "So *that's* settled. So we're getting a new chair."

She broke into a laugh and slapped my hand.

"It's yet a lucky thing for the world that my Heshie didn't all of a sudden decide he wants to wear his hat on his feet," she said.

I looked at her.

"What?"

"Because otherwise," she said, "you could be sure that before long the world would be walking on its head."

"Aw, don't say that, Ma," I said. "I don't want you to think I'm trying to *force* a new chair on you. If you don't want it, you just say the word, Ma, and I won't—"

"All right, all right, all right," she said, still laughing. "So we'll get a new chair. Maybe it'll be easier to keep clean. What else?"

I looked around the room at the dinky table, the cheap radio, the old horse of a mirror, the oilcloth rug, the old-fashioned pictures on the wall, the string portieres.

"Aah, hell," I said, waving my hand to take in the whole room. "Everything. We'll throw the whole damn junk out and—"

"What kind of throwing out?" she said, sitting up in the chair. "Who do you think you are, Rockefeller? You want to buy new things, all right. But we're not throwing out anything. You want to get rid of it, so all right, we'll sell it to the junk dealer or somebody. But what do you think, money grows on trees?"

"For some people it does, Ma."

"For dopes," she said. "Only dopes they think money grows on trees. A smart person doesn't think like that. A smart person, even he's *got* plenty money, he still doesn't go around like a dope thinking money grows on—"

"All right, Ma," I said. "Money doesn't grow on trees and

we won't throw this junk out. We'll sell it. Then we'll get new stuff. All right?"

"All right," she said. "Now, Mr. Millionaire, what are you going to do with the rest of that money?"

"Plenty," I said. "But first I'm going to take you out and buy you some fancy new clothes."

"What's the matter?" she said sharply. "All of a sudden my clothes aren't good enough for you?"

"Sure they're good enough for me, Ma," I said. "But they're not good enough for *you*. I want you to have——"

She got up and put her arm around me.

"Remember, Heshie," she said, "The banks need customers, too."

"Don't worry," I said. "I'll be getting around to them."

"To the banks, Heshie, you should go *first*."

"There's no rush, Ma," I said. "The longer I wait the more they'll have to shell out with when I get ready to take them over."

She laughed and shook her head.

"Come on," she said, "you're such a good boy, I'll make you some blintzes."

"But what about the stuff you already got on the stove?" I said.

"Don't stick your nose in my pots," she said. "Let me worry about the cooking. You want blintzes, so I'll make you blintzes. The other things we'll save for to-morrow, or we'll throw it out or——"

"What kind of throwing out?" I said, imitating her voice and scowling. "Who do you think you are, Mrs. Rockefeller?"

"Good things you learn quick," she said, laughing.

"Not good things, Ma," I said. "Smart things."

"Is the same," she said.

"Maybe," I said.

"So all right," she said. "So we won't throw it out. So we'll save it for to-morrow."

We went into the kitchen arm in arm, laughing. I sat down at the kitchen table, and she began to mix the batter.

I rolled up my shirtsleeves and stretched my legs far under the table and watched her. It felt good to be looking at her. I realized suddenly that this was the first rest, the first real rest, I'd had in weeks. It was always that way when she was around. It was like putting your arm on a log after a tough swim. That's why I didn't like to see the gray hair. It scared me a little to think that some day there wouldn't be a place to reach out and touch and draw a deep breath and rest a while.

"Here, Ma," I said, taking the bowl of batter from her. "Let me mix that. You mash the potatoes and fry the onions."

After a few moments she looked up from the gas range and said, "What are you looking at, Heshie?"

"Nothing, Ma," I said. "I was just thinking, why don't you —why don't you go to the beauty parlor once in a while, like the other women?"

Take it from me, it's no cinch telling your own mother she isn't perfect.

She stopped pounding the potatoes to stare at me.

"What are you all of a sudden, Heshie, a little crazy?"

"What do you mean, crazy?" I said. "All the other women do it."

"If all the other women are going to run up on the roof and jump off, so I'll have to do it, too?"

"That's not the idea, Ma," I said. "It's just that you're still a young woman. Why shouldn't you—?"

"Aah, Heshie, please! Don't talk like a baby," she said, bending over the pot in her lap. But I could see her blush a little and I knew she was pleased. "What are they going to do in the beauty parlor, make a young chicken of sixteen out of me again?"

"No," I said, "but they could make you look as young as you really are, and not older."

"Yeah," she said, trying to sound sarcastic and taste the mixture of mashed potatoes and fried onions at the same time, "they're going to make me look young!"

"Of course they will, Ma," I said. "They touch up your

hair a little and they manicure your nails and they fix up your eyebrows—"

She set the pot of potatoes down suddenly and shook with laughter.

"What's so funny about that?" I asked.

"You," she said. She held up her clean, worn hands, with the dishwater scars all over them. "In the first place, the girl in the beauty parlor, she'll take one look at these hands, she'll get the cholera. And secondly, other boys, they come your age, they go into business, they make a little money— they start looking around for a nice quiet girl she should make a good wife. But you, instead you should look around for a wife, you start sending your mother to beauty parlors."

"So what's wrong with that?"

"It's not wrong," she said. "It's just crazy, that's all."

"All right," I said, "so it's crazy. But don't forget, there, I like some cheese blintzes, too, not only potato ones."

"Aah, you always eat with your eyes, Heshie," she said. "This is enough."

"Never mind," I said, grinning at her. "By me it's not blintzes unless I get both kinds."

She went to the icebox and took out the cheese.

"I'd just like to see if your wife, when you get one, if she'll cook for you two kinds of blintzes also."

"Don't worry," I said. "I'll find that out in advance. No blintzes, no wife."

She looked at me slyly.

"Maybe you got already a girl, you're keeping it a secret?" she said.

I looked at her as though I had been highly insulted.

"Ma!" I said. "Would I keep a secret from you?"

"So all right, then," she said. "If you haven't got a girl, I'll get you one. I got one that's for you just right."

Maybe it wouldn't have so many curves. But it'd be kosher all right. Leave it to Mama.

"Don't do me any favors, Ma," I said. "Just watch out for those blintzes, there."

Unless my nose had suddenly lost its sensitivity, my guess

was that the old lady had been giving this matrimonial business a little more than just a passing thought. If I knew what was good for me, I'd get her mind onto other things, quick.

"Did you ever hear of such a thing?" she said, addressing the frying pan as she poured the batter in. "Instead of thinking about a wife, he's worrying about stuffing his stomach."

"That's the way it should be," I said. "Wives are easy to get. But blintzes like these—aah, Ma, that's not so easy to find. You ought to see some of the junk they give you in restaurants."

She picked the hot thin pancake out of the frying pan with a fork, put it on a plate, and rolled it full of mashed potatoes. She worked swiftly and silently at this, the most important part of the process. But I knew she was thinking deeply, because when she set the first plate of hot blintzes before me, she said:

"Maybe you're right, Heshie," she said. "Maybe you got time with a wife. Maybe you got other plans, hah?"

If my biographer ever wanted to find out from which side of the family I got my brains, I guess he wouldn't have much difficulty.

"Sure I got other plans," I said. "I always have other plans, Ma."

"Maybe now you've got a little more money, now you don't work so hard, Heshie, maybe now," she said hopefully, "you'll go to school at night like Papa wanted you should, and you'll become a lawyer?"

My dear Mrs. Bogen, unless you drop your recently acquired critical tone, and pay more strict attention to business, I'm afraid we'll have to drop you from the payroll.

"Aah, Ma, please," I said gently. "Let's not start that all over again."

"Why not, Heshie?" she said, sitting down across the table from me. "You know it's what Papa always wanted you should be. And now, now you got a business, you're making money, you're still young, you could go at night easy. Plenty boys they study at night and they become big lawyers. What's the matter? They're smarter than you? You're just as smart as they are." Smarter yet! "If by Mrs. Heimowitz that dumb Murray of hers, *he* could become a lawyer by studying at night, then you could do it in a one, two, three, Heshie. You know that."

"Sure I know it, Ma," I said. "But what's the sense of me wasting my time? You know what lawyers are making today? You know how many of them are starving? Why, for crying out loud, Ma, I make more in one week in that delivery business of mine, than most lawyers they make in a *year.*"

"That's nothing, Heshie," she said. "For a good one, there's always room."

"You must've been listening to Mrs. Heimowitz again," I said, reaching for more blintzes. "That's what they all say. For a good one there's room. They're crazy. For a good one there's *never* enough room. Well, I'm good, Ma, and there's plenty of room all right, but not in the law business. Not for me. I got bigger plans than that."

"All right, Heshie," she said, "so you *don't* make so much money at the start. But look at the respect. Look how nice it is for Mrs. Heimowitz she should walk down the street and everybody should say that's the lawyer's mother. Don't you want people should look after *your* mother and say that?"

"No," I said. "I want people should look after my mother in the street because she's wearing diamond rings and fur coats and they should say there goes Mrs. Bogen, she's got a good son."

"But Papa, when he was alive, he always wanted—"

"Yeah, I know," I said. "I know what Papa wanted. But that's just what was the trouble with Papa. That's why we lived on the East Side and in the Bronx all our lives on twenty bucks a week. Because Papa couldn't be bothered figuring out what was the best and quickest way to make money. He had to waste his time figuring out what was the highest-class fancy—"

"Heshie!" she said sharply. "Is that a way to talk?"

"I know, Ma," I said. "I'm sorry. It's just that every time

we get started talking about it, we end up the same way. Now, look. If I'd've listened to you and to what Papa said I'd still be working as a shipping clerk for fifteen dollars a week and tearing my eyes out going to school at night. Like this, I'm still young, I got my own business, we got plenty of money, we can begin to live right, we can buy what we want, we can—"

"All right, Heshie," she said with a sigh. "All right."

I got up and came around the table toward her.

"So come on, Ma," I said, kissing her. "Let's stop fighting and arguing and let's go out for a walk and to buy a couple of things. All right?"

"All right," she said.

I helped her with the dishes and then she got dressed and we went out.

We walked down the street together, stopping every once in a while to talk to the neighbors sitting in chairs on the sidewalk. What I liked about her was the way she could make even a simple thing like that seem important and dignified, not kikish and washwomanish like the rest of them.

As we came near the 179th Street corner she nudged me and spoke in my ear.

"There's that Mrs. Heimowitz," she said. "That's the one that her Murray is a lawyer."

"She looks it," I said. "You'd think a lawyer'd be ashamed to have his mother wear a worn-out pair of shoes like that. What's the matter, can't he afford to get her a new pair?"

"Ssshhh," Mother said, and then, "hello, Mrs. Heimowitz."

"Hello, Mrs. Bogen," she said. "Your son is home early, isn't he?"

I smiled and nodded and Mother said, "Yes."

"The lawyer isn't home yet," Mrs. Heimowitz said with a sigh. "He works so hard, and such important work, yet too, he doesn't get home till I don't know when."

"Tsk, tsk," Mother said. "My Heshie, he took a half a day off from his business he should come home to take his mother out shopping a little."

"Nice going, Mom," I said out of the corner of my mouth as we moved on.

"She always shows off that lawyer son of hers in front of me," she said bitterly.

"Don't worry about it," I said, patting her arm. "I'll get you a couple of things to-night that'll give you a chance to show off to her until she'll get blue in the face."

We turned into Tremont Avenue and walked until we reached a dress shop.

"This is our first stop," I said, as we went in.

I didn't even give her a chance to look over the first selection that the salesgirl trotted out. I took one look at the price tags and sent them back.

"Haven't you got anything more expensive than this?" I said.

"Why, yes, sir. I didn't know—"

"Bring out the best you've got," I said.

"Heshie!" Mother whispered to me sharply. "That's no way to buy! They'll think you're a dope and charge you anything they want."

"Don't worry about it, Ma," I said. "You just pick out what you want. I'll handle the rest."

For a while she couldn't seem to make up her mind. There were six on the rack. Three of them were simple and quiet and expensive-looking. The others were flashy and cheap and just the kind of stuff I hate. But this was her party and I wasn't butting in. She could have whatever she wanted.

"I don't know which one to take," she said finally.

"What do you mean, 'which *one*'?" I said. "You go ahead and pick yourself two or three."

"What's the matter with you, Heshie?" she said, laughing. "Are you crazy to-day?"

"I'm not crazy," I said, "and you're not taking only one dress. You're taking at least two. Understand?"

She stood there, hesitating.

"What's the matter, Ma?" I asked.

"I can't make up my mind," she said. "I like these." She pointed to the three simple, quiet ones. "But—"

"But what?"

"But since you gave me that long speech about the beauty parlor," she said, "I'm just thinking, maybe I ought to get these—" she pointed to the flashy ones—"maybe they'll make me look a little—a little younger."

I laughed out loud and gave her a big hug, right in the middle of the store. All of a sudden I felt a new way about my mother. All of a sudden I felt proud of her.

"Gee whiz, Ma," I said, "you're a corker, all right. Go ahead and take the ones you like," I said, "and don't take all that beauty parlor talk too seriously. I was only kidding anyway."

"All right, then," she said to the salesgirl. "I'll take this one."

She pointed to one of the nice-looking dresses.

"What's that?" I said sharply.

"I said I'll take this one," she said.

"That's what I *thought* I heard," I said. "What did I say about this one dress business, hah?"

"Oh, Heshie," she said, "Don't act like a baby. One dress is enough for—"

"Never mind," I said, and turned to the salesgirl. "Are all these dresses my mother's size?"

"Yes, sir."

"All right," I said, "then wrap them all up."

"All three, sir?"

"All three."

"But Heshie—!"

"But Mama!" I said, imitating her voice. I felt so good about her having had the taste to pick something dignified, and not something that would make her look like a loud Bronx blouse, that I was willing to buy out the shop for her. "How are you going to make Mrs. Heimowitz eat her heart out if you haven't got enough dresses to wear a new one every day?"

"All right, Heshie," she agreed, shaking her finger at me. "But remember, that's all."

"That's all nothing," I said. "The Bronx is full of shoe stores and hat shops and underwear shops, isn't it?"

She slapped my shoulder playfully.

"I don't want you should waste your money like that, Heshie," she said.

"Who says it's wasting it?" I said, hugging her. "I don't know why, but to me it's a pleasure, Ma."

II

Take me, for instance. I can read the handwriting on the wall long before it's even written.

The trick is simply to recognize that it's writing. Sometimes it doesn't look like it. Sometimes it looks like Miss Marmelstein.

"And what did you say your last name was?" I said, letting my eyes take their time as they crossed the Alps.

"Marmelstein," she said.

"All right, Miss Marmelstein," I said, "then you know what's wanted of you." Or did she? "You can take your things off and get to work."

"Thank you, Mr. Bogen."

I nodded briskly and turned back to the papers on my desk. Baby, I thought, wait till we get around to the point where I'm thanking *you*.

I got up and walked to the filing cabinet at one side of the room. I opened the top drawer and began to thumb through the papers in it. I didn't have to. I wasn't looking for anything. But standing in that position, leaning over the pulled-out drawer, I could get a clear view of her in profile, as she sat at the switchboard, with her chest sticking out in a way that did my heart good.

She knew I was looking at her because I could see her face grow red and she put her hand up to the back of her neck to adjust the wave in her hair. Once or twice she almost turned around to face me, but she caught herself in time and kept her eyes fixed on the switchboard.

I laughed to myself when I thought of what her face would look like if I went up to her and told her what I was thinking. The temptation was so great that I almost walked over and began to speak.

Hello, Miss Marmelstein. How are you? That's good. Oh, all right, thank you. Can't kick. Don't strain yourself, Miss Marmelstein. You don't have to lean forward *that* far. In fact, Miss Marmelstein, you could have taken a day off to-day. I mean, for a change, you could have worn a brassiere to-day. What? Oh, pardon me. I didn't *think* I was being subtle. No, of course not. I don't mind. What I mean is, Miss Marmelstein, it's no go to-day. There, there, now. Don't take it that hard. You do? Well, I don't really blame you. From what I understand, that's the best way to take it. No, please, please, it's not that. No reflection on your ability at *all,* Miss Marmelstein. Look, Miss Marmelstein, suppose you stop working so hard waving that chest of yours under my nose. Fine. There, that's better. But—ha, ha, ha— I'm not displeased, though. It's a good thing to find out. But not to-day. Some other time, maybe. To-day, Miss Marmelstein, to-day you're a piece of handwriting on the wall, that's what you are. Ha, ha, ha. You don't? Why, that's easy. Let me translate. You, of all people, should know how a good thing gets around. Doesn't it, though? The competition gets terrific, doesn't it, Miss Marmelstein? Before you know it, there are *too* many people around. And then, of course, there's only one smart thing to do. And that's to go and find something else. Yes, indeed, Miss Marmelstein, we're both in the same boat. A thing that's as good as my business can't help getting a reputation. And all you need, Miss Marmelstein, is a reputation. You know that. My bet is that before long there'll be dozens of people in the delivery business. But I won't be one of them, Miss Marmelstein. Because I've seen the handwriting on the wall. And I'm getting out, Miss Marmelstein, while I'm still the only one that can see it. Do I make myself clear? That's it. That's it exactly. I'm going to cash in while I'm ahead. I *do* make myself clear? Good. You do? Well, that's too bad. Because frankly, Miss Marmelstein, if I was as talented in one direction as you are, I wouldn't *want* to learn anything else. Oh, now, please. It's not that at all. I *would* teach you, if I could, Miss Marmelstein. But I'm afraid it won't do. When it comes to a talent like that, Miss Marmelstein, it's a lot like your figure. Votes don't count. You're either born that way, or you aren't. So it doesn't help to stuff the ballot boxes or pass out dime cigars. Miss Marmelstein! Please! I told you I wasn't— Oh, well, all right. Let's.

I walked back to my desk and moved around the papers on top of it for a few minutes. Then I took my hat and went over to the switchboard.

"I'm going out, Miss Marmelstein," I said, staring hard at her. They looked like the money, all right, but the way they built brassieres nowadays, you never could tell. Still, this looked like it was worth the trouble of finding out. "I'll be back a little late. You can put my messages in the book and I'll—but wait. I'll tell you what. I'll try to get back before six. You wait for me, will you? I'm going out to see some people, and I may want to dictate a couple of letters when I get back. I'll try to get back as early as I can."

Well, I said I'd *try*, didn't I?

"All right, Mr. Bogen," she said.

As I walked down the street I kept meeting my clients. I nodded and said hello and moved on. By the time I reached the bank I was good and sore. My business was good. But compared with some of the heels whose bundles my men schlepped at two bits a piece, my take was chicken feed. I had more on the ball than they had, and there was no reason why I couldn't deal myself a couple of hands from the same deck. Why should I be jockeying their bundles? Why shouldn't I be in a position where I was hiring guys to make deliveries for me?

I didn't bother trying to figure out the answer to this one. As far as I was concerned there wasn't any. I was glad I'd

run into those clients. Now I knew what my next move was
going to be.

"Give it to me in fives," I said to the teller.

It was Thursday, Mama's payday. I got a kick out of giving it to her in small bills, so that it felt like a lot. It was a
pleasure to hand it to her. In fact, if I didn't keep close
watch on myself, I would've found myself not only giving
it to her in a big wad, but also made up of big bills. That's
the kind of soft-hearted dope I am. But there was no hurry.
When my next move went through, she'd get her cut. I'd see
to that. For me, the world owed her a little extra.

When I got out, I stood in the street, hesitating. Three-
thirty in the afternoon, and nothing to do. That was progress
for you. But I wasn't satisfied. There were guys who had
nothing to do after as early as twelve o'clock. And there
were some who didn't have to go to work at all, weren't
there? Well, at least I had a goal.

I decided to go up to the Capitol.

When I got out, the clock on the Paramount said six-thirty.
But I didn't hurry. I knew my customers. She'd be there.

I came into the office briskly, though, like I'd just settled
a deal for moving Pennsylvania Station over to Forty-Second
Street and shifting Grand Central over to Thirty-Third.

She was at the switchboard, typing away busily.

"Sorry to be so late," I said, "but I was detained at a
conference."

"That's all right, Mr. Bogen," she said.

It was, eh? Well, we'd soon see.

I breezed into my private office, slammed the drawers of
my desk around a little, then came out again, holding a
blank sheet of paper.

"What's that you're working on?" I asked.

"The bills," she said. "Mr. Maltz said it's the first of the
month—"

"Good for Mr. Maltz," I said.

"I beg your pardon, Mr. Bogen?"

"Don't bother," I said. "Mr. Maltz was just telling you it
was the first of the month and—"

"And he said I should type up the bills," she continued. "He said they had to be in the mail to-night."

"That's right," I said. "By the way, where *is* Mr. Maltz?"

"Why, he's not here, he—"

"You mean that?"

She looked startled, then she saw my smile and she smiled too.

"I mean, he left a short while ago. He said he had an appointment."

"Oh," I said. "For a while, from what you said, I thought he was hiding under a desk or something."

That one was pretty lousy, but what the hell, when you're paying them a salary, they laugh at the lousy ones, too. She laughed.

"No, Mr. Bogen. He left. He said he had an appointment."

"We-ell, I'll tell you," I said, scratching my head and looking at the piece of blank paper in my hand, "I wanted to give you a couple of letters on this, but—" I looked at the typewriter. "—But Mr. Maltz was right. Those bills have to be in the mail to-night. Otherwise we don't get our checks in on time. I'll tell you what," I said suddenly, like Morgan deciding to float a small loan for England. "Those bills are a good hour's job. It's almost seven now. Suppose we both go down for a bite, then, when we come back, I can give you these letters, and after you've finished typing up the bills, and while you're typing these letters for me, I'll give you a hand with folding the bills and putting them in envelopes. Like that we'll both get out earlier. What do you say?"

"All right," she said quickly.

Well, well, well. This was going to be interesting.

"Wait'll I get my hat," I said.

There goes another rule, I said to myself as I adjusted the brim in the mirror. And a good one, too. Never crap where you eat. But I don't worry much about breaking rules. As long as I know them, that's enough for me.

And besides, this was different. I was paying her a salary anyway, wasn't I? And the office rent was the same whether I used it eight hours a day or twenty-four, wasn't it? And besides, that rule was only for rummies, to see that they don't get themselves tied up. Which was something I didn't have to worry about. I don't get myself tied up.

12

A week later I was watching Tootsie through the crack in my door. I waited until he put on his topcoat and hat and began to pull on his gloves.

"Say, Tootsie!" I called.

He stopped short and looked quickly toward my room, but I knew he couldn't see me. The opening wasn't wide enough.

"Can I see you for a minute, Tootsie?"

I spoke in a loud voice so he could hear me through the partitions.

"Sure," he said, coming back. "Be right in," he said and began to wrestle out of the coat.

"You can come in the way you are," I said. "I won't keep you long."

He stopped fooling with the topcoat and looked like a kid that's been caught in the icebox. Then he tried to get back as far into the coat as he'd been when I called him, at the same time walking toward my room. The result was that when he came in, he looked like something the cat forgot to drop at the door. It's a funny thing about clothes. If you've got the build, and you know how to carry them, you can look like a million bucks in a nineteen-seventy-five. But if you haven't got that natural feel for clothes, it doesn't make any difference how much you spend on them. There was Tootsie, standing before me in one of the snappiest numbers that Kolmer-Marcus ever put out. I'd helped him pick it myself and I'd seen him lay seventy-five dollars in American money on the counter for it. But for all the good it was doing his appearance, he could have left it hanging in his closet.

"I'll tell you what I wanted you for," I said, and stopped

as though I had just noticed something. "Say, your coat there, it's on all cockeyed. The collar's bent in."

"Yeah—I—I was," he began, flushing and stuttering all over the lot as he tried to straighten the coat out over his form. He could have saved himself the trouble. Nothing would ever fit him right. He was built like a dumbbell.

"Well, I'll tell you," I said, turning back to the papers on my desk, "if you're in a hurry, then suppose we let it go till to-night."

"I'm not in any hurry," he said. "If you want—"

I turned around to look at him.

"You're not in any hurry?" I said.

"Well, I mean—I—I mean, if there's anything you *want*, I—"

"That's all right," I said. "It'll keep. I'll see you about it some other time. There's no rush. To-night is time enough."

"Okay," he said, and turned to go.

"That is," I added, "if you can tear yourself away by to-night."

He whirled around.

"What do you—?"

"Skip it, Tootsie," I said, smiling at him. "Skip it."

After all, I'd done him out of it once before. But that was the first night, when I had to show him who was boss. Now, though, there was no need for another demonstration. I might just as well give him a break. God knows, there weren't many times when a guy could afford to be generous. Why be a louse, when I didn't have to be? A guy has to give up his principles *some*times.

"Let's make it for to-night," I said. "Okay? I want to talk to you about something."

"Well, I won't be back to-night," he said.

I raised my eyebrows. Maybe another demonstration *was* in order.

"I beg your pardon?" I said elaborately, putting my palm behind my ear. "Did I understand you to say you're *not* coming back to-night?"

He dropped his eyes from mine.

"I mean, Harry," he said, "I mean I made arrangements to go up to the mountains for the week end. I didn't know you—"

"Oh!" I said, dropping back in my chair and waving my hand at him. "That's *different*. I didn't know that. I just thought I heard wrong, that's all. You go right ahead, Tootsie. Monday is all right."

"I'm here now, ain't I? If you wanna—"

"Shall we make it Monday morning?" I said with a grin. "Say, about nine-thirty or ten? That ought to give you time enough."

"Listen, Harry. You can't—"

"Nine-thirty Monday morning, Tootsie?"

He opened his mouth and then closed it. "Okay," he said, "I'll be back Monday," and went out.

I wasn't positive yet, of course. But I was certain that before long I would know what I needed Tootsie for. I had a hunch I'd know why I hadn't tossed him out on his tail as soon as the delivery service was going good.

I picked up the receiver and spoke to Miss Marmelstein.

"Get my home," I said.

A few moments later Mother was on the wire.

"Hello, Ma."

"Hello, Heshie," she said. "What's the matter?"

"What do you mean, what's the matter?" I said. "Does something have to be the matter before a fellow can call up his mother?"

"God forbid," she said. "But just the same, what's the matter?"

"Nothing's the matter," I said. "I just wanted to try out the new telephone. How does it feel to have a telephone in the house? How do *you* feel?"

"How should I feel?" she said. "The same as I felt when you left in the morning. All right. And how do you feel?"

"I feel all right, Ma," I said.

"So I feel all right and you feel all right," she said. "So it's perfect. Now, Heshie, what's the matter?"

I laughed.

"You're okay, Ma," I said. "Try and put one over on you, hah?"

She laughed too.

"Well, you can try, Heshie," she said.

"All right, then, Ma," I said, "I'll tell you why I called. I wanted to know how the blintzes situation was."

"Oh, my God!" she said. "How could a person eat so much? Three times you had them last week. And now, now you want them again!"

"Can I help it, Ma, if you make them so good?"

"Never mind with the fancy talk," she said. "By you it's easy to talk. You say a couple words, you tell me they're this, they're that, they're wonderful, and me, like a dope, I have to start working over the hot stove. So it'll be without blintzes to-night, Heshie. Kill you, it won't. It's not good you should eat so much the same thing. I'll make you a nice piece spring chicken for to-night. You'll have blintzes again in a couple days, maybe next week."

"Aah, Ma, don't be like that," I said. "I wanted to bring a friend home for supper to-night. Here I been talking about your blintzes to everybody, and now, now I'm bringing somebody home to try them, so you're not going to make them! I ask you, Ma, is that nice?"

"Oh, you're bringing somebody home, hah?" Her voice dropped a bit. "Who is it?"

"Just a friend, Ma."

"A boy, or a girl?"

"Ma, will you stop trying to marry me off," I said. "It's not a girl. It's just a friend of mine. A business friend. And I want him to—"

"All right, Heshalle," she said cheerfully. "I was just fooling. What time will you be home?"

"Oh, I don't know, Ma," I said. "Around six or seven. That be okay?"

"Yeah, sure, plenty time," she said.

"Okay, then, Ma, thanks. I'll see you to-night."

"All right, Heshie. Good-bye."

I took my hat and coat and stopped at the switchboard on my way out.

"I'm going over to Pulvermacher, Betschmann & Kalisch," I said. "If a Mr. Babushkin calls me from there, tell him I'm on my way over. If anybody else calls, just take the message. Tell them you don't know where I am. Got that, Miss Marmelstein?"

"Yes, Mr. Bogen," she said, giving me one of those tragic movie glances that made her look like she ate something that didn't agree with her. But I kept on moving toward the door. I don't let those things worry me. Just because I slipped her the business once, that doesn't change our relationship. She was still an employee of mine, and I was still paying her a salary.

When I got up to Pulvermacher, Betschmann & Kalisch, Inc. I went into the shipping room and spoke to the man in charge of it.

"Hello, Singer," I said. "Everything all right?"

"Yes, Mr. Bogen," he said. "Everything's fine."

"Packages moving out on time?"

"Oh, yes. Everything's okay."

"That's fine," I said, making a notation in my pocket notebook for his benefit. "Remember, now, any complaints, or anything like that, you just let me know, and somebody'll get hell."

"I know that, Mr. Bogen," he said. "But so far everything is fine."

"Good," I said. "Now, on these air-mail packages, Singer. If that's going to be a regular thing with you, I mean, if you're going in for it big, you let me know and I'll have one of my boys ready for you every day at two-thirty so you can get them on the first plane west. I noticed here—" I looked at my notebook—"you had almost twenty for Chicago and Los Angeles last week. You might as well take advantage of the extra couple of hours, and it's no extra bother for us, you know."

"Oh, I don't think that's necessary, Mr. Bogen," he said.

Neither did I. "When I call your office, that usually gives us plenty of time."

"All right, then," I said. "But in case you want the boy special, you can have him." I grinned at him. "That's what the word 'Service' stands for in our name."

"Thanks," he said. "I'll call you if we need it."

I turned to go, and stopped.

"Oh, by the way, is Mr. Babushkin around?"

"Why, yes. I think so. He should be in the cutting room, I guess. Did you want to see him about business?"

"Why, yes," I said, "if he's not busy. I just wanted to ask him some questions about a new scheme I'm working out for delivering cut work to contractors."

"Just a moment, Mr. Bogen, and I'll find out."

He left the room and returned in a few moments.

"He's in the cutting room, all right, Mr. Bogen. Straight through this door and turn to your right."

"Thanks," I said, and went through the door.

Babushkin looked up at me from the other side of the cutting table and almost dropped the wax chalk he was working with.

"Hello, there, Meyer," I said heartily.

"Hello, Bogen," he said, looking to right and left at the people working around him.

I guess that was another thing I'd have to teach him— manners. I call him Meyer, and he calls me Bogen!

He came around the cutting table quickly to head me off.

"You want me, Bogen?" he said nervously.

"Yeah," I said, "I just wanted to ask you if—"

"Ssshhh," he said under his breath, "not so loud. Don't talk about that here, Bogen. I don't want—"

"About what?" I said, playing dumb.

"About the—you know—about—"

"Oh!" I said, putting my hand on his shoulder. "Why, Meyer, don't be silly," I said in a low voice. "What do you think I am, a dope? Would I talk about a thing like that in front of all these people?"

He looked relieved.

"Well, you know how it is, Bogen," he said apologetically. "While I'm still working here, I wouldn't want—"

"Of course, Meyer," I said. "I understand those things. I only came up here to invite you up to my house for dinner to-night, that's all."

"Gee, thanks, Bogen," he said, scratching his head. "But I don't know if—"

"Come on, Meyer," I said, "don't turn me down. I called up my mother already, and she's making those famous blintzes I told you about."

"I certainly would like to come up, Bogen," he said. "But I don't know if I can make it. My wife, you know, and the baby—I don't know if—"

I suppose according to the book of etiquette I should have invited his wife, too. But I don't like women around when I'm talking business.

"Aah, come on, Meyer," I coaxed. "It's only for once. Tell your wife you've got a business conference. That's what it is, isn't it? You know we can't talk down here, Meyer."

He looked around quickly and said, "Ssshhh."

"So what do you say? Call your wife up and tell her you'll be home a little later. Say, that's an idea!" I said. "We can have an early supper, and we can talk for an hour or so, and then you can go home in plenty of time for her not to worry. How's that?"

"It *sounds* all right," he said, still doubtful.

It was. Like that I'd get him off my hands as soon as we were through talking. Or rather, as soon as *I* was through talking.

"Go ahead," I said, taking his arm and leading him toward the phone. "Call her up and tell her."

He looked embarrassed.

"I'll call her later, Bogen," he said. "But don't worry. It'll be all right. I'll call her and tell her."

"Swell," I said. "So I'll pick you up here about five-thirty or so, all right?"

"No, no," he said hastily. "You better not come up here

for me, Bogen. Just give me your address and I'll meet you up at your house."

"You won't stand me up, now, will you?" I said. "Because my mother is making dinner special, you know."

"No, don't worry," he said. "I'll be there."

I wrote out the address and then added complete instructions about which subway train to take and how to walk. I wasn't taking any chances.

"Here," I said, handing it to him. "How about six o'clock, all right?"

"We-ell, I don't know," he said. "Better make it six-thirty, Bogen, or seven. Between six-thirty and seven."

"All right, then," I said, reaching for the door. "My house to-night. Follow those instructions, and you can't go wrong."

Not about the directions, anyway.

"All right," he said, and nodded.

"You won't go wrong, now, will you?" I said again.

Do I love being subtle!

"No, no, Bogen," he said. "I'm sure I won't."

I wondered what made him so positive.

13

Mother was waiting for me at the door when I came home.

"I got a surprise for you," she said with a smile, and began to lead me by the hand toward the living room.

"What's the matter, Ma?" I said. "My friend get here early?"

It was only a few minutes after six, and Babushkin didn't look like the kind that could talk his wife out of or into things very easily.

"No," Mother said, "it's not your friend."

We reached the doorway of the living room and she stood aside, beaming, so I could look into the room.

A dark-haired girl in a black and white dress was sitting in the new armchair, looking up from the pages of the maga-

zine she had been turning on her lap, and smiling. She didn't
have to turn sideways to show the long, drooping nose for me
to realize that it was just the kind of Jewish-looking squash
I'd been spending three-quarters of my waking hours since I
was thirteen trying to avoid.

"This is Ruthie Rivkin," Mother said, smiling toward her.
"Mrs. Rivkin's daughter. You remember Mrs. Rivkin,
Heshie, she had the grocery store when we used to live on
Fox Street?"

"Sure, I remember," I said. But I didn't smile. I could see
right away that the only way out of this situation was to
make as few encouraging remarks as possible. "How do you
do?" I said. What the hell, you can't be impolite to your
mother's guests.

"Hello," she said, and smiled.

Her voice was pleasant and her teeth were square and
white. And the smile accented the softness that was in her
face in spite of the profile. And she could thank heaven for
one thing: while she was definitely on the plump side, she
was just as definitely not fat. But it would only have been
fair to tip her off in advance that it was going to take a lot
more than a couple of redeeming features if she even wanted
to place in the competition for my lily white hand in marriage that her mother was obviously entering her in.

"I made a mistake with the blintzes," Mother said to me
with an innocent smile. "I'm such a thick head, I forgot you
said you were bringing only one friend, and I made enough
for God knows, maybe even a dozen. So I thought to myself
instead they should go to waste and I should have to throw
them out, I'd invite up Ruthie she should help us finish
them."

"I wouldn't exactly call that a compliment to Miss Rivkin,
Ma," I said with a smile of my own. "Seems to me you
should invite your guests because you like them, not because
they can eat a lot of blintzes."

"First of all," Mother said, "where did you get so high
class, so fancy, with this Miss Rivkin talk? Her name is
Ruthie. And secondly, I invited her for two reasons, because

I like her *and* because she knows how to eat blintzes. So now maybe you're satisfied?"

"When you do something, Ma," I said, "I'm always satisfied."

I pinched her cheek and we all laughed.

"Will you excuse me for a few moments while I get rid of some of these packages?" I said, lifting them for her to see.

"Of course," she said, still smiling, and mother and I walked toward the kitchen together.

"Nice work, Ma," I said sarcastically in a low voice. "Why don't you open up a marriage broker's office? Or maybe you could just stick a sign in the window? I'll bet you could pick up a nice piece of change that way."

She stopped to look at me with an injured expression.

"Why, Heshie! Is that a nice way to talk? Can't I even invite an old neighbor's daughter to have a bite to eat with us without you should begin right away——?"

"Yeah, I know, Ma, I know," I said, patting her shoulder. "You just wanted to have somebody to try out the new armchair, didn't you?"

She laughed and pushed me gently.

"You're only afraid somebody is going to grab you and marry you, aren't you, Heshie?"

"I'm not afraid," I said. "The only thing is, of all the days in the year for you to pull your fancy stuff and try to get me a wife—yeah, I know, I know, you weren't even thinking of that—but of all the days in the year for you to do your stuff, Ma, you have to go ahead and pick out the one night when I've got an important business friend coming up to see me. Why don't you let me know in advance when you're going to do these things, Ma?"

She smiled wisely.

"I should tell you in advance, so you shouldn't come home for supper that night?" she said.

I pounced on her quickly.

"Oh, so now you're admitting it, eh?" I said.

"Who, me?" she said, shrugging. "What am I admitting? What did I say? I didn't say nothing. I just——"

"Yeah," I said, "I know. Well, let's not waste time arguing about it. I don't mind, Ma, except this one night you had to—"

"Aah, Heshie, don't be a baby. What did I spoil for you, what? You want to talk business, so talk business. A girl by the table is going to spoil everything?"

"You bet she's not," I said. "Because as soon as we finish eating, I'm taking my friend into the living room where we can talk and you can do what you want with your Ruthie."

"All right, all right," she said, pushing me back toward the living room. "In the meantime, show at least the little bit good manners I taught you. Don't leave a girl she should sit alone in the front room by herself."

I straightened my tie and went back into the living room. She smiled as I came in. I hated to admit it, but when she smiled in that soft appealing way, she had something. Why does a gift like that have to be given to a girl from the Bronx?

"I'm afraid I'll have to call you by your first name," I said, walking over to the sofa across the room from her. "My mother is a pretty determined woman, and she's put her foot down about it."

I stopped for a moment, surprised. I wanted to say it again, just to make sure I'd heard myself right.

"I learned that already," she said with a little laugh. "She threatened to spank me if I didn't call you Harry."

"Well, I guess that makes it even," I said.

It was too bad there wasn't a stenographer present. That brilliant conversation should really have been recorded for posterity.

"I'll tell you," she said. "My name is Ruthie, of course— but all my—I mean—all my friends, they call me Betty." She blushed a little. "I mean, if it's all the same to—"

"I get it," I said, smiling reassuringly, and marking it up as dumb trick number one. "All right, then, Betty it is."

But it wasn't. Betty didn't fit her. Ruthie was the word for that softness that was the first thing you noticed about her. Not even Ruth. Just Ruthie.

"Where have you been keeping yourself all these years since we lived on Fox Street?" I said. "I don't seem to remember you at all."

"Oh, we've been living there all this time," she said.

"Gee whiz," I said, "that must be every bit of, let's see— we moved from Fox Street before I was *bar mitzvah,* a couple of years before, so I must've been about ten or eleven—say, that makes it every bit of twelve or thirteen years, doesn't it?"

"It certainly does," she said.

"Boy," I said, "how time flies!"

Well, I guess we were both doing our bit toward making this one of the high spots in my conversational career.

"What do you do during the day?" I said.

She began to look more at home at once. Well, I asked for it.

"I'm secretary to one of the partners in a large law firm downtown," she said, smoothing the dress over her crossed knees. "It's interesting work, but the hours are long. I don't usually get home as early as this." Was I flattered! "You don't get home so early yourself, do you?"

"No," I said. "I'm rather busy downtown until six or seven and I don't usually get home before eight or so. But to-night I'm having an important business friend to dinner, and so I came home a little early."

"Oh," she said, and the smile went out of her face.

Ah, well, another conquest!

"I'm terribly sorry," I said, leaning forward with my elbows on my knees. "It'll probably be very boring for you to listen to us discuss business all night. But I didn't know you were coming, and it's too late now to head this friend of mine off. He's due here any minute," I said, looking at my watch.

What the hell was I apologizing for?

"Oh, that's *perfectly* all right," she said in that pleasant voice of hers, and her face broke into the smile again. I leaned back on the sofa and found myself smiling, too, in spite of myself. "I suppose I really shouldn't have butted in on you on such short notice."

"Don't be silly," I said. "It's a pleasure."

"Well, it's nice of you to *say* that, anyway," she said.

"I mean it, too," I said, and just then the bell rang. "Excuse me a moment, while I answer that," I said, jumping up. Now I knew what the bell between rounds meant to a fighter. Another minute and I'd have said something I'd be sorry for. What the hell was the matter with me? Maybe I was trained too fine.

"Hello, Meyer," I said, taking his hand with a good deal more warmth than he was entitled to. It felt strange to be thankful for the arrival of a kluck like Meyer Babushkin. "Right on time, eh?"

"Yeah," he said.

"Well, come on in," I said, leading him toward the living room. "Meyer," I said, "I want you to meet a friend of mine, Miss Betty Rivkin. Miss Rivkin, Mr. Babushkin."

While they were shaking hands, Mother came in and I introduced Meyer again.

"Well," Mother said, "now we're all here, I could put the supper on the table, no?"

"Ma!" I said reprovingly, "Not supper. Dinner!"

"Well, Mr. Smart One," Mother said to me, "it's not dinner either. What do you think of that? It's just blintzes!"

Everybody laughed and I said, "Well, whatever it is, let's go in and eat it."

I moved over toward Ruthie and took her arm to lead her to the kitchen. I saw Mother looking at me with a suppressed smile, but I couldn't avoid giving her that much satisfaction. I wanted to find out if she was as soft to the touch as she was to the look. She was. Not flabby, but firm, and at the same time soft and tender and warm. In spite of Fox Street and the Bronx and her background and her nose, there was something appealing about her. She wasn't my speed, but I figured that while I was saddled with her for dinner, I might just as well amuse myself by trying to find out what it was.

Mother had four chairs arranged around the kitchen table,

and she had Ruthie sitting directly across from me, so that
while I couldn't do much talking, I could watch her.

As soon as the blintzes were served, I had another mark
to chalk up in her favor. She handled a fork like it was
something with which to carry food to your mouth, not like
it was a thermometer that had just been used on a typhoid
case.

"Oh, Mrs. Bogen," she said, leaning toward Mother and
smiling, "these are *delicious!*"

Mother beamed.

"You like them, hah?"

"I certainly do," she said, "they're wonderful!"

"All right," Mother said, "so after supper, I'll show you
how to make them. It's a handy thing for a girl to know."

Hey, Mom! Enough is enough!

I turned to Babushkin.

"How're they coming, Meyer?" I said.

"Fine," he said, with his mouth full. "Very good."

It was a good thing I had an opinion of my own about
those blintzes, because I never would have been tempted to
try them on *his* recommendation.

"Have some more," I said, loading up his plate.

When we finished I lit a cigarette and passed the pack
toward her.

"Have one?" I said.

"No thanks," she said with a pleasant little shake of the
head, "I don't smoke."

I was glad she didn't say it like she was showing off a
medal.

"Well, then, now, look," I said, leaning on the table with
my elbows. "Mr. Babushkin and I, here, we have a little
business to discuss. So if you ladies will sort of excuse us,
we'll go into the living room and get it over with. But don't
you run away, now," I said, shaking my finger at her and
kicking myself at the same time. "We won't be long."

"Don't worry," Mother said, waving us away. "I'm going
to teach her how to make blintzes. So go already, go, with

your business. All the time business, business, business, business, business, business, business!"

I laughed and got up and Babushkin followed. We went through the foyer to the living room and I pointed to the armchair.

"Take a seat, Meyer," I said, and sat down on the sofa, facing him.

"Well, Meyer," I said, cheerfully, "how are things up at Pulbetkal?"

"Oh, you know. Just about the same."

"Struggling along, eh?"

"You know," he said, shrugging.

"How's my friend Mr. Pulvermacher? I'll bet he don't feel so good this week. He probably only made three million dollars this week instead of the six he usually makes? Hah?"

He smiled a little. The way he did it you'd think it was against the law.

"Well, that's the dress business for you," I said. "If you've got a good combination, you can make money faster than the mint. That Pulvermacher, he must be worth all kinds of dough."

He didn't look very happy and he began to chew on his thumbnail.

"You make up your mind yet on that thing we were talking about the other day?" I said.

He swallowed the piece of thumbnail he had in his mouth and began to talk to the floor.

"I'll tell you, Mr. Bogen," he said slowly, "I been thinking about it, you know, I been thinking about it a lot, but, well, I don't know, it's such a big thing you know, that, well, aah, I don't know——"

"Sure it's a big thing," I said. "But all good things are big." Oh, yeah? "That's not really an objection, is it? Because if that's all that's——"

"No," he said. "It's not that. It's just that, well, you know, you can't be sure what's gonna happen. Like this, now, at least I know I got a good job, and every week, regular, like clockwork, I get——"

I love this.

"Listen, Meyer," I said quietly, putting my hand halfway across the small room so I could touch his arm. "You're no baby and I'm not going to talk to you like you were a baby. I'm not going to give you any of this nothing ventured nothing gained stuff. You and I we're about the same age, maybe you're even a little older—how old are you, Meyer?"

"Twenty-six and a half."

"So it's just like I said. You're even a little older than I am. So there's no sense in my trying to give you advice or anything like that. But one thing you and I know, Meyer. When you go into business, nobody goes around giving you a written guarantee you'll make a million dollars the first month. It's a risk. Everybody takes a risk. Don't forget, Meyer, I have a running business of my *own* that I'm stepping out of. I don't have to tell you that. And how about Mr. Ast? He's the crack salesman there for Toney Frocks, you think he's not thinking twice before he goes in for this thing? You can just about bet he's thinking about it. And so am I, too. We're all thinking about it. But a man's gotta make a break sometimes. You can't go on working for another man all your life. You have to make a break *some* time. You've been on Seventh Avenue longer than I have, Meyer." This was true. "And you know a little more about it than I do." But this wasn't. "But in my business, the way I have to keep circulating around all the time, keeping in contact with all my clients, my accounts, I pretty nearly get into every dress house in the industry. I sort of get the feel of the way things are running a little better than somebody else. Every place I go, what do I hear? All I hear is what a great line Pulbetkal is got this season. Every place it's the same thing. 'Pulbetkal is got a line that's hot.' 'That Pulvermacher is some little smart one, all right.' 'Look at the business he's doing.' 'Look at the line he's got.' All day long, wherever I go, that's all I hear. But nobody is kidding me, Meyer. Why is Pulbetkal's line hot? Why is Pulvermacher, Betschmann & Kalisch, Inc. making so much money? Because Pulvermacher is got a bald head, or because he wears glasses with a black ribbon, or because he smokes twenty-cent cigars, or maybe because he's president of the Associated Dress Manufacturers? All that stuff is the bull. Pulvermacher is cleaning up because in the back, in his factory, he's got the best factory man on Seventh Avenue, a man that also happens to be one of the best designers in the business. He's got Meyer Babushkin."

It's a funny thing about spilling the crap. If you don't watch out the way you sling it, you're liable to get snowed under yourself.

"So Pulvermacher's got the dough," I said, "and what has this Meyer Babushkin got?" I know, teacher! He's got a corking puss to sling manure at! "He's got a job, a good job, with a good salary, too, but just the same, that's all it is, a job. But if this Babushkin was to step out for himself, if he was running his own factory, and it was his own line he was making hot, not only would he still be the best factory man and designer on Seventh Avenue, but he'd also be getting the money that's really his, and that right now he's not getting, but that Pulvermacher *is*."

He kept nodding slowly as I talked, although the worried look still remained on his face. The look didn't mean anything, though. It was the way he always looked. The important thing was that he was nodding. But I wasn't really convincing him. He was convinced right from the start, before I even began. The same would've been true of any one of the thousands of heels you find on Seventh Avenue. Go out into the street blindfolded and reach out. The first guy you'll touch will react the same way. Every one of them, every salesman, every factory man, every shipping clerk, every one of them is dying to go into the dress business for himself. And every one of them does, sooner or later. So I wasn't really convincing Babushkin. He was just yellow, that's all. And I was playing substitute for a backbone.

"Like I said before, Meyer, we can't get any written guarantees. But I ask you, how can we miss?" I was asking, but I wasn't waiting for any answers. I was young and healthy and wanted to enjoy life. I couldn't afford to waste the best

years of my youth waiting for a molasses-brain like that to
frame an answer to a question. "We've got a combination
that's practically sure-fire. Look. We've got you, the best
factory man and designer on the Avenue. You've been coining money for Pulvermacher, Betschmann & Kalisch, Inc. for
years. Is there any reason why you shouldn't continue to do
the same for yourself? And even better, too? The chances
are that when you're in your own business, Meyer, you'll be
even better than you ever were. So all right. We've got you.
Then we've got Teddy Ast. Maybe he isn't so wonderful a
salesman as you're a factory man. I mean, that's just between
the two of us, and I wouldn't want it to go any further. But
he certainly is one of the best in the business, isn't he? Look
what he's been doing for Toney Frocks. They haven't had a
line worth a—a—excuse the expression, Meyer, but they
haven't had a line worth a fart in I don't know how many
years. Yet year after year they turn in a profit. Why is that?
Because they've got Teddy Ast. They've got a salesman there
that could sell—I don't know, he could sell *any*thing. And
then there's me. Why, between the three of us—I don't know
what to say. There's just no limit to the money we can make."

I lit a cigarette and gave him a breathing spell.

"And then," I went on, "if you're really worried about
those things. I mean," I said carelessly, "if the worst comes
to the worst, in case the whole world is all of a sudden
crazy, and we *don't* make a go of it, why, then, Meyer, you
can take my word for it, you'll still have nothing to worry
about. Pulbetkal will grab you back so fast, I mean just in
case you ever *want* to go back, they'll grab you back so fast,
you'll be dizzy. And you'll be able to come back on your
own terms, too. They'll respect you more, too. Aah," I said,
waving my hand at him, "but what am I talking about! We
won't make a go of it! What am I, crazy? I'm so positive
we're gonna clean up, Meyer, I'm so positive, that I'm even
gonna borrow some extra money so that we can start off with
a little more decent capital." I reminded myself not to get
excited. I was only talking. I never borrow. "That's how positive I am about this thing."

He turned his worried squash in my direction, but there was no change in the way it looked. So I was willing to consider it a step forward. After all, Einstein says everything is relative.

"You really think we'll have enough to go into business?" he asked doubtfully.

"Do I *think* we'll have enough?" I said. "Look. Let's see what we've got. First there's you. You said six last time, didn't you?"

He nodded slowly.

"All right, then, we have six. Then there's Ast. I think he said something about thirty-five hundred or four, wasn't it? Well, all right, it doesn't matter. Let's say four. So your six and his four makes ten. After all, we can't expect him to have more. You know how those things are. He's a salesman. They can't save any money. If it isn't clothes it's entertainment and this and that and God alone knows what. They spend twice as much as they make. Every cent they make is on their backs. Every one of them has twenty-seven suits and twenty-seven cents. It's yet a wonder to me, Meyer, that he's got the four. But anyway, that's the way it is. So far we have ten. And me, last time I said seven, didn't I? Well, I'm gonna borrow three or four extra, like I just told you. That'll make ten or eleven from me. So what've we got? We've got twenty thousand dollars or over. Why, for God's sakes, Meyer, you know what we can do with twenty thousand dollars? We can start *three* dress houses not one. I'll bet three-quarters of the dress houses in the neighborhood start with a capital of less than ten. And plenty of them start with five, too. But what's the sense of my telling you things like that? You've been in the dress business too long for me to tell you these things. You know all about these things." I certainly was taking a lot for granted. "Of *course* we've got enough. We've got enough to not only start, but to start off with a *bang*."

Suddenly I heard the front door open and close and then I heard Mother's footsteps walking back through the foyer to the kitchen. And all at once I had it. I knew what it was in that girl's face that had puzzled and attracted me and had kept going around and around in my mind all the time I had been talking. I saw, too, the resemblance between them that I had missed because of the difference in their ages. She had that same way of making you feel rested just by looking at her that Mother had. I could sit there, in the same room with a dope like Babushkin, and think of that girl's face as it had looked across the table from me in the kitchen, and I got that same feeling of having reached a place where I could drop my guard and draw my breath after having gone through something tough.

I didn't like the idea of Mother's footsteps having gone back to the kitchen alone. I wanted to see that girl again and talk to her. But I couldn't until I got rid of Babushkin.

"So don't worry about it, Meyer," I said, talking quickly. "We're as good as in right now."

He waved that worried face of his up and down in front of me a few times. It was the best thing he did.

"So what do you say, Meyer?" I said, getting up and coming toward him. "Are we in this thing together?"

He nodded slowly, but that didn't mean anything to me any more. For all I knew he might have been saying no.

"I think so," he said, and I was surprised that his voice didn't break. "Just give me a little more time to think it over, give me a chance I should talk it over with my wife, and I'll let you know," he said.

Suddenly I had an idea. Maybe I ought to meet his wife. I wanted to hurry this along a little. If he couldn't make up his mind, she'd make it up for him soon enough. And if he could talk her into marrying him, I could talk her into anything.

"I'll tell you what, Meyer," I began, and stopped. Maybe it would be better if I didn't go around looking for trouble. She might not be as dumb as he was. And anyway, I didn't want to spend any more time with him just then. I wanted to get back into that kitchen.

"What?" he said.

"Nothing," I said, giving him his hat and walking him toward the door. "You think it over and I'll get in touch with you in a couple of days." It was better not to get him nervous by trying to clinch it right then and there. Besides which, it was faster, too. "Okay, Meyer?"

"Yeah," he said, nodding a little. "I guess that'll be best."

"Good night, then," I said.

"Good night," he said.

I closed the door behind him and hurried toward the kitchen.

14

Mother was alone in the kitchen, darning socks, when I got there.

"Hello, Mom," I said, "where's your company?"

"What do you mean, where's my company?" she said. "What are you, anxious or afraid? Take a look at the clock."

I did. It was a quarter to eleven.

"Holy smoke," I said, "was I in there that long?"

"Well," she said with a shrug, "you wasn't out here, so you must've been in there, no?"

"What happened to Ruthie?"

"She went home. What do you think happened to her? To sit here and wait for you to get finished with the business in there, a person could have a hemorrhage, God forbid. The girl has to go to work to-morrow. She can't sit around a half a night with an old woman like me while you're inside with those high-class friends of yours."

"What's the matter with my friends?" I said.

"Nothing is the matter with your friends," she said. "Did I say something was the matter with your friends?" Only tell me, Heshie," she said, cocking her head to one side, "is that gonna be your new partner, the one you were telling me about?"

"That's *one* of them," I said. "What do you think of him?"

"He's all right, I suppose," she said, biting off the thread from a freshly darned sock. "He's *your* partner, not mine."

"Okay, okay," I said, sitting down at the table with her and grinning, "let's have it. What do you think of him?"

"Of course, it's none of *my* business—" she began.

"I know," I said, "but since when does that stop you?" She flicked a sock at me and I ducked.

"Well, to me," she said, "if you really want to know—"

"Yeah, I want to know."

"To me," she said, "he looks like a high-class dope."

"Good," I said, slapping the table. "That's all I wanted to hear. Now I'm positive I'm going into business with him."

"What's the matter?" she said. "Can't you find any smart people in this world, you gotta go around picking out such *schlemiels* like that—?"

"I don't need smart people," I said. "I'm smart enough for three. But dopes, the right kind of dopes, they're hard to find."

"Remember only one thing, Heshie," she said. "To be entirely smart is to be half a fool."

"Yeah, I know, Ma," I said. "Papa used to tell me that, too.

"Well Papa was right, Heshie."

"Let's not go into that now, Ma," I said. "Let's stick to my dope of a partner, Meyer Babushkin"

"I don't know why a person with a little smartness in him should even want to *talk* about a dumbbell like that. Let's talk better about smart people. How do you like Ruthie?"

"Not Ruthie, Ma," I said, raising my hand with the thumb and forefinger forming a circle, "*Betty,* Ma. She doesn't want to be called Ruthie. She wants to be called Betty."

"All right, so it's Betty. Betty, Ruthie, what's something the difference? How do you like her, that's the question?"

"How should I know how I like her?" I said with a shrug. "Before I even got a chance to take a good look at her, she ran away home."

"Well, she didn't run away to Europe. You know where she lives. I got the telephone number. Maybe you don't want to call from here," she said slyly. "You want to take a good look at her, you want to see what she looks like, so you take a nickel, you go into the drugstore, you call her up, and then you go over to her house on Fox Street and you take a look at her. Is that so hard to do?"

It wouldn't be hard. It would be crazy.

"It's not hard," I said, "but it takes too much time. I'm too busy. I can't bother with those things."

"What's the matter, the whole world business fell all of a sudden on your head? One night a week to call up a nice girl like that you haven't got?"

I wouldn't even spend a whole night on the *right* kind of girl. So what chance did a *nice* girl have?

"It's not that, Ma," I said. "I'm planning a new business, too, you know. I've got to see my partners. I've got to arrange for capital. You know, Ma, all that—"

"Who says that by calling up Ruthie—?"

"Betty," I interrupted, smiling.

"All right—Betty. Who says that by calling up Ruthie you'll be wasting time?"

Nobody had to say it. I could tell by looking at her.

"I didn't say I'd be wasting time, Ma," I said. "She's a nice girl and all that, and I got nothing against her."

Not yet, anyway.

"You got something against her!" Mother cried, shaking her head from side to side. "She'll gain ten pounds when I tell her that my Heshie said he's got nothing against her! Since when, Heshie, since when you think you're yourself Count Itufski's son? He's got nothing against her!"

I laughed and lit a cigarette.

"All right, all right, Ma," I said, "I didn't mean it that way. I only meant that I can't spare the time now. I have to look after my new business, that's all."

"All right," Mother said. "Now that you're so smart, and you talked so much, so I'll tell you something. It wouldn't hurt you or that new business of yours if you should go out with Ruthie Rivkin. Now what do you think of that?"

"What do you mean?" I asked.

"Nothing," Mother said with exaggerated casualness. "Only Mrs. Rivkin told me that the boy that marries her

Ruthie, that boy gets ten thousand dollars to go in business with, that's all."

He ought to get a medal, too.

"Stop kidding me, Ma," I said. "No grocer on Fox Street is giving away ten thousand dollars with a daughter."

"So maybe you know better than the whole world," she said. "But I'm telling you one thing. The boy that marries Ruthie—"

"Betty," I said.

"All right—Betty. The boy who marries Ruthie Rivkin, he gets ten thousand dollars to go in business. Now what do you think of that?"

She'd never forgive me, if I told her.

"What's the matter?" I said. "Is she so hard to get rid of?"

"What do you mean, hard to get rid of? You saw her, didn't you?"

"Well, I sort of did get a quick look at her before she breezed out of here," I admitted.

"Never mind," Mother said, "don't get so smart. If you didn't see her for long enough, it was your own fault, you were so busy with that big lemon of yours, that Babushkin. But you saw her. And you know there's plenty boys they would thank God seven days a week for the rest of their lives if they could only get a nice girl like that even *without* ten thousand dollars. And *with* ten thousand dollars, don't worry, there's plenty boys in the Bronx, so smart like you any day, Heshalle, that they figure it's worth while they should spend a couple nights a week in the parlor there by the Rivkins on Fox Street."

She probably had a younger sister that was a knockout.

"Then how come nobody grabbed her off yet?" I said.

"What's the matter? She looks like a cripple to you, maybe? She's got a glass eye? One leg is by her shorter than the other? She's a good-looking girl, dope. *She's* particular, too, you dope, you!"

"Ma, please," I said, "don't call me a dope."

"Why not?" she said. "Maybe you're something better?"

"Maybe," I said. "But don't call me a dope."

"If you had any sense in that head of yours—that head that you think is the smartest one the Above One ever made —instead of wasting you time on *lemishkes* like Meyer Babushkin, you'd make a try for that ten thousand dollars, and you could go into business the way you want to and you wouldn't need any stupid partners they should get in the way of your feet when you walk."

"I don't need Babushkin for his money only, Ma," I said. "I need him because he's a designer, a factory man. Don't you understand that?"

"Anything *you* understand," she said acidly, "you can be sure *I* understand, too. Don't think the whole world smartness settled all of a sudden in your head, Heshie. What do you think, it's going to hurt that business of yours if you have an extra ten thousand dollars in it?"

"Of course not, Ma. Ten thousand dollars—"

"—Is ten thousand dollars," she finished. "And it isn't every day in the week a young boy your age gets a chance to put his hands on so much money and at the same time get a nice girl like that Ruthie—"

I started to correct her again, but stopped. I liked the idea of Mother's not being able to talk of her in any way but as Ruthie.

"And I'll tell you something else," Mother said, leaning across the table to poke her finger with the thimble on it at me. "She *likes* you."

"Yeah, she likes me," I said. "What did you do, show her a picture of me? She hardly even saw me. How do you know she likes me?"

That was one to stop the presses for. Harry Bogen reaching for a compliment!

"She told me," Mother said.

"Yeah, she told you! When?"

"After supper, when I was teaching her how to make blintzes," she said.

"Oh, boy, Ma," I said, grinning suddenly and shaking my head, "if I told you before, I'll tell you again—would *you* make a marriage broker! Oh, boy!"

"Never mind with that talk," she said. "I'm not a marriage broker. But for my own son, I want he should get a nice girl. Is there anything wrong in that?"

"Not if she's got ten thousand dollars, too," I said, "there isn't."

"So what do you say, Heshie?"

"Well, all right," I said, "give me her phone number. For *you,* Ma, I'll do it."

She grinned at me.

"You should live so, you little tramp, you," she said, the grin turning into a laugh. "For *me* you'll do it!"

15

I was sitting there, looking at the phone on my desk. When I finally made up my mind to put the call through I glanced at the clock. It was six-thirty. That meant Miss Marmelstein was gone and I'd have to go out to the switchboard to dial the number myself. I opened the door from my private office and walked out into the large room. She was still sitting behind the switchboard, toying with the plugs and staring at her hands. She looked up as I came into the room.

"Why, what are *you* doing here so late?" I said. "You don't have to stick around as late as all this, Miss Marmelstein, you know."

"Oh, that's all right, Mr. Bogen," she said eagerly. "I haven't got anything special to do to-night, anyway."

My heart bled for her.

"Did you want something, Mr. Bogen?" she asked.

"Yes," I said. "Get me Intervale 9-929—no, never mind. Forget it."

I turned on my heel and went back into my private office. For another moment I stood at my desk, hesitating. Then I said, "The hell with it," and reached for my hat.

"I'm going up to Toney Frocks for a few minutes, Miss Marmelstein," I said to her on the way out. "If anybody calls me, and it's important, you can probably reach me there for the next quarter of an hour or so. Otherwise, don't bother. You can close up any time you want to. Good night."

"Good night, Mr. Bogen," she said lingeringly.

I didn't even turn back. She couldn't kid me. I wasn't *that* good.

When I reached Toney Frocks the girl at the information window was fixing her hat in her pocket mirror which she had propped up against her switchboard.

"I'd like to see Mr. Ast," I said, "Teddy Ast."

"Mr. Ast is gone," she said without looking up. "Any message?"

"No," I said, "no message. What time does he usually get in in the morning, do you know?"

"Yes, I do," she said, "but he won't be in to-morrow morning—"

"Why not?"

"He went away for the week end. He won't be back till Monday."

"Oh!" I said, and stood there, hesitating. I couldn't make up my mind whether I was sorry or not. The evening was free now, and there was no excuse for not making the call. "Where did Mr. Ast go for the week end, do you know?"

"Totem Manor," she said; then, "say—!"

"That's all right," I said, "I'm a friend of his."

I went back to the elevator, pushed the button, and got in. I was watching the lights at the top of the car that winked on and off to indicate the floor we were passing. When the light for "18" went on I made up my mind. "Okay," I said to myself and put my hand in my pocket for a nickel.

I went into a phone booth in Liggett's and dialed Intervale 9-9294. A woman's voice got on the wire.

"Hello."

"Hello," I said, "is this Intervale 9-9294?"

"Yes."

"Is Ruthie home?"

"You mean Betty, no?"

I guess whoever she was, she had her orders.

"Yeah," I said, "that's right. Is she home?"

"No, she's not home yet. But I expect her any minute. Maybe you wanna leave a message?"

"We-ell, I don't know. I'll tell you, who's this talking?"

"This is her mother."

"Oh, well, I'll call again. Never mind."

"You sure you don't want to——? Oh, hello, hello?"

"Yes?"

"Here she is now, she just came in this minute. Hold the wire, please."

Well, here I go, I thought. After a few moments of silence another voice got on the wire. I recognized it immediately.

"Hello?"

"Hello," I said. Damn it, I should have cleared my throat. "Who's this, Betty?"

"Yes. Who's this?"

"This is Harry Bogen. Remember me?"

"Why, of course," she said with a laugh. "What ever made you think I wouldn't?"

"I don't know," I said. "You know how those things are."

I guess she had me hypnotized all right. I couldn't even make the properly sarcastic comebacks that her remarks really earned for her. And the hell of it was that I didn't think it was the ten thousand dollars Mother said they were passing out to the guy that carried her to the altar, either.

"Oh, I don't forget people as easily as all that," she said.

"That's where you've got it over most girls, then," I said.

"Oh, I think you're too critical of girls in general," she said.

"I don't think I am," I said. "Not of girls in general anyway."

The next step was epigrams. God, how do I get into these things?

"Well——" she began, and paused.

That was better. At least we were back on safe ground again.

"Look," I said, "I didn't call so we could have a long discussion about girls in general. I like to be more specific than that."

She laughed and I was glad I was at the other end of the phone to hear it.

"All right," she said, "be more specific."

"Well, what are you doing to-night?" I asked.

"Oh—I don't know. Nothing special, I guess. Why?"

I'm the inquiring photographer, and I'm conducting a poll to discover how many girls—aah, nuts.

"Then suppose we do it together," I said. "What do you say?"

"All right," she said.

"Fine," I said. "Now, where would you like to go?"

"Oh—I don't care. Any place at all that you say. It doesn't make any difference to me."

If she didn't come from Fox Street and Mama hadn't introduced her to me and there wasn't something about her face and voice that warned you all over in spite of the fact that your common sense told you at a glance that she wasn't pretty—if it wasn't for all that, I'd know where to take her all right. But like this I was stopped.

"It doesn't make any difference to me, either," I said. "But anything you like I'm sure I'll like too. So just say the word," I said.

"Well, then, let's see. Oh, I know. I'll tell you what I'd really *like* to do."

"What?"

"I'd like to go up to the Stadium Concert," she said.

Well, that's what I got for asking for suggestions.

"Okay with me," I said, "if you really want to go."

"Oh, I'd love it. They're having a special Viennese program to-night and Albert Spalding is the soloist."

"Who?"

"Albert Spalding."

"Yeah, well, I guess we'll have to go then, that's all. Let's see, now, what time is it?"

I looked at my wristwatch.

"Seven o'clock," she said.

"That's right," I said. "Now, then, when do these—when does this concert start?"

"Eight-thirty, I *think*."

"That gives me an hour and a half to get the tickets and to come up to your—"

"Oh, you don't have to do that," she said quickly. "Why should you travel all the way up to the Bronx and back?" That's just what *I* was trying to figure out. "Why don't you go up to the Stadium, get the tickets, and then I'll meet you at— well, any place you say."

"Well, I'll tell you the truth," I said, "I don't know much about the neighborhood up there—"

"All right," she said, "here, I've got it. The Stadium, you know, is on Amsterdam Avenue between a Hundred and Thirty-eight and a Hundred and Thirty-seventh Streets. Across the street, I mean across the Avenue, is the Hebrew Orphan Asylum. Suppose we meet there, right in front of the main entrance to the Orphan Asylum?"

"That's the first time I ever met a girl in front of an orphan asylum," I said with a laugh. Come on, Bogen, be natural. She's not paying you. You don't have to laugh at *all* of them. "But for you I'll do it."

"Thank you, kind sir," she said sweetly, "I'm—"

I felt my face wrinkle up as I scowled into the mouth-piece. Before I knew I was talking, I said, "Don't ever say that," sharply.

"Don't say what?"

"Nothing," I said quickly. "I mean—I'll tell you when I see you."

"But I don't understand. What were we talking about?"

"I was saying that this is the first time I ever arranged to meet a girl in front of an orphan asylum, but for you I'd do it."

Her voice, when she spoke, was suddenly sharp and cool.

"And *I* was about to say," she said, "that I was going to consider that a compliment. Would you mind telling me what's wrong in that?"

"Nothing," I said quickly. "And you're right—it is."

"It is what?"

"A compliment," I said.

"Then what did you mean when you said——?"

"It's not important," I said. "I'll tell you when I see you."

"All right," she said, laughing the way I liked to hear her, "then it's the Hebrew Orphan Asylum at, say, eight-fifteen."

"Right," I said, and hung up.

During the next hour and a quarter I had a chance to call myself as many different kinds of a horse's ass as I could think of. And I could think of plenty. But after I'd gone through the whole list, it still didn't help. The fact remained that I was going to a concert and, worse than that, that I was actually looking forward to it.

I could think of an answer, of course. I knew how to read and understand English, and I'd seen a movie or two in my day, so I knew what the answer was supposed to be. But I was damned if I'd admit that a thing like that could happen to me.

But being certain of immunity couldn't change the fact that I was pacing around nervously in front of an orphan asylum on Amsterdam Avenue, all but biting my nails, waiting for what my common sense told me was as Jewish-looking a broad as I'd ever seen in my life.

Hell, I said finally, I guess the smartest of us will do more for ten thousand dollars than we're willing to admit.

When I saw her turn the corner into Amsterdam Avenue, I went forward to meet her.

"Hello," I said, taking her arm, "I was beginning to get scared that you wouldn't show up."

"Oh, I don't think you were *scared,*" she said.

That's how much *she* knew about it.

"Well, maybe——" I said, staring at her.

She looked frightened and began to examine her dress and purse and hands.

"Is there anything wrong?" she asked.

"No," I said, still staring hard, "nothing's wrong. I'm just trying to discover two things."

"What?"

"Whether you look the same as you did the other night

when we had blintzes," I said, "and whether you're as pretty as my mother keeps saying you are."

She blushed suddenly and looked down at her hands with an embarrassed smile and for the first time in my life I knew what it meant to want to kiss a girl. I mean, just to *kiss* her.

"Oh, I think your mother is—I mean, she's too—"

"Maybe she is," I said, still staring. "But I don't think so."

"Well," she said in a slightly higher-pitched tone of voice, "shall we go in?"

"We might as well," I said, putting my arm through hers. It was amazing how warm she was, even through the thickness of a dress and a light summer coat. "I got the best seats in the house."

"You mean the ones at the tables downstairs?" she said, stopping.

"Yeah."

"Oh, you shouldn't have done that. It's—"

"Forget it," I said, patting her arm. "They're only a dollar and a half a piece."

"It isn't that," she said. "But it's so much nicer in the fifty cent seats, high up in the Stadium."

"You mean way up there on those stone seats?"

She nodded.

"It's not as comfortable as the ones downstairs," she said, "but they're not as uncomfortable as they look. And it's really much more—well, sort of private. But it doesn't matter. If you have these already, why—"

"Just a moment," I said. I took the tickets out of my pocket and tore them in half and tossed them in the gutter.

"Oh!" she said, "you shouldn't—"

"Why not?" I said, remembering to kick myself. I don't like that kind of cheap flash. "No sense in sitting out in the open like an actor on a stage with the whole world staring at you. I should've had more sense than to buy those tickets, anyway. Come on, we'll get a couple of those other tickets."

There was quite a crowd going in when I stopped to buy two of the cheaper tickets. It never occurred to me that there were that many people in the world who were willing to spend money to sit on stone steps and listen to music. Well, and I guess it never occurred to me that I'd be one of them, either.

"Let's go over toward this end," she said, leading me toward the left. "We can climb up to the top row there, and it won't be very crowded. Most of the people sit lower down and toward the right."

"You seem to know a lot about this place, don't you?" I said.

"Oh, I come here pretty often," she said.

"Alone?" I asked.

She blushed and I was sorry I'd asked.

"Sometimes," she said awkwardly. "Sometimes with some other girls or some—"

"Hold it a second," I said. "I want to get a couple of these."

I bought two straw mats from a boy that was selling them, and we continued to climb the wide cement steps.

"You don't really need them," she said. "It's just as comfortable sitting on the stone."

"I suppose," I said. But I couldn't imagine her sitting on anything so hard and not hurting herself seriously.

"This ought to be about right," she said finally, and I spread the mats on the cement step and we sat down.

The huge Stadium stretched away below and to the right of us. It was getting dark quickly, but there was still enough light to see the tiers, arranged like the rays from a flashlight, and how crowded they were. Down below, at the focus of the rays, was the orchestra, with the men tuning their instruments. The sky was blue with a few stars beginning to show and a handful of clouds moving across it slowly. I hadn't looked at the sky for a month. Somehow you get out of the habit downtown.

"It's nice, isn't it?" she said.

I nodded and looked around at the people near us. Most of them were couples of about our own age; they were sitting very close to one another and were whispering and hold-

ing hands and laughing for all the world as though they were
alone up there. And none of them paid any attention to the
others. I considered it a good sign. They had sense.

Just as the music started she turned to me suddenly and
said, "I've been wanting to ask you, but I forgot in all the
excitement about the tickets. What was it you meant when
you said to me on the phone before, 'Don't ever say that,' or
something like that?"

It was pretty dark, now, and the only lights were down in
the center of the Stadium, with the orchestra.

"Oh, I guess I didn't mean anything," I said. "Let's just
forget it."

That marked another first in my life. For once I was afraid
to say something to a dame.

"But you must have," she said, looking at me. "I could
tell by the way you said it, all of a sudden."

"Well, I'll tell you," I said. "I don't know if I can exactly
tell you what I mean. And then, again," I added, "maybe
you won't like it. So suppose we skip the whole thing and
listen to—"

"But, Harry, please," she said. "I'd rather you told me."

It was the first time she'd called me by my given name.
And the way she said it made the skin and the little hairs
on the side of my jaw stand up and tingle. Well, at least I
could say she had better manners than Babushkin.

"Well, it's like this," I said. "Maybe I don't know you
long enough to go around telling you these things, but hell,
the way I figure, I figure it's important. So don't get sore, or
anything like that. Okay?"

"I promise," she said, smiling, and I was sure she meant it.

"All right," I said. "Now don't ask me for explanations
or anything like that, because I can't give them to you. All
I know is there's something about you, let's say about the
way they put your face together when they made it, or the
way you sit and walk and even talk—I heard it on the phone
to-night—there's something there that's sort of soft and, well,
I guess honest is the best word. Anyway, that's the general
idea, see? And it reminds me a lot of my mother. And any

girl that can do that, I mean remind me of my mother, must be pretty good. You follow me?"

She nodded a little, quickly, without looking at me.

"Now," I continued, "this is where it gets a little thick, but it's the best I can do in the way of an explanation. I mean, if you only let yourself alone, if you only act natural, you can take my word for it you're all right; you can't go wrong. Anything you say or do, any way you sit or walk or I don't know what, if you only do it natural, without adding anything fancy, you don't have to worry; it'll come out right and it'll look and sound right, too. But the minute you try to add some of those touches, you know, the minute you try to do something different than what you would do if you let yourself alone, it sticks out like a sore thumb; it just doesn't ring right. Now take for instance to-night. We were talking there on the phone and everything was okay; then, I don't know exactly where it was, but all of a sudden you said something—yeah, I remember, now—I think you said something about 'Thank you, kind sir,' or something like that. Anyway—now don't get sore—it was, well, it was fake; just like me tearing up that couple of tickets a little while ago was fake. It didn't sound like you and if you wanna really get right down to it, it *was*n't you talking. So the second you said it, it hit me so wrong that before I even knew what was happening, I forgot all those high-class manners my mother taught me and like a dope I was yelling 'Ouch,' and I was telling you not to talk like that. Naturally, I got no right to tell you what—aah, *hell,*" I said suddenly, "what's the sense of talking?"

"That's all right, Harry," she said quietly. "I know what you mean."

It was nice to know that at least *one* of us did.

"Then suppose we forget it," I said, "and listen to the music."

"All right," she said.

We sat quietly for a while, and the music coming up made everything seem all right. Then I thought of something, and I said, "There's one more thing."

"Yes?"

"What do you want to have people go around calling you Betty for?" I said. "That's not you. You're Ruthie. You know what I mean?"

She nodded slowly.

"Ruthie," I said, trying it out. "Ruthie. See, that sounds right. Because that's you, you know. Ruthie," I said again. "Well, that's settled. Your friends, they call you Betty, but me, I'm different."

Boy, I was as casual as a freight car.

I turned back to the orchestra below us. The music came up thin and tinkly and it suddenly occurred to me that I liked it. It was just right for that sort of place.

"I never listened to this stuff before," I said, "but it's pretty good, isn't it?"

She didn't answer.

She sat with her elbows on her knees, supporting her chin in her hands. A man in a white suit stood up under the lights and put a violin under his chin.

"That's Spalding," she said, as he began to play.

I put my arm around her and she leaned against me, resting her head on my shoulder. I leaned my head down and kissed her hair gently. She didn't move.

The music stopped and we left the Stadium with the crowd.

"How about a little bite of something to eat?" I said.

"I'm not hungry," she said, "but if you are—"

"I'm not either," I said. "Shall we walk a while?"

"All right," she said.

We went west, toward the river, and then walked downtown, arm in arm, without talking. In a dark spot, under a tree, we stopped and I tipped her face up toward me with my hand and kissed her on the mouth. It was all right.

She shivered a little and said, "I'm afraid I'll have to be getting home, Harry."

"All right," I said, and hailed a cab.

I sat with my arm around her, holding her hand in mine, and didn't think of anything.

After a while she coughed a little.

"Well," she said, "I guess we'll, well, I guess we'll be getting home soon."

"Yeah," I said.

"Wasn't it nice?" she said.

"Yeah," I said, without thinking. Then I looked at her quickly. "It was all right," I added.

She turned to look at me.

"What's the matter, Harry? Didn't you like it?"

So far, what had there been to like?

"Yeah, sure," I said. "I liked it."

That was just the trouble. What *did* I like about it? It wasn't the music, that was sure. And as far as I'm concerned, a stadium is just a big draft. I guess I liked my mother so much, I got a kick out of taking her girl friends out.

"It was all right," I repeated. Maybe it still would be, at that. "Only I sort of hate to, well, you know, break the whole thing up right now."

A dame was a dame.

She moved closer to me and put her head against my shoulder. I guess it's all in the words you use.

"Harry—" she began.

I put my other arm around her and drew her close. The cab stopped. What a spot! That's what you get when you haven't got a place to go.

"Well, here we are," she said in a quick, relieved voice.

Yeah, home.

We got out and I paid the driver. She stood on the stoop, hesitating.

"Well, good night," she said slowly.

"Good night," I said; then, quickly, "hey, wait a minute!" Where did she get off, making me behave like a gentleman? "What are you doing to-morrow, Ruthie?"

What was I going to do, let her go thinking I went out with her for the sake of her company?

"Nothing," she said. "Why?"

"How would you like to run up to Totem for the day?"
What the hell, I had business up there anyway. I'd kill two
birds with one stone. "We could leave early—"

"Oh, I couldn't go to-morrow, Harry," she said.

"Why not?"

"It's Saturday. My mother wouldn't let me ride on Saturday."

It was just as well to be warned in advance. Maybe her
mother wouldn't let her do other things on Saturday, either.

"Then suppose we make it for Sunday, then?"

"All right," she said, opening the door and stepping into
the hall. "I'll tell my mother."

"Okay," I said, smiling. "Tell her not to worry."

She'd be doing that soon enough.

But somehow, as I walked down the street to the subway,
I couldn't help thinking that if I had to knock off a dame to
prove I didn't like her, there was something wrong.

16

I didn't say much on the train because I didn't know what
she was thinking. Whatever it was, I could tell by her face
that it was harmless. And I didn't want to jolt her into a
series of questions. But I sat with my arm around her and
every once in a while I asked her if she was comfortable.

"I'm comfortable, Harry, thanks," she said, "only—"

"Only what?"

"I'm just a little worried if I'm dressed right for a place
like that," she said.

"Don't be silly," I said. "You're all right."

She was wearing a blue sports dress with a pleated skirt
and white trimmings, including a sailor collar with a white
star in each corner.

"You're dressed better than most of the girls you'll see up
there," I said.

There were a half dozen busses around the station when

we got off the train. I looked for the one with the sign TOTEM MANOR over it and walked toward it.

I recognized a few people from Seventh Avenue in it when we took our seats, and nodded to them.

"You know those people?" she asked.

"Sort of," I said. "Not that they're my friends, or anything like that, but it's just that I do the delivery work for some of them. This Totem is a regular hangout for the garment industry."

I tried to figure out what I wanted to avoid most: these heels thinking I couldn't pick myself anything better-looking than Ruthie Rivkin, or her thinking that these heels were my friends.

About a dozen people got into the bus in all, and then it drove away. It went down the state road for a few miles and then turned into a private road for a half mile. It drew up in front of a big wide two-story building with screened-in porches all around it. People were sitting in chairs on the lawn and on the porches. To the left were the tennis courts and the swimming pool, both crowded, and to the right, on a hill, was the first tee of the golf course that they spend sixty per cent of their advertising copy in describing. Around the large main building were the half dozen or so smaller ones, the annexes, in which they accommodated the guests that couldn't be taken care of in the main house. Between the main house and the first annex was the very wide and square casino, where the social staff did its stuff after dinner.

"Come on, Ruthie," I said, "let's go in and register."

We walked up the steps into the large lobby with the rustic furniture and the Seventh Avenue kibitzers.

As I signed the register I asked the clerk, "Is there a Mr. Ast registered here for the week end, a Mr. Teddy Ast?"

"Yes, sir," the clerk said. He pointed to the porch on the right of the desk. "There's Mr. Ast now."

"Thanks," I said, and to Ruthie, "Just a second, I want to see if that's the guy I'm looking for."

I walked over to the screen door and looked out. It was Ast all right, sitting in a steamer chair with a half dozen

snappy-looking blondes surrounding him. I ducked away
from the door quickly and walked over to Ruthie.

"Look," I said, walking her toward the other end of the
lobby, toward the porch on the left of the desk, "I've got to
go out and talk to that guy for a few minutes. On business.
You sit out here like a good girl for a while, and wait till I
come back for you. All right?"

"Can't I sit out on the other porch while you're talking
to him?" she asked. "I'm a little afraid to be alone. I don't
know any of these people, and—"

"Don't be silly," I said, laughing and pinching her cheek.
"Nobody's going to eat you up."

That's all I'd need. Ast with his six blonde nifties, and me
with Ruthie Rivkin of the Bronx!

"You want anything to read?" I asked, when she was
finally seated. "I'll get you a magazine or something."

"No, that's all right, Harry, thanks. I'll just sit here and
wait for you. Hurry, though, will you?"

"I sure will," I said, patting her cheek again.

As I left the porch to go into the lobby again I took a
quick look around. I didn't know any of the people sitting
there nor did they pay any attention to me. So *that* was all
right.

I walked across the lobby and threw open the door behind
Ast. He looked up and recognized me.

"Hello, Bogen," he said, reaching out his hand.

"Hello, there, Ast," I said.

"Meet the stable," he said, waving his hand to take in the
girls.

They giggled crazily as though he'd said the smartest
thing they'd ever heard. I had to hand it to the little kike.
He was a skinny little runt, with a face that looked like it
had been worked on often enough but never quite finished,
and a nose that could have hidden the Statue of Liberty and
a couple of ferryboats besides. But with all those handicaps,
when it came to the women, he was all there.

"Pull yourself over a chair," he said, pointing toward an
unoccupied rocker with one leg.

"Thanks," I said, and sat down.

"When'd you arrive, Bogen? I didn't see you around last night."

"I just got in a few minutes ago," I said.

"When are you going back?"

"To-night," I said.

"Hell of a trip for just one day," he said. "What's the matter, no more dames left in New York?"

The blondes laughed like they were getting paid for it and they'd been promised a raise if they turned in a good performance.

"No, not dames," I said. "I came up here on business."

"Business?"

"Yeah," I said. "I came up here to see you."

He dropped his legs to the ground and sat up in the chair.

"Okay, girls," he said, waving his hands at them, "scram for a while, will you? I've got business with Mr. Bogen, here. I'll see you all later."

"Oh, Teddy," one of the blondes said, pouting.

"Come on," he said, raising his voice. "Shoo!"

They shooed.

"What's up?" he said.

"I had Babushkin up to the house for dinner the other night," I said.

"Yeah? What happened?"

"Oh, my mother filled him full of food, and then I took him into the living room and talked his ear off for a couple of hours."

"How does it look?"

"Pretty good," I said. "I think he's in. He just wanted a little time to talk it over with his wife. He's got one of those things, you know."

"Yeah, I know," he said. He waved his hand understandingly. "A designer. *Nu.* He's gotta have a steady position."

It wasn't funny. But he was expecting it. I laughed.

"And he promised to let me know definitely on Monday. That's to-morrow."

"But how does he look to you? I mean, do you think there's any chance of his getting cold feet or anything like that?"

"I don't think so," I said. "He looked pretty well set to *me*. It's only that wife of his that I'm worried about."

"Well, we can't help that," he said. "But otherwise it looks okay, right?"

"Right," I said. "Now, how about you?"

He lit a cigarette and shrugged.

"It's hard to say, Bogen," he said. "Right now I feel pretty sure I'm in. But I'm a funny guy."

He didn't have to advertise it.

"Well, hell," I said. "You can't—"

"But don't worry about me," he said, holding up his hand to quiet me. "The way I look at it, I figure if we get the factory man, if we get Babushkin, then I'm in. That enough?"

"Plenty," I said.

We shook hands.

"I guess you'll want to go back to the stable, now," I said, getting up. "So I think I'll—"

"I'm not anxious," he said. "There's dozens of them around. But how about you? You want a knockdown to something?"

"No, thanks," I said, "I've got my hands full right now."

"Private stock, eh?" he said, leering.

"Yeah," I said. "Pre-war."

He let out a short laugh and shook his head.

"Not for me," he said. "I don't like them that old."

"They have their points," I said. "They know a little more when they're that age."

"I don't care about that," he said. "I teach them all they have to know."

"I guess they couldn't want a better teacher, eh?" I said.

Look at me, handing out compliments!

"Oh, I'm not bad," he said with a pleased shrug. Of course he wasn't. He had too mild an adjective. "Say," he said, "when are you going home—to-night?"

"Yeah," I said, "I've got to be in my office in the morning."

"All right," he said. "I'm going back to-night, too. I'll give you a lift home in my car. Okay?"

"Nah, I'll tell you, Ast," I said, "this tomato I got up here with me, she don't like automobiles."

"What's the matter," he said, "is she *that* old?"

"No," I said, "but she was in an accident once, and since then she's been sort of—"

"Well, okay, then," he said. "Suit yourself."

"Thanks anyway, Ast," I said, "but I'm afraid it'll have to be the train."

"Okay," he said.

"So we'll leave it this way, then," I said, getting up. "As soon as Babushkin gets in touch with me—or maybe I'll get in touch with him—yeah, that'll be better, I'll get in touch with him. And as soon as I get word from him one way or another, why, I'll contact you. Okay?"

"Yeah, that'll be all right."

"Maybe the three of us ought to have a little lunch or something together on Monday, so we could clean up the whole thing once and for all."

"That's not a bad idea," he said.

Well, that made it even. I got my compliment back.

"So I'll see you Monday, then, Ast," I said, holding out my hand.

"Right," he said, shaking it. "Just in case we miss each other in the shuffle, then, so long."

"So long," I said, and went out into the lobby.

I stopped at the desk and spoke to the clerk.

"Do me a favor, will you?" I said. "I just registered here this morning, and I'm leaving to-night. For the two meals I'm going to have here, I'd like to have a small little table at one side of the dining room. In a corner, if possible. Do you think you can arrange it?"

He looked at me with a wise grin and puckered up his lips. I took out my wallet and slipped two singles across the desk.

"A small table for two in as unnoticeable a corner as you can find in the dining room," I said. "And the name is Bogen. Okay?"

"Why, I guess so, sir," he said, taking the money.

I went toward the other porch and stopped in the doorway for a moment, to make sure nobody I knew was in a position to see me going out. I took a look at Ruthie in the chair, staring out over the lawn, before I went over to speak to her. I should have known better than to take her to a joint like this. Somehow she didn't look as good in the sunlight at Totem Manor as she'd looked in the moonlight at the Lewisohn Stadium.

"Well," I said, sitting down next to her, "did anybody take a bite out of you?"

"No," she said, smiling that gentle smile of hers. "It's lovely. I'm really beginning to enjoy it."

"That's fine," I said. "That's why I brought you out here." There I go, lying again.

"Did you meet the man you wanted to see?" she asked.

"Yes," I said.

"I hope everything was all right," she said.

"It was."

"Good," she said.

Maybe it was, for me. But if I was as successful with the second purpose of the trip as I'd been with the first, maybe she wouldn't think so.

17

Everything was all right until lunchtime. I kept her moving around the place, showing her the sights, pointing out the Seventh Avenue big shots at play, avoiding people I knew.

And when lunch was served, our table was far enough in one corner of the large dining room to prevent my having to make embarrassing introductions.

I had one narrow squeeze when I saw Ast enter the dining

room late and stand for a few moments near the doorway, staring about him.

"Be back in a minute, Ruthie," I said, slipping out of my chair and walking toward Ast.

"Hello, Bogen," he said, still staring across the room as he spoke. "Alone again?"

"Yeah," I said, moving past him as I talked. "The girl friend went out for a minute. I guess she must've fallen in or something."

"Well, don't get your hands wet," he said, and hurried across the room. The idea got me sore.

I walked out into the lobby, bought a pack of cigarettes I didn't need, and came back. I looked the dining room over carefully before I sat down, but I didn't see Ast again.

"I think what we'll do, Ruthie," I said, "is go out for a walk right after lunch and see if we can't find a nice quiet spot where we can lie down and take a little nap for a while. What do you say?"

"All right, if you want to," she said. "I thought maybe we'd take a swim, though. The pool looks so—"

"I don't think you better go in," I said. "It's still too early in the year. I don't want you to catch a cold, you know."

"All right," she said again. "I only mentioned it because I saw those other people there, when we came in—"

"Aah, they're crazy," I said. "Come on."

We walked across the lawn past the tennis courts till we were on a narrow footpath that led through the trees. Once we were out of sight of the other people I took her hand and walked along swinging it.

"This is nice, isn't it?" I said.

She nodded slowly, with a smile. I guess she thought she had it all figured out. There it was, right on her face: he'd rather make love than go swimming!

"It's a relief to get away from those damn crowds for a while," I said.

She nodded again and I put my arm around her. I wanted to make up for any stitches I may have dropped during the morning by my maneuvers to avoid Ast.

We walked in silence for a while until we reached a small cleared space at the side of the footpath. It sloped gently up from the path toward a knot of trees, and ended with a big log lying across their base. Like in the movies.

"This looks all right," I said, "let's try it."

I took off my slipover and spread it near the trees so she could sit on it and lean against the log. I helped her sit down and while she was arranging her skirts I parked myself on the log, a little to one side of her and slightly above her.

She leaned back and looked up at the sky through the branches of the trees. From the angle at which I was watching her, alone in the woods, without any fast blondes from Seventh Avenue to compare her with, she began to look again like she had looked the night of the concert. But it wasn't getting me this time.

I looked around the cleared space carefully, to make sure I'd recognize it in the dark. For the rest, the darkness didn't worry me. When you get into my class, it's more of a help than a handicap. The only thing that was going to be new to-night was the stage.

I should have spent more time in the park.

I let my hand drop to her shoulder and she reached up and took it, holding it there against that warm soft skin of hers that would have put a dame with an ounce of intelligence and a decent-looking face in a Park Avenue penthouse before she even learned how to make out bank-deposit slips.

The sweat began to gather in my palm, but I didn't take my hand away. We sat that way for a long time, with me stroking her hair every once in a while to keep her in the right state of mind. But under my hand her flesh grew warmer and warmer, melting away until I could feel the pulse come beating up against me. Now and then she dozed off, clutching my hand more tightly and smiling a little. My legs began to ache from the strain of holding myself against the trunk of the tree, and inside my head I could feel the blood pounding against my ears. The veins in my temples began to hurt. It got so that for a minute I forgot she was there. I couldn't think. But I didn't let it worry me. My own feelings,

I knew I could always take care of. I was on my way, and the detour signs didn't mean a thing.

"We better be getting back," I said finally. "Or we'll miss dinner."

She smiled through her yawn and stretched delicately. The dress grew tight across her chest. Her head rolled back against the tree and she moved her shoulders in a quick happy shiver. I helped her to her feet. But from the way she got up I could tell she didn't want to go.

We walked back slowly, without talking.

After dinner the crowd went over to the casino.

"Let's go over, too, Harry," she said.

"I don't know," I said. "That dump gets so crowded with all those—"

"The social staff is putting on a show," she said.

"Don't listen to their bragging," I said.

"I heard the girls talking in the ladies' room," she said. "They're going to give *Counsellor At Law*."

These overpowering inducements were hell on a guy's resolutions.

"All right," I said, "if you really want to."

I figured as long as it was going to be a show, it would be dark, anyway.

The stage at the far end of the large social hall, or casino, was hidden by curtains, and the room was covered with loosely strewn chairs. At one side a six-piece band was playing and several couples were dancing. Most of them were in evening clothes, although there were quite a few, like us, who wore the same things they had worn during the day. The slot machines and the bar at one side were getting quite a play.

Ruthie and I stood near the stage, watching the dancers weave in and out among the scattered chairs and listening to the noises behind the curtains.

She touched my arm and said, "Would you want to—to dance a little, Harry?"

What was she doing, trying to make it easy for me?

"Gee, I don't think we ought to, Ruthie," I said, smiling. "We're not in evening clothes, you know, and, well, it's not so—"

"You're right," she said quickly. "I just thought maybe you wanted to, that's all."

"*I* don't," I said, "but if *you* do, why, just say the word and we'll—"

"No, no," she said, "That's all right."

"Sure?" I said, looking down into her face.

From now on everything was build-up. Everything I said and did had to count.

"Positive," she said.

"Then let's take a crack at those slot machines," I said, taking her arm and leading her toward them.

I broke a five-dollar bill into quarters and gave her a handful.

"Oh, no, Harry," she said, pushing them back. "*You* play if you want to. I'll just watch."

"Oh, come on, Ruthie," I said, taking her hand. "Don't be like that."

"No, please," she said. "I'd rather just watch."

"All right, then," I said, "Maybe you'll bring me luck."

But she didn't. I went through the five dollars, and another three, without cracking the jackpot. Somehow, aside from the ten thousand, she and money didn't seem to go together.

By this time the people were beginning to take their seats for the show, and I found two near the door. It was a lucky thing I'd seen the play on Broadway. Otherwise I'd never have recognized it from the way it was being murdered. The first act was lousy. And it didn't take me long after the curtain rose on the second act to see that it wasn't much of an improvement. I leaned close to Ruthie and whispered in her ear.

"What do you say we get out of here and go for a walk?" I said. I took her hand and squeezed it a little. "This thing is terrible, anyway."

"All right," she said.

She was pretty good at these sweeping statements.

We tiptoed out onto the lawn and stood for a moment, looking up at the sky.

"It's a lot like the night at the Stadium, isn't it?" I said.

"Yes," she said.

We walked across the lawn toward the tennis courts, swinging hands, until we reached the footpath. It was dark under the trees and I moved closer to her and put my arm around her. She rested her head against me as we walked. When we reached the little cleared space, I stopped and said, "Let's rest a while."

I spread my jacket near the log and helped her down. Then I sat down next to her and we sat in the pale light that filtered through the branches and the leaves, hugging our knees and watching the stars come out over us. It was very quiet.

"Happy?" I asked softly.

"Uh-huh," she said.

I leaned back against the log and eased her to me, resting her head in the bend of my arm. She tipped her face up and I kissed her, hard, holding her to me. Her arm crept up around my neck and we remained like that for a few moments.

This was going to be a pushover.

I kissed her again, very softly, on the forehead, and her tense body relaxed in my arms. I put my hand on her belly and began to stroke her gently, feeling her warm flesh, soft and yet firm, through the dress and the underwear. Once she half raised her free arm, but she dropped it back on the grass. I began to fumble with the buttons of her blouse, but she didn't stop me. The last thought I had in my head was that I wasn't feeling the way I thought I would. I felt quiet and warm and didn't care what happened. I liked the feel of her against me. I wanted to stay like that.

She drew a single sharp breath—almost a gasp, but not quite—and her head rolled so that her face was toward me.

It was pulled all tight! She looked like a kid too scared to cry.

It was as though I had suddenly smacked my head into something hard.

She didn't move in my arm. She didn't move my hand from her blouse. But there was no mistaking the look on her face. She wasn't enjoying it. She hated it. She had her teeth gritted, but she didn't budge.

It came to me all in a rush. The whole thing didn't mean a damn to her. She'd just made up her mind to take anything I gave. I realized that what she wanted was *me!*

She reached her arm up around my neck again and drew herself toward me. I responded without thinking. Still dazed, I took her to me. I guess I felt happy. There was something to her that all the others had never had. She made me feel good, like for once I had everything I needed. I could tell from the motions that the last barrier was down. If I wanted to go on, I was home. It was up to me.

But all of a sudden I didn't want to. Even as I held her in my arms, I began to feel sore. For Christ's sakes, what was I gonna do, become a sucker for atmosphere? Anything money can't buy, I don't want. Why the hell couldn't she play according to the rules? Why the hell couldn't she act like other girls? Like Miss Marmelstein, for instance? Why did she have to look at you and make you feel that you were changing her whole life?

The hell with this, I figured. I wasn't that hard up. If I wanted to get laid, I knew where to go without having to take on responsibilities.

I loosened my arms around her and stood up. She dropped against the tree, shivering. I smacked my pants hard to get the dirt off and reached for her hand.

"Come on," I said roughly.

I swung her up into a sitting posture.

The hell with this, I said to myself. They could keep the ten thousand dollars. I'd get the capital for my business some other way. What did I have Tootsie Maltz for?

"Come on, come on," I said again. I didn't care how tough I sounded. "What do you think we've got, all night? It's late. We've got to make a train yet."

She stood there, slightly dazed, smoothing her dress, her lips quivering.

If she was going to tell me she'd never done this before, she could save her breath, I knew it better than she did.

"For Christ's sakes," I said. "Shake a leg, there, will you?"

She followed me without saying a word.

18

On the way into my private office, as I passed Miss Marmelstein at the switchboard, I said, "Get me Pulbetkal on the phone."

The bell rang as I hung up my hat and I picked it up and said, "Hello, Pulbetkal?"

"Yes."

"Mr. Babushkin, please."

"Just a moment, please."

He got on the wire and said, "Hello?"

"Hello, Meyer," I said. "This is Harry Bogen. How's everything?"

"All right."

"Have a nice week end?"

"Yeah, all right."

"I'll tell you why I called, Meyer," I said. "How about you and I and Ast having a little lunch together to-day?"

"Let's see," he said slowly. "I don't know——"

He should have had those last three words embroidered on his linen as his motto.

"I'll tell you why, Meyer," I said. "I saw Ast yesterday and he thought it wouldn't be a bad idea if we sat down around a table and discussed the whole thing once and for all. What do you say?"

"Well, all right," he said.

"Let's see, now, Meyer," I said. "What time is convenient for you?"

"Oh, I don't know, Bogen——"

"Well, then, let's say two o'clock. That all right with you?"

"I guess so," he said.

"Well, now, look, Meyer," I said, "let's make this definite. Because I want to tell Ast, too, you know. Is two o'clock okay with you? Because if it isn't, let's make it for any time that's convenient for you. What do you say?"

"All right," he said. "Two o'clock."

"Fine," I said. "Two o'clock at the Beaux Arts. Ask the waiter for my table. I'll reserve one."

"All right, Bogen," he said. "Two o'clock."

I hung up and looked at my watch. It was a quarter after nine. I picked up the receiver again and said, "Get me Toney Frocks."

A few moments later I was talking to the switchboard operator at the other end.

"Is Mr. Ast in yet?"

"No, sir, he's not in *yet.*"

Just as I thought.

"Well, will you take a message for him?"

"Certainly."

"Please get this right. It's very important."

"I'll get it right. Don't worry."

"I'm not worrying," I said. "But get it right. Tell Mr. Ast that Mr. Bogen called him. Mr. Harry Bogen. And tell him that the appointment is for to-day at two-fifteen at the Beaux Arts with Babushkin. Got that?"

"Right."

"Read it back to me like a good girl, will you?" I said.

"Mr. Harry Bogen called," she read. "Appointment is for to-day at two-fifteen at the Beaux Arts with Mr.—who?"

"Babushkin," I said, and spelled it for her. "Got the whole thing now?"

"Right," she said.

"Fine," I said. "Now if Mr. Ast gets that message right, just as I gave it to you, I'll come up there personally one of these days and give you a nice box of candy."

"Don't kid me, Mr. Bogen," she said. "You sound just like a dress salesman."

"Stop insulting me," I said, laughing. "Is that a way to talk to a person you've never met?"

"I could talk to you differently, Mister," she said, "but they'd pull the telephone out on us if I did."

"You tempt me, lady," I said. "I think I'll have to come up there one of these days and put you to the test."

"Better send your picture up first," she said. "And don't come without that box of candy."

"Okay," I said. "When you give that message to Mr. Ast, just ask him about me. He'll give me a good recommendation."

"Well, that'll be news," she said. "Any time *that* guy gives anything away, I'd like to be there just to watch."

"All right," I said. "You just give him that message right, and I'll see if I can't arrange that little treat for you."

"Fine," she said, "that's a promise."

Just as I hung up, Tootsie walked in. I looked at my watch. Nine-thirty on the dot. I had him trained right.

"Well, here I am, on time," he said proudly, like he'd just discovered a cure for cancer.

"Yeah," I said, and got up to sit down on the edge of my desk.

He hung up his coat and turned to face me.

"Well, Harry, what's on your mind?"

"Nothing special," I said, waving my hand and smiling at him. "Just things in general, that's all."

"I mean, what was all the excitement about on Friday? You told me to be here this morning nine-thirty, no?"

"That's true," I said. "I did."

"Listen, Harry. You starting that kidding stuff again? You told me Friday I should be here nine-thirty this morning, and I'm here. Now what's all the excitement about?"

"Excitement?" I said. "What excitement? Why, I'm as calm and cool as—"

He shook his head and pulled out his cigarettes.

"Oh, all right, go ahead, go ahead," he said, trying to sound disgusted. "I see already you won't be ready to talk until you've had a chance to be a wise guy for a few minutes.

Okay, go ahead, go ahead. I know you by this time, Harry."

That's what he thought.

"Okay," I laughed and got up to slap his shoulder. "Here," I said, pushing him into a chair, "sit down." I took a seat facing him.

"All right," he said. "So now I'm sitting."

"Good," I said, and then, "Tell me, Tootsie, how do you like this delivery business of ours?"

For a few seconds he stared at me. Then he said, "Jesus Christ alive! Did you haul me back here this morning just so's you could ask me that?"

"Sure," I said. "Why not?"

"Say, are you crazy or something?"

"No. Why?"

He rubbed his hand over his face and then through his hair and then squeezed his lips together and leaned forward in his chair.

"Listen, Harry," he began.

Sorry, but that's where I draw the line.

"You listen to me, Tootsie," I said. Not tough. Just friendly. Dutch uncley, sort of. "What's wrong with me asking a question like that? We're partners, aren't we? Can't I ask you even how you like the business we're in together? Can't we have a little executive conference once in a while, without you thinking I'm crazy or something?"

He leaned back and threw out his hands.

"I don't know," he said to the ceiling. "Maybe *I'm* the one that's crazy?"

Where did he get that maybe stuff?

"I'm not kidding, Tootsie. I just asked you a simple question, that's all. How do you like the business?"

He hesitated a moment, still looking at me as though he couldn't make up his mind whether he was being taken for a ride or not, and said, "It's okay. I like it."

"That's all?" I said. "You just like it?"

"Well, hell, Harry, I mean what can a guy say to—?"

I put on a long face.

"I'm glad you like it, Tootsie. No kidding either. I mean that. I'm really glad you like it."

"What's the matter? Anything wrong?"

"No. Not exactly," I said; and then, brightly, "You saving any money out of this, Tootsie?"

He shrugged.

"Well, sure," he said, "I been saving."

"That's good," I said. "Remember what I told you when we started. There's no sense in pissing it all away. I'm not saying you have to go around being a mizzo or anything like that. But a guy who saves his money is no dope, let me tell you."

"Well, I been saving. I've saved all right."

"Yeah? How much?"

"Oh—I don't know." He waved his hand. "A coupla thousand. You know."

That was just the point. I didn't know.

"Don't you know exactly?" I said. "For crying out loud, Tootsie, the least a guy can do is keep track of how much money he's got. Don't you know how much you—?"

"Sure I do." He dug into his pocket and pulled out a bank-book. "Here. I got—thirty-seven, thirty-seven-fif—oh, about thirty-seven hundred."

"Not bad," I said. "Not bad at all."

He put the book down and looked at me.

"Say, what *is* this, Harry, anyway?"

"I'll tell you, Tootsie," I said quietly. "I just came from the doctor."

"What's the matter?" he said. "You sick or something?"

I sighed and looked sad. It's easy to do.

"That's about the size of it, I guess," I said.

"That's tough all right. What is it?"

"Oh, I don't know. Complications and things like that. You know. You can't get anything straight out of those doctors. You know how they are."

"Gee, that's tough, Harry."

Was it?

"Yeah, Tootsie. I'm not as healthy as I look."

He leaned forward in his chair and frowned a bit.

"Well, what did he say?"

"I have to lay off for a while. He said I have to knock off for a while and take a good rest."

He leaned back and his face relaxed.

"Well, that's easy," he said. "You can go and—"

"I'm afraid it's not as easy as it sounds, Tootsie. He said I have to knock off. Not just for a couple of weeks or so, either."

"That's all right, Harry. Why don't you go away and just—?"

I shook my head.

"No, Tootsie. It's not all right. He said I have to go away for over a year. Maybe even more."

His mouth hung open, like a basketball goal. I wanted to crumple up a blotter and toss it in, to see if I could shoot the two points.

"A whole *year?*"

I shook my head.

"Maybe even more," I said.

"Gee *whiz.*"

I got up and scratched my head.

"That's what I wanted to see you about," I said, talking without looking at him, moving around his chair slowly. "A guy can't just leave a business like this for over a year and then expect to come back like nothing happened. It wouldn't be fair. It wouldn't be fair to you, Tootsie."

"Aah, hell, Harry," he said. "You and I, we went into this thing together—"

"I know what you're gonna say, Tootsie, and don't you think for one minute I don't appreciate it. I want you to know I appreciate it all right, and I think it's damn nice of you, too. But, well, you know how it is, Tootsie. A guy can't do those things. It sounds all right in the movies, but it just doesn't work out."

He didn't say anything for a few moments, just chewed his lip. He was so fat that if he ever got shipwrecked, he could keep himself alive for quite some time by doing that. Then he said, "What are you gonna do?"

"Oh, I don't know, Tootsie. But you don't have to worry about me. I've got a few thousand saved up. I'll just go away some place, maybe Europe or some place like that, you know, and then, maybe when I come back—but hell, I'm not worrying about that now. My health comes first."

"Sure," he said.

"That's one of the reasons why I asked you if you saved any of your money, Tootsie," I said. "I want to sell you my interest in the business."

His mouth dropped down to his third rib. Once more and I wouldn't have to use a crumpled blotter. A regular basketball could get in.

"You wanna *sell* me your interest in the business?" he said.

"Sure," I said, turning quickly to face him. "Why not? You and I started this thing together, didn't we? It's yours just as much as it's mine, isn't it? Why should I go ahead and sell out to a stranger? Would that be fair to you? Why, you can run this whole shooting match by yourself. If you need any help in the office, if you need anybody to help you with the assignments or handling the boys or anything like that, hell, you can hire a guy for thirty or forty bucks a week, and you can keep the whole profits for yourself. You wouldn't have to go around splitting with anybody. You'd be your own boss. Just you and nobody else. The whole works would be yours. Look at what you saved in the few months we've been in the business. Thirty-seven hundred. Almost four thousand bucks. Remember, Tootsie, up to now we've been splitting twenty-five and seventy-five, and you've been on the short end. But like this, from now on, when I'm gone, you'll be getting the whole damn thing, one hundred per cent."

And I wasn't just batting them out to him, either. He'd be getting one hundred per cent, all right. The only trouble with that was that in another month or so, with the way the competition would begin to roll in, that one hundred per cent would be less than the twenty-five he was getting now.

"Well, gee whiz, Harry," he began, "I don't—"

"Don't worry about it, Tootsie," I said, putting my hand on his shoulder. "There's absolutely no other way out of it for me. The way I am now, what the doctor told me, I've got to get away and I've got to do it quick. And I don't care what the hell it costs me to do it, either. I'd rather have my health than anything. Maybe in a year or two, when I come back, and I'm all right again—*maybe*—then, if you still feel the same way about it, maybe then we'll be able to get together and work something out, maybe we'll be able to tie up again the way we did. But right now, Tootsie, I'm just a sick man, that's all. I can't waste any time. I've got to get out and I've got to get out in a hurry. There's nobody I know I'd rather turn my end of this thing over to than you, Tootsie, and I want you to have it."

He scratched his head. That made the third time.

"I know, Harry," he said, "I guess I understand how you feel about it and all. But the only thing worries me, is whether I got enough money to *buy* your end. I mean, what the hell, a thing like this—"

"You just said you had thirty-seven hundred, didn't you?"

"Sure, but what's thirty-seven hundred dollars for a—?"

Well, if he felt *that* way about it!

"All right, then," I said, smiling at him. "If it's really gonna make you *feel* bad, suppose we make it this way. Thirty-seven hundred in cash, and let's say another—oh, another eight hundred that you can slip me in a week or so, or you can mail me a check, when the collections come in. So that'll make it an even four thousand five hundred bucks, and everything'll be one hundred per cent okay right up to the minute. All right?"

"Well, gee, Harry, *still*—"

"That's all right," I said, patting his shoulder. Big-Hearted Bogen. "Just forget it and don't worry about it. For you, Tootsie, it's all right. You can have the whole works for the forty-five hundred dollars."

"Well, gee, Harry—"

"What do you say?"

"Well, if that's what you want, Harry, then it's all right with me. You know that."

Well, I'll admit, I *did* have a suspicion.

"That's fine," I said, taking his hand and shaking it. "We'll go down to Golig to-morrow and we'll have him take care of the whole thing."

"So quick?"

"Well, it's Monday now," I said, "And if we clean up the whole thing to-morrow, then I'll be able to get away by Wednesday. I can do all my packing to-night and to-morrow, and I'll be all set."

"You certainly must be sick, Harry," he said. "I swear I'd never think it just by looking at you."

In a way he was right, too. My stomach was giving a combined imitation of the Chicago fire and the San Francisco earthquake.

"Well, that's how those things are," I said. "You never can tell how you stand." Where have I heard that before? "So we'll go down to Golig to-morrow, okay?"

"Okay," he said, and got up. He put on his hat and coat, but I didn't move. I figured if I remained seated, and didn't do anything, there was less chance of my giving myself away.

"I'll be here all day, and maybe a little late to-night," I said, "just in case you want me for anything. I want to clean up my desk and write a couple of letters and things like that."

"All right, Harry," he said. "I'm going out to see a couple of the clients. They've been kicking about the rates a little, something about they can get it cheaper from somebody else and all that."

"They're crazy," I said quickly. "Just go up and talk to them and if they get tough, tell them to show you some figures. But don't worry about those little things."

"I'm not," he said.

The dope.

"Okay, then," I said, "to-morrow at Golig's."

"Right," he said and went out.

As soon as I heard the outer door close I picked up the

receiver and said, "Get me Toney Frocks again, will you?"

"Hello," the girl at the other end said.

"Mr. Teddy Ast, please," I said. "Is he in yet?"

"Yes, he's in. Who's this, Mr. Bogen?"

"Yes," I said. "How'd you know?"

"Well, for one thing, I recognized your voice, and for another—"

"You can stop right there," I said, "I feel flattered enough."

"—And for another thing," she continued, "the girl at your switchboard just told me who's calling when I asked her."

"Well, now that the preliminaries are over," I said, "what are the chances of talking to Mr. Ast?"

"Very poor," she said. "He's busy in the showroom with a customer."

"Aah, hell," I said. "Is that guy ever free?"

"Once in a while," she said. "But you always call at the wrong time."

"Well, that certainly is lovely," I said. "Here I have an appointment with him, and I can't even get him on the phone to find out if—"

"But I have a *message* for you from Mr. Ast," she said sweetly.

"Is that right?" I said. "Well, hell, what's your rush? Why don't you wait until—?"

"Now don't be sarcastic," she said, "and I'll tell you what he said."

"Okay, shoot."

"Mr. Ast said," she said, reciting like a kindergarten kid, "that if Mr. Bogen calls him, Mr. Harry Bogen, I should tell Mr. Bogen, Mr. Harry Bogen, that Mr. Ast, Mr. Teddy Ast, told me that he, Mr. Ast, Mr. Teddy Ast, would be on time to keep his appointment with Mr. Bogen, Mr. Harry Bogen, at the Beaux Arts to-day at two-fifteen. Is that all right?"

I love them when they get cute. If I had her near me, I'd've pushed her face in.

"I guess so," I said, "but I'm not quite sure yet. I'll have to decipher it first."

"Well, I'm sorry," she said, "but that's the best I can do."

"The *best?*" I said.

"Well, I mean, on the *phone.*"

"Oh, that's different." Maybe it was all in my voice, after all. "Well, thanks," I said, "and if everything turns out all right, I'll bring up that box of candy one of these days."

"You don't have to wait till you're free," she said. "You can send it up with a boy."

"What's the matter," I said, "you think the boy'll be able to do better than me?"

"I wouldn't be surprised," she said, "and don't get so fresh," she added and hung up.

After a week end with dimwits, it was a pleasure to talk for a few minutes with someone that gave you a chance to sharpen up your shots.

I put on my hat and took my coat over my arm and went out to the switchboard.

"I'm going to the barber, Miss Marmelstein," I said, "and then I've got a luncheon appointment. I'll probably be gone most of the afternoon, but I think I'll be back later."

"All right, Mr. Bogen," she said.

You bet it is, I thought.

19

I entered the restaurant five minutes late on purpose, but Babushkin was already there. He was at the small table I'd reserved way over in the corner, hunched over the menu because he was scared of the waiter that stood a little way off and kept looking at him.

Everything he did was so in keeping with the way I'd figured him out, that it looked like a gag. But he wasn't playing dumb. He wasn't that good an actor.

I came late because I knew he'd be there ahead of me.

He was the type that was always on time for appointments. That was a good sign. When a guy can manage to hit the time of an appointment right on the nose, the chances are he's been devoting quite a bit of time to reminding himself that he should be there, which means that his mind isn't exactly what you'd call a beehive, which means that he's at least a couple of notches lower than a genius, which means he was right up my alley. Another thing I'd decided on was that he wasn't exactly a lion tamer, and here a waiter had him buffaloed, just by looking at him. If I had any doubts about him, this clinched it.

"Hello there, Meyer," I said, shoving out my hand and giving him a healthy shot of the old personality smile, grade A.

"Hello, Mr. Bogen," he said, getting up to take my hand.

"Stay right where you are," I said, pushing him back into his chair and taking one that faced him, with my back to the wall. That's my Chicago training, you know. Keep the whole room in front of me. "Sorry to be late, but I couldn't help it. They had me tied up on the phone till just a couple of minutes ago. I came down as soon as I could."

"That's all right," he said, "I know how those things are."

Maybe I had a genius on my hands after all. He knew how those things were!

"How's the missus?" I asked.

"She's all right, thanks."

"One of these days," I said, "I'll have to invite her up to my house to try some of my mother's blintzes. You ought to hear the bawling out my mother gave me for not inviting her up the other night when you were there. She was so sore I thought she was going to hit me with a frying pan or something. They were all right, those blintzes, weren't they?"

"Yeah," he said.

"I guess your wife'll like them, too," I said. "What's a good night during the week for her? I mean, there's no rush, but any time you have a free night, just let me know."

"Well, I don't know—"

"All right, then, I'll tell you what I'll do. I'll let *you* know, and then, if it's not okay, why, we can change it for some other night."

"All right," he said.

"Don't forget, now," I said.

"I won't," he said.

Well, at least that made one of us who wouldn't.

"And the baby?" I said. "How's the baby?"

"All right," he said. "A little cold it had, but my wife she took it to the doctor and he gave her some kind of oil she should rub on, but now it's all right."

"Only one you got?" I said. "Just one, right?"

"Yeah," he said, "just one."

"Well," I said, with a laugh, "just wait till we get going good, then you'll be able to afford to have another dozen if you want to."

"Yeah," he said.

Well, that was enough of *that*. No sense in ruining my appetite completely. I picked up the menu and put it down again.

"I wonder what's keeping Mr. Ast?" I said, looking at my watch. "It's almost a quarter after two already."

"He's probably tied up with a customer, I guess," Babushkin said. Sure, either that, or it was because I'd told him the appointment was for later. But Babushkin didn't have to know that. There were going to be a lot of things that Babushkin wouldn't have to know about. "You know how it is with salesmen," he said.

He was taking a hell of a lot for granted. That made two things I knew how they were.

"You bet," I said, laughing. "I'm practically in the same boat myself." I picked the menu again. "I'll tell you what. There's no sense in our waiting for Mr. Ast. We don't know how long he'll be. And while I don't know about you, Meyer, I know *I'm* nearly starved. Suppose we order, and when he comes, he can catch up."

"All right," he said.

"Waiter," I called, but I didn't really have to. He was practically sitting on my neck from the minute I'd drifted in.

I took my time about the order, making it sound complicated, and when I finished the waiter turned to Babushkin. He looked at the menu for a few seconds, rubbing his face a little like he had a toothache. Then he looked up and said, "Uh—I'll—I'll take the same."

Just a make-it-two guy. Every time I met him he showed more qualifications for the job of being my partner.

He didn't look very happy, and when the waiter brought the fruit cup and put it down in front of him, he picked up his spoon and went to work on it without a change of expression. I let him fiddle around with the cherry on top, until he got it onto the spoon and carried it to his mouth. Then I said:

"Well, what did your wife say about that proposition we were talking about the other night up at my house?"

He swallowed the cherry and began to talk to the plate of fruit in front of him.

"Well, she said it was a good idea, Bogen," he said slowly. "Only one thing she said—I hope you don't think there's anything personal in this, Bogen—she only said a man has to be very careful of the men he goes into business with. I mean, she said you can't pick your boss when you go to work for somebody, but, well, she said you ought to pick your partner pretty carefully when you go into business."

So far that looked like his only drawback as a partner— his wife. Was I glad I didn't act on that brainstorm I'd had about meeting her!

"She's perfectly right, too," I said as the waiter changed the plates in front of us. "Why do you think I went all over Seventh Avenue with a fine-tooth comb before I decided you were the best designer and factory man there was? If I wanted to rush this thing, hell, I could have picked up any one of a hundred dopes who know a little something about designing and cutting and things like that. But like your wife said, I knew that when you're going into business with a man, the thing to do is be very careful and pick him like, hell, I don't know, like you were picking an eye to put in your head."

I dipped my spoon into the plate, but I didn't carry it to my mouth. I'd rather have the soup get cold than Babushkin.

"That's just what Teddy Ast told me the first time we even talked about it," I said. "I said what we need more than anything else, Teddy, is a corker of a factory man. I don't care so much about the other things, I said, if any of the other things aren't so okay it isn't so bad. But a factory man, that has to be absolutely the top, I said. And he agreed with me right away. 'Get Babushkin of Pulbetkal,' he said to me, just like that, without even batting an eye, that's what he said."

He nodded slowly. Maybe he was finally beginning to realize himself that he was a good factory man.

"So what do you say, Meyer?" I said, leaning across the table toward him, and looking serious. "When Ast shows up, do we tell him we're in?"

"All right," he said, "all right."

I didn't have time to let out the sigh of relief that I should have let out. And I didn't waste any time complimenting myself, either. Because this was nothing. This was easy. The hard part was yet to come. I just leaned back in my chair and let my joints ease up a little. But in a moment they tensed up again. Because as I leaned back I saw two things. The clock on the restaurant wall, and that said twenty-five to three. And Teddy Ast, dressed to kill, bouncing across the restaurant toward us.

There were times when, seeing him as I did just then, my feelings toward Teddy Ast amounted almost to admiration. With all the handicaps of a body shaped like a toothpick and a face that had about as much distinction in it as a spoonful of mashed potatoes, he was still a snappy number. He was wearing a draped herringbone topcoat with a fly front and a gray velvet collar, tab shirt with a black knitted tie, peg-top pants, suede shoes, and a brown pork-pie hat with a black band and a tricky little feather stuck into it. I took it all in at a glance and filed it away for future reference.

"Here comes Mr. Ast now," Babushkin said. But I didn't have time to be astonished at the fact that he should have noticed something all by himself. I was too busy reminding myself that for the next few minutes I would be talking to Teddy Ast and not to Meyer Babushkin.

"Yeah," I said, "That's him all right."

Right about—*face!*

"Hello, Bogen," he said, nodding briskly, and, "Hello, Babushkin."

He slipped out of his coat and handed it to the waiter with his hat. The suit was a pepper-pot tweed, rough and shaggy-looking, but double-breasted. I marked that down on my list, too.

"Hello, there, Ast," I said. You have to put the "there" in. You can't say "Hello, Ast." It sounds dopey. "How's the boy?"

"Pretty good," he said, studying the menu. "Can't kick. Say, waiter," he said, tossing the menu down. "Just bring me a tongue on rye and a glass of beer. But the bread has to be thin, remember, and I don't want any of that lungy stuff on the tongue. Tell him to cut all that stuff away, understand?"

The waiter nodded. They were all doing it. I guess it was an epidemic.

"Okay, then," he said, dismissing him. "Step on it. I'm in a hurry."

Then he turned to us and rubbed his skinny hands.

"Well, gentlemen? What's the good word?"

"Pussy," I said, and grinned. "That's always the good word, isn't it?"

"Right, my friend," he said, jerking his face into a smile. "You getting much?"

I shrugged my shoulders and ducked my head and gave an imitation of a Seventh Avenue grease ball.

"End iff I go around makink complaindts, so it'll help me maybe?"

He laughed and showed his teeth. They weren't so hot. They were even and strong-looking, but they were yellow and sloped inward, so that his mouth looked like that of an old man, without teeth, sucked in.

"Well," he said, "any time you run short, just call on Uncle Teddy, and I'll get you fixed up."

He was going to get *me* fixed up!

"That's a promise?" I said.

"A promise," he said.

The waiter brought the sandwich and set it before him. He dug in. I lit a cigarette and watched him. Babushkin just looked worried.

"Did you ever hear about the way they catch fish up in Alaska?" I asked.

He pushed the food into a corner of his mouth, and said, "Not since I stopped wearing diapers, I didn't hear it."

"No, this one is new," I said.

He washed down the lump of food with a swallow of beer.

"They're all new," he said.

A wise guy. Well, that was all right. He was sure of himself. I liked them that way.

"I know," I said. "But this one is new."

"Yeah," he said. "Like my girl friend."

"See, it's this way," I said. "First they cut a hole in the ice. Then they—"

"Yeah," he said, taking another bite of the sandwich and examining it to see how much damage he'd done. "Try again, Bogen," he said.

"Well," I said, "they can't *all* be new."

"No," he said, "but they don't have to be *that* old."

He swallowed some beer and attacked the sandwich again.

"How about the he-virgin and the nurse?" I said. "Hear that one?"

"Probably," he said.

But when I finished and said, "Get it?" he squinted his eye and stopped chewing for a second.

"No," he said.

That was the wise guy that knew all of them. They were *all* new!

"Lemme explain," I said, and did.

"Oh, yeah, sure!" he said. "That's right."

Yeah, sure, that's right! He knew it all the time!

"Not bad, eh?" I said, laughing.

He finished the sandwich and lit a cigarette.

"Say, that's pretty good, you know?"

No, I didn't know. He was telling me.

"When you get to the gag line," I said, "You have to get the break in when you say the second 'cheap.' Like this: 'Cheap is *chea*-eap!' "

"Cheap is cheap," he said to himself, memorizing the words. "That one's pretty good, all right. Wait'll I tell that to a couple of the buyers. They'll die laughing when—say, that reminds me." He looked from me to Babushkin and then back at me. "I hate to rush out on you like this, gentlemen, but I've got a couple of important buyers coming in, and, well, you know how those things are—"

"Sure," I said, "we know."

What the hell, I figured, Babushkin might have known, too. Maybe I wasn't lying when I spoke for both of us.

"So how do we stand, gentlemen?" he asked.

"We stand okay," I said. "It all depends on you now. Mr. Babushkin here and I, we're all set. We've got our money ready, both of us, and we're all set. Any time you say okay, all we have to do is make an appointment to go down to the lawyer and we're all set to go. We're just waiting to hear from you."

"Then you don't have to wait any longer," he said, spreading his skinny fingers out like a fan. "I'm all set any time you are. My money is ready now."

"Then we're all set?" I looked at Babushkin, who nodded, and then at Ast, who jerked his head up and down. "Fine. Let's see. To-day is Monday. Suppose we make it for Wednesday? Wednesday all right with you? All right, then. Wednesday at Golig's office. I don't know exactly what time, but I'll call you both up to let you know. Then it's Wednesday at Golig's office?"

They nodded. Ast stood up and shoved his arms into the sleeves of his coat that the waiter was holding for him. I got up, too, and Babushkin followed.

"How's my old friend Mr. Schmul of Toney Frocks?" I asked.

"You know Schmul?" Ast said, surprised.

"Do I know him?" I laughed. "I've been trying to forget him for over a year. I *worked* for the punk."

"You *worked* for him?"

"Sure."

"When?"

"About a year ago."

"A *year* ago? That's funny. I've been with him over two years already, and I don't remember you."

"That's because you never go into the back," I said with a laugh. "No salesman ever goes into the back."

"What do you mean, in the back?"

I figured I might as well give him a little jolt. It might shake a little of the cocksureness out of him and make him realize that he wasn't dealing with a schmoogie.

"I was one of his shipping clerks," I said.

He stared at me. It isn't every shipping clerk that can dig up ten thousand bucks with which to go into the dress business.

"You mean that?"

"I sure do," I said.

"A *year* ago?"

"You bet."

I bent down for the check, but I could feel the look of surprise he had trained on me, and I fumbled a little with the tip on purpose to give him a chance to recover. I didn't want him to get sore or anything. I just wanted him to think about it.

On the sidewalk, in front of the restaurant, we stopped.

"Which way you headed?" I asked.

"This way," they both said, pointing down.

"I'm going up," I said. I wasn't, but I said it anyway. No anticlimaxes for me. "Then it's Wednesday at Golig's office. I'll call you both up and give you the exact time. Okay?"

"Okay," they said, and walked off together.

I laughed a little to myself as I saw them go down the block, and I hoped they wouldn't get themselves run over or killed. They didn't know it, but they were worth their weight in—well, no, not even *they* were that valuable, but they were worth a lot to me. Two men make a dress business. A designer and a salesman. I was neither, but that didn't stop me. I took it easy. I picked and chose. And out of all of Seventh Avenue, I picked them. I hoped they would have brains enough to feel properly honored.

I grinned when I thought of what Pulvermacher's face would look like when he found out I'd taken away his factory man. But when I thought of that son of a bitch Schmul, and what *his* face would look like when he found that Toney Frocks, Inc. had lost the services of Theodore (Teddy to his pals and partners) Ast to me, I laughed out loud. A couple of people looked at me, but I didn't care. Meal or no meal, this called for a drink.

I went into Schrafft's for a soda.

When I got out I felt pretty good. I walked down Broadway slowly, whistling a little and window-shopping. A black and white tie in Gillette's window looked good to me, so I went in and bought it. On the corner of Thirty-Eighth Street I saw a women's accessory shop and I remembered that I'd promised Mother a purse to go with her new brown suit. I went in and bought her a good large one, the kind she liked. As I turned to leave the shop, a blue bag in a stand on the counter struck my eye.

It was made of soft blue suede, with a white leather border and two large white metal stars, one in each corner, for ornaments. Looking at it reminded me of Ruthie, and the dress she had worn to Totem Manor over the week-end. For a moment I couldn't think what the bag she had carried had looked like. And this one, aside from the color that matched her dress, seemed to have been made for her. Before I knew it, I had put my hand out and touched it, squeezing the soft sides gently.

"Did you want to see this purse?" the salesgirl said, moving down the counter toward me.

"Why, yes," I said. "Sure, you can wrap it up for me."

It was not until I reached the street and had walked half a block or so that I began to feel sore. It wasn't the money. It was just the feeling that I must have been going soft in the head. What the hell was the sense of buying things for a dame when you knew you weren't going to get anything back in exchange? What was I all of a sudden, Santa Claus? Where the hell did I get off playing around with a kike broad like that, anyway? Go buy her eight dollar purses! What the God damn hell for? Because my own mother had introduced her to me? The hell with that crap. If I was going around buying gifts, at least I ought to know enough to buy them for people who knew what was expected of them in return. A dame like Miss Marmelstein, for instance. She wasn't making any of the members of the Harvard faculty worry about their jobs. But she was smart enough to know that if I gave her a purse it wasn't because I all of a sudden thought it would be a good idea for her to have something that would match the color of her eyes.

I stopped walking and looked at my watch. Five-thirty. She *should* have been there yet. She'd been hanging around till after six for over a week. But it would be just my luck for her to skip out early this one night when I didn't want her to. Suddenly I began to walk quickly, and soon I was almost running.

I burst into the office breathlessly, and stopped short. She looked up at me from behind the switchboard in surprise.

"Why, Mr. Bogen!" she said. "What in the world—?"

I felt relieved and after I'd had a second or so to catch my breath I said, "I'm in a terrible hurry to get some very important letters out, Miss Marmelstein. I hope you don't mind staying a little later to-night."

"Why, of course not, Mr. Bogen," she said, smiling quickly. That was a dame for you! "I'm not doing anything special to-night, anyway."

It began to look like she did special things very seldom. Well, I'd see what I could arrange for her. After all, it wouldn't make any difference after to-night. But she didn't have to know about that.

"I'll tell you," I said, scratching my chin and looking at my watch. "It'll take me about a half hour or so to get my papers in shape before I'll be ready to dictate. I'll tell you what you do. You go down and have a bite, or go out and buy yourself a new brassiere or something. And say you get back here about six-thirty. That'll give me plenty of time."

She was all smiles.

"Okay," she said, and got up quickly.

"By the way," I said, holding out the package with the blue and white purse in it, "Here's a little trinket I picked up for you during the day."

She took it quickly and tore the wrapper off.

"Oh, Mr. Bogen, how am I ever going to thank you?"

I'll give you one guess, sister.

"That's all right," I said. "Just don't disappoint me. Six-thirty to-night."

"Don't worry," she said, "I won't."

As though I didn't know that.

"I'll be all ready by the time you get back," I said.

"That'll be good," she said.

Good my eye. This was going to be lots better than just plain good. This was going to be my swan song.

I went into my private office and began to clean out my desk and put the things I wanted to take with me aside. When I finished, my watch said twenty after six. Which meant I had ten minutes to think about how Miss Marmelstein was going to look on the couch in my private office as she performed her last official act as a salaried employee of the departing president of the Needle Trades Delivery Service, Inc.

20

The building had two entrances. One on Thirty-Eighth Street and one on Broadway. I walked in through the Broadway entrance, slowly, then out the Thirty-Eighth Street side. I did it a few times, maybe five or six. Each time I got the same brisk, excited feeling that the place was full of people moving, working, coining money. I was glad now I'd had the fight with Ast. Even though it had meant taking a chance on his

getting sore and walking out while I still needed him, I was
glad I'd insisted on this building over the one he had wanted.
The hell with what he wanted. The sooner he learned who
was boss, the better. I was in the right place.

I walked through the lobby once more, the last time, but
this time I didn't go out the Thirty-Eighth Street entrance. I
went into an elevator.

"Twenty-nine," I said, and the young guy with the tiny
nose and the marcelled hair punched the button. I wondered
how long it would take him and the rest of the operators before they would remember my floor. What the hell, I wasn't
a shipping clerk in the building any more; I was a tenant.

As we stopped at the various floors, I noticed that the
doors that faced the elevator had the names of the firms that
occupied those floors painted on them. Before I stepped out
of the car onto the twenty-ninth floor, I noticed that our
name had not yet been painted on the door facing the elevator. I made a mental note to remind the super about that.

It was a lucky thing I made a mental note of it. Otherwise
I would have forgotten it. Because the second I stepped into
our showroom I saw the carpet.

There were a lot of things and people in that showroom.
First of all, it was still full of ladders and pails of paint and
brushes. Then some of the wrapping paper and excelsior
and rope from the furniture was still lying around. And the
pictures on the walls were new. They must have arrived since
I had left in the morning. And there were three or four workmen moving around, too. But that didn't matter. I noticed the
carpet right away. It didn't fit in with the way I had that showroom laid out in my mind. And after the fight I'd had with
Ast over the money I was laying out on furnishings, I felt I'd
earned the right to have everything just so. That was why, as
soon as I walked in, I could see something was cockeyed. The
carpet was supposed to be purple. But the stuff they had
standing up in big rolls was the funniest looking purple I ever
saw. It was red.

None of it was down yet. The workmen were just unrolling
some of it and getting their tools ready.

"Hey, *bey*zon!" I called sharply from the doorway.

They looked up from their bent-down position.

"Whatsa matter?"

I came a little further into the room and they stood up straight.

"What the hell do you guys think you're doing?"

They were all wearing overalls, but one of them, a thin one with a cigarette in his mouth, had a regular vest and shirt and tie on underneath. He did all the talking.

"Whaddaya mean, what're we doing?"

"Listen," I said. "I only had two meals to-day. I don't feel so strong. Don't make me go around repeating things. I said what do you guys think you're doing?"

"We're layin' a carpet, ain't we?"

"I'll tell you," I said. "You just let me ask the questions."

He shrugged and took the cigarette out of his mouth.

"Not in *my* showroom you're not laying that carpet," I said. "Not here you're not."

He just looked at me. All right, I'm handsome. But I'm not that much of an attraction.

"What's the matter with it?" he asked finally.

"Nothing's the matter with it. It looks all right to me. Only it's red, that's all."

He turned to look at it, then turned back to me.

"See?" I said. "I told you. I'm a regular whiz at those things. I just looked at it once and I saw right away it was red. Just like that."

He dropped his cigarette on the floor and stepped on it. Then he lit another one.

"Ah, nuts!" I said. "I ordered purple carpet. Purple, see? Not red. Purple. You can just roll that *tiniff* up and take it away. I ordered purple."

He inhaled deeply without removing the cigarette from his mouth and bent his head a little, squinting his eyes, to see around the smoke that rose straight up from the cigarette.

"Mr. Ast saw it," he said. "He said it was all right."

Now, wasn't that nice of him!

"Listen," I said, "you heard me. Take that junk back and

bring purple. And don't worry so much about Mr. Ast. He made a mistake. He's funny that way. He's liable to make those mistakes every so often. You just take that crap back and bring purple."

I waited till they began to roll up the piece they had opened, and then I went into the back.

Babushkin was sitting on a cutting table, watching the men around him setting up the machines. And Teddy Ast was standing next to him, leaning on the table and talking earnestly to him.

I didn't even bother to walk up on them quietly. I wasn't even interested in what they were talking about. It was just nice to know that Teddy Ast and I had gone to the same school. But I wasn't worried. I was an honor student.

I called to them from the entrance to the factory. They turned around and Teddy smiled.

"Come on over, Harry," he said. "Meyer and I were just talking about you."

Surprise! Surprise!

"What's up?" I said, coming over and swinging up onto the cutting table.

"Nothing," he said, which isn't a bad way to begin. "Only we'll be opening up soon here, in a couple of days, maybe a week, so Meyer and I were sort of splitting up among the three of us the various duties of, well, of running the business. You know what I mean?"

"I sort of get a rough idea," I said. "But don't let me stop you, Teddy. You go right ahead."

"Oh, it's nothing," he said, waving his skinny hand, "just who's gonna take care of this and who's gonna take care of that and all that sort of stuff. You know."

"That isn't a bad idea," I said. "Did you come to any agreement yet? I mean, anything definite?"

"Well," he said, "I'll tell you. It's like this. First of all there's Meyer here. He's the factory man. Right?"

I nodded.

"Then there's me. I'm the salesman. Right?"

I nodded again. But I didn't smile the way I wanted to.

This guy was smooth, and no maybes about it. If baloney were religion, he'd've been the next Pope.

"That leaves only you, Harry, see? So Meyer and I, we both thought the perfect set-up for you was to be a sort of office manager. Sort of superintendent of the whole works. You could run the office, and keep your eye on things in general while I was out selling and Meyer here was in the back in the factory, and sort of, well, you know, sort of superintend the whole works."

I lit a cigarette and blew the smoke up toward the ceiling before I spoke.

"I get the idea, Teddy," I said. "You want me to sort of superintend the whole works."

"That's right," he said, shaking his head and looking at Babushkin. "That's what we sort of figured out, wasn't it, Meyer?"

Meyer nodded. Meyer was the greatest little nodder you ever saw. But I didn't mind. In a three-cornered set-up you can't afford to have the pair-off two and one. Especially if you're on the short end. The best way out is for one of the three to be a hammerhead. At least then it's one against one. And so long as I'm not outnumbered, I don't worry.

"What do you think of the idea?" Teddy asked.

"It's great," I said. "It's one of the greatest ideas I ever heard of." Teddy grinned. "There's only one thing wrong with it."

Teddy stopped grinning.

"What's that?" he asked.

"What am I going to do with the rest of my day?" I said. He stared at me.

"What do you mean, the rest of your day?"

"You don't think a thing like running an office is going to keep me busy all day, do you?" I said. "Of course, I could go sit in the crapper with a newspaper for a couple of hours every day. But I'll tell you the truth, it would be a waste of time. My bowels move pretty good without coaxing, so I'm in and out in five minutes. And I never read the papers anyway. I just look at the pictures."

"You mean you don't think that's gonna keep you busy enough?" he asked. His face wrinkled into sharp little regular furrows, like a washboard.

"That," I said gently, "is the general idea, Teddy."

"Well, then, what do you want—?"

"Look, Teddy," I said, "there's a couple of things we might as well get straightened out right now. You and me and Meyer here are partners in a new dress business. But it's not just an *ordinary* dress business. I can see from the way you and Meyer were laying things out, figuring on just one salesman, yourself, that you've been thinking this is just an ordinary small dress concern. But that's where you're wrong. You don't think I'd go to the trouble of getting the best factory man in the business and the best salesman in the business just to start another heel dress concern, do you?" Who's a dope? "You don't think I'd sink a young fortune into a showroom if I thought we were gonna match for cigar store coupons, do you? Oh, no, Teddy. Apex Modes, Inc. is gonna be *the* house on the street. Forget about Schmul and Toney Frocks and those other *schwanzos*. We're stepping right into Pulvermacher's class. And when we learn all they got to teach there, we're gonna get promoted. We're going into the big time, Teddy, and we'll need a lot more than just one salesman."

"All that's very nice," he said quickly, before I could continue. "And I'm with you right from the start, Harry. But just remember. I've been in this game for a long time. I know it inside out. You can't just start a million-dollar dress firm just by talking about it."

"I know that, Teddy," I said. Get this Teddy and Harry bull. Just a couple of buddies. "I know it. But you just watch our smoke. I've got a couple of tricks up my sleeve that'll make this market sit up and take notice. You just leave that to me."

He sucked in his cheeks like he was getting ready to whistle, but he didn't. He just looked at the ceiling, and said, "So what about what we were talking about first? About you

being office manager and superintendent and it wasn't enough
to keep you busy?"

I get it! Sarcasm!

"Here's my idea," I said. "I'll be office manager and superintendent and all the rest of that bullshit. But I'll be a salesman, too. We're gonna need an extra one before long, and it
might as well be me, instead of us hiring somebody."

He laughed a little at that.

"That just shows how little you know about the dress business," he said, putting his hand on my arm to pull the punch
a little. "You're no salesman, Harry. You know that."

"That's nothing," I said, laughing back at him. "You
ought to hear what my public school teachers used to say
about me and how fast I could learn things. So what if I'm
not a salesman, now, so what? Haven't I got the best salesman on Seventh Avenue for a partner, Teddy? Can't he teach
me?"

The general idea, gentle reader, was that no *pyoick* with
canary teeth and a snowplow nose was going to bury Harry
Bogen of the Bronx Bogens in the back some place, while all
the souvenirs and nickel-plated favors were being passed out
up front.

Teddy laughed again.

"You're really funny, Harry," he said. I must have been.
I was positively panicking him. "You can't learn to be a
salesman overnight."

"So it'll take me *two* nights," I said, hopping off the cutting table to end the interview, but not forgetting to grin up
at him in friendly fashion. This politeness was beginnning to
make my jaws ache. "So it'll take me *two* days," I said again.
"So what?"

21

Ast stuck his head into the office from the showroom and
scowled a little.

"What do you say, Harry?" he said irritably, shoving out his wrist to look at his watch. He was wearing his hat and coat and he had *Stampers Arrival Of Buyers* in his hand. "It's ten to nine already."

I looked at my own watch.

"Throw the watch out, Teddy," I said. "It's only twenty to nine." Then, before he could open up again, I said, "All right, all right, all right. I'll be out in a minute," and turned back to the girl. He went back into the showroom.

"All right, then, Miss K," I said. "I have to go now. I guess I've explained everything there is, and you know what we want. If there's anything you don't understand, anything you want to know, just ask Miss A here," I pointed to the bookkeeper, "or wait'll I get back. But I think you got everything down all right. No?"

"Yes, Mr. Bogen," she said, shaking her head so the glasses shivered on her nose.

"One more thing," I said, turning back. I like to get these things off my chest while they're hot. "I'm a pretty easy boss to work for, but there's one thing I can't stand. Nothing personal, now, Miss K, and I don't mean to insult you or anything, but I can't help it. I'm funny that way." I pointed to the glasses pinched up on her nose with the long silver chain stretching down and around her neck. "Every time I see a nice young girl, a girl like you, for instance, Miss K, wearing those kind of glasses, I get good and sore." She blushed and her hand shot up quickly to the glasses. "If you have to wear glasses, get yourself a pair of simple frames. But for God's sakes, get rid of those things. All right?" I said, and smiled reassuringly. I know it's a little silly, and maybe in a way it was stupid, too, to risk getting her sore, in case she was merchandise, I mean. But I was telling her the truth. I can't stand that kind of fake ritz. Every time I see a dame with those things on I feel like putting a couple of extra dents in her profile. "All right?" I repeated, smiling.

"Yes, Mr. Bogen," she said, and took the glasses off.

"Okay, then," I said, patting her on the head, and then went out into the showroom.

Teddy was sitting at one of the little tables, smoking a cigarette and looking through *Stampers*. He jumped up as soon as I came in.

"Jesus, Harry," he said, folding up his face like an accordion, "I can't sit around all day waiting for you. We gotta get over there."

"Aah, quit bellyaching, will you? We got a good fifteen minutes yet."

"What the hell takes you so long to get out in the mornings?"

"I gotta paste up my stamp album first," I said. Go tell him what takes me so long to get out in the mornings! "What do you think, all I do is worry about getting over to the buying offices? Just in case you forgot, just in case it slipped your mind, Teddy, I also happen to be the office manager around here. Remember?" He made a funny face. Or rather, he tried to make it funnier. But it was a waste of time. "When do you think I take care of that, when I'm sleeping?"

He reached for one of the two large sample cases.

"All right, Harry, all right. But Jesus, every morning. To-day—"

"To-day I happened to be hiring another girl to help out in the office," I said.

"Don't you ever do anything else?" he said. "All the time you're hiring new girls for the office. Or if it's not that, then you're firing them. What was the matter with the girl you hired last week?"

I figured the time wasn't ripe yet for us really to square off. Although a little shadow boxing like this every day tended to keep me in practice. When the time came, I wanted to be in condition to give him his lumps. So I grinned and winked at him.

"You know me, Teddy," I said. "Not that I got any designs on them or anything. If I wanna get put I know where to go. I don't like to mess up my own doorstep. But just the same, hell, while I'm hiring somebody I might as well make it pleasant around here. I don't like to have a bunch of dogs floating around. While I'm at it, I might as well hire some-

thing with a well-turned ass and a decently uplifted tit. Am
I right or no?"

He shook his head and that accordion face of his folded
up again. Only this time it was a smile. It looked the same
as before, but it was a smile. After you knew him a while
you got so you could tell the difference.

"Okay," he said, picking up one of the sample cases.
"Grab hold of that one and let's go."

I picked it up and put it down again.

"Listen," I said, "I'm getting good and sick and tired of
lugging these lousy things. Why can't we get a boy to carry
them for us? What are we, shipping clerks or something?"

He put down his case and looked at me.

"That's a hot one all right," he said. "You're the guy that
started all those delivery businesses in the neighborhood,
you're the guy that did away with shipping clerks on Seventh
Avenue, and now you're the guy that's crying!" He started
to laugh and shake his head. "Boy, that's a hot one on you
all right, Harry. That's a hot one. But I guess it's just too
tough. We got no shipping clerks. We got a delivery service.
So we have to carry our own sample cases. Boy, that's good.
We got a delivery service to deliver our packages and our
orders, but we have to carry our own sample cases. It's
tough, Harry. Boy, is it tough!"

"It certainly is tough," I said, laughing with him. "But
not on us. Because I got an idea how it won't be tough on us
any more. Maybe it'll be tough on somebody else, but it's
not gonna be tough on the president and treasurer of Apex
Modes, Inc. any more."

I turned toward the office, and he said quickly, "Hey,
where you going?"

"Come on," I said over my shoulder, "I'm gonna make it
a little less tough for the both of us."

"Holy Christ, Harry," he said, "it's late already. We'll
never get there on time, and then it'll—"

"We'll take a cab," I said. "And anyway, this won't take
a minute."

The girls looked up when we came into the office.

"Take a letter, Miss K," I said, standing over her. "This goes to the Needle Trades Delivery Service, Inc. Put in that I. N. C. They're at two-twenty-four West—well, I don't remember it right now, but it's in the phone book, or wait, you can dig out one of their bills from the file. You'll get the address there. All right. Needle Trades Delivery Service, Inc., attention Mr. Maltz. No, leave out that attention business. Just Needle Trades Delivery Service, Inc. Gentlemen. Please be advised that we are discontinuing your service as of the thirty-first of this month. Be good enough to render your final statement as of that date, and oblige. All right, Miss K, get that ready and Mr. Ast'll sign it when he gets back."

Miss A looked up from behind her books.

"By the way, Mr. Bogen," she said.

"Yes?"

"That Mr. Maltz called you again yesterday. He's been calling you pretty—"

"Yeah," I said, "I know. Just don't pay any attention to him. He probably wants to borrow money or something. Any time he calls, just tell him I'm out, that's all." I turned to the new girl. "You'll be at the switchboard most of the time, Miss K, so you just remember that too, will you? If a Mr. Maltz calls, I'm not in."

"Yes, Mr. Bogen," she said.

"All right, then," I said. "And remember. Mr. Ast'll sign that letter when he gets back."

"But why me?" Teddy said.

"Aah, I know this guy Maltz," I said. "It'll look better if you sign it. I'm supposed to be in Europe or some place, anyway. How's it gonna look if when he calls up they tell him I'm out, but the next day he gets a letter signed by me? See what I mean?"

"Yeah, well, all right. But, hell, Harry, how about our deliveries?"

"We're gonna be old-fashioned," I said, slapping him on the shoulder. "We're gonna start a back to the land movement or something like that. We're gonna hire ourselves a couple of old-fashioned shipping clerks."

"Yeah, but it's more expensive, isn't it?"

"So what? I'd rather pay the few extra dollars a week than tear my arms out schlepping those damn sample cases around."

"Yeah, but—"

"But nothing," I said, pushing him toward the sample cases and taking one myself. "I'll tell you about it some other time. We got less than ten minutes. Come on, Teddy, shake your ankle. We gotta hurry."

The cab got us to Thirty-First Street in a few minutes. I paid the driver and we went into the long arcade, past the classy-looking passenger elevators, toward the ones at the far end under the sign SALESMEN WITH SAMPLE CASES WILL USE THESE CARS. Only one car was down on the ground floor, and that was too jammed for us to get in, so we set the cases down and waited for another one. A lot of other salesmen kept coming down the arcade toward us and set their sample cases down to wait for a car. I knew most of them by this time, and Teddy probably knew all of them just as they probably all knew each other, but they did not speak. They just smoked and watched the indicator over the elevator door. They even seemed a little sore at each other. I didn't blame them. I felt a little sore myself, having to lug those heavy sample cases around. Some of them had boys with them to help with the cases, but most of them carried their own. Well, I thought, Teddy had certainly been right. They could thank me, and I could thank myself, for having to carry those cases. Pretty soon, though, they'd be able to thank me for *not* having to carry them any more. Well, that's life. To-day you're on bottom, to-morrow they're on top. Nuts.

I suddenly thought of something.

"Say, Teddy," I said in a low voice, "how is it I never see any of Pulvermacher's salesmen around here? This partner of his, this Kalisch, he's supposed to be such a holy wonder of a salesman, how come I never see him around here?"

"Them, they're different."

"What do you mean, different? Don't they have to sell the same as we do, the same as everybody else does?"

"Sure, but they're so big, they make such high-priced stuff, they don't have to do this."

"What do you mean, they don't have to do this? Everybody comes to see the buyers here, don't they?"

He looked disgusted as he watched the hand on the indicator swing around slowly toward zero.

"Yeah, they come. But they don't bring any sample cases. They come with a couple of models, the models wear one of their hot numbers each, and that's all. The rest of their stuff, the buyers come to their showroom. They throw a big opening when they show their new line and all the buyers come. But that's the high-priced stuff. The twenty-nines and over."

"Maybe for the fall line, Teddy, we'll take a crack at that higher-priced stuff. What do you say?"

"You're crazy," he said. "We're a sixteen-seventy-five house. Come on," he said suddenly, reaching for a sample case and moving into the elevator.

We were jammed together face to face in the crowded car.

"What's so crazy about it?" I said. "We got Babushkin. That high-priced stuff is his meat. He was with Pulvermacher for years. And we got the showroom, haven't we? We got as nice a showroom as Pulvermacher has."

"Forget it," he said. "You're crazy with the heat."

Phooey! He had a breath that an exterminator would have paid to bottle.

"All right," I said. "So I'm crazy with the heat."

The car stopped and the whole mob rushed out. I followed Teddy up to the wooden railing that divided the long room in half and waited while he scribbled blue slips for the buyers he wanted to see. In a few seconds the salesmen were waving wads of these blue slips and yelling at the office boys on the other side of the railing.

"Whaddaya say, Tony, take this in to Miss LeBeau, will you?"

"Hey, kid. For Miss Smith. Here's one for Miss Smith."

"Mrs. Hopper's in, ain't she? Take this in like a good fella, will ya?"

The hungry mob kept moving and shoving and yelling and waving slips. Every once in a while one of the office boys would come over, take a slip and carry it into one of the dozen doors that stretched along the wall of the room that faced us across the railing. In a few seconds he would come out again, return the slip to the salesman, and take another one. The salesman who received the slip back would scan it quickly. If the box that said "Will see" was checked, he grinned and picked up his sample case and went through the gate in the railing, waving his slip at the guard as a pass. If it was the "Will not see" or the "Call again on—" box that was checked, he scowled and spit on the floor and said, "The bitch," and began to yell for one of the office boys again. The yelling and the shoving didn't stop for a minute, and the salesmen grew more excited as the hands of the big clock on the wall crept toward ten. All they had was an hour, from nine to ten, and a lot of them wanted to see as many as eight and ten buyers.

They fought each other for a place at the rail and swore when they lost an inch, but nobody started punching because the minutes were too precious. Every once in a while one of them would try to shove through the door in the railing. But three or four of the office boys would come together in a wedge and force the intruder back. These office boys were the snottiest little punks you ever saw. They moved their feet like they were stringing pearls, and when they took a slip they acted like they didn't expect you to forget them in your will.

I looked at Teddy. He was dividing his time between swearing, lighting cigarettes, and yelling at the office boys.

"Why don't you slip one of them a buck?" I said. "Give him a buck and he'll take it in for you."

"Where do you think we get our money, it grows on trees?" He stepped on his cigarette, lit another one, and turned back to his yelling.

"Gimme that," I said, grabbing the slip out of his hand.

Before he could say anything I wrapped a dollar around it, shoved it into an office boy's hand and said, "Give that to Miss Bonthron of Jessup Jordan. Bonthron of Jessup Jordan."

"Okay," the kid said and moved across the room.

"What the hell do you think we are?" Teddy said. "Millionaires?"

"Aah, what's a buck?"

"What do you mean, what's a buck? You're all the time throwing money around like—"

"Aah, nuts," I said, "Stop worrying about it."

When the kid came back Teddy took the slip, looked at it quickly, and turned to me.

"See? What'd I tell you?"

I took the slip. The "Will not see" box was checked.

"All right," I said, throwing up my hand, "You do this your own way."

I lit a cigarette and sat down on the sample case. Let him keep on yelling his head off if he wanted to. I wasn't even listening to him. There was nothing more he could teach me. I had my own ideas of how to sell dresses. This was the last time anybody was going to find me down here tearing my arms and lungs out and begging some baloney to let me come in and see her for a minute. If a midget brain like Pulvermacher didn't have to do it, then I didn't have to do it either.

At ten o'clock the gong rang. The salesmen tried to get one last slip in, but from the way the office boys quit you'd think it was a fire alarm. In another couple of minutes the buyers began to come out, dressed for the street, carrying their order books, swinging their cans, and shaking their heads at the salesmen that hung around them like flies.

"What do you say, Miss Rhinelander, just give me a minute?" Sorry, sorry. "You coming up to see our line, Miss Crowley? We got a couple numbers—" Not to-day, sorry. "Aw, Miss T, be a good scout. Lemme just show you—" Sorry, sorry. "Just a second, Miss Rhinelander. Can't I see you just a second?" Sorry, sorry.

I didn't know exactly what they were sorry about, or for

whom. But one thing was sure, they weren't being sorry for me. Because I was just watching them and laughing.

When the private elevator closed on them and carried them down, the salesmen went back to their sample cases and the elevators reserved for them.

Teddy was quiet until we reached the street. Then when I hailed a cab, he said quickly, "Don't you ever believe in walking?"

"Not when I can ride," I said.

"Where do you think all this money's coming from, anyway?" he said.

"Aw, climb in and stop crying so much," I said, shoving in the sample cases.

He went in after me and the cab started.

"Did you see any buyers?" I asked, although I knew the answer.

He gave me a dirty look and I grinned back at him.

"I don't see Pulvermacher breaking his ass chasing down to these lousy buying offices with dresses," I said.

He lit a cigarette and whistled when he blew out the smoke.

"And what's good enough for Pulvermacher is good enough for me," I added.

"Aah, you're crazy."

"So I'm crazy," I said. "But I still—"

He turned around to face me.

"Listen, Harry, forget all that dopey stuff about making a higher-priced line. Just try to get ready a little earlier in the mornings, so we shouldn't have to throw money out on cabs. That's all. Stop worrying about Pulvermacher and his line. Worry a little more about ours."

Well, it's nice to have a guy around to pick your worries for you. But if I didn't have any greater need for Teddy Ast than that, maybe it would be better if we kissed each other good-bye.

"Just answer me one question," I said. "What the hell are you crying about? So what if it costs us a couple of bucks in cabs? So what? We're making dough, aren't we?"

22

I was signing checks in my private office when I remembered something. I picked up the receiver and said, "Get me Listokens and Tsitsarnes." Then, "Hello, L. and T.?"

"Yes."

"Mr. Listokens, please."

"Speaking."

"Oh, hello, Listokens. This is Bogen of Apex Modes."

"Yeah, Bogen."

"How's that silver fox collar coming along, Listokens?"

"What silver fox col—? Oh, yeah, yeah. Sure, sure. I got a man working on it now, Bogen."

"Well, you don't sound so enthusiastic about it. Don't tell me you forgot all about it. Because if you did, I'll—"

"No, no, Bogen. I didn't. It just sort of slipped my mind for a moment. It's in work now."

"Well, just don't forget it. I want that by Monday during the day or Tuesday night at the latest, understand?"

"You'll have it, Bogen, don't worry."

"I'm not worrying," I said. "But if I don't get it on time, then *you* better start worrying. Because Apex'll never buy another inch of fur from you, understand?"

"Just don't worry about it, Bogen. You'll get it."

"Okay," I said, and hung up.

There was a knock on the door.

"Come in."

Babushkin shoved his worried-looking face around the door.

"You busy, Harry?"

It was nice of him to knock before he came in. In a dress house with three models it was a good idea. But Babushkin didn't do it because it was a good idea. He did it because he was scared he might see something he'd heard about, but had never seen. Or maybe he was a gentleman. He had the first requirement. He was dumb enough.

"Come on in, Meyer," I said, "what's on your mind?"

He stood in the middle of the room and rubbed his nose.

"Nothing special, Harry," he said. "I just thought maybe, you know, if you weren't busy—"

"Sit down," I said, waving toward the couch, "take a load off your feet."

"Thanks," he said, taking the chair that faced me across the desk. "I'll, uh, I'll sit here."

"What do you know?" I said, lighting a cigarette and leaning back in my chair.

He shifted around in the chair and rubbed his nose a little harder. Well, the wear and tear would never hurt it. He had the kind that was built to last.

"Well, I'll tell you, Harry," he said slowly. "It's nothing *special,* you know—"

Maybe I did, at that. But I just sat back innocently and blew smoke at him. It was his move.

"Teddy told me to come in and speak to you," he said suddenly.

Poor Teddy. It must be tough to be so tongue-tied that you have to pick a spokesman like Meyer Babushkin. Or maybe guys like Teddy were only tongue-tied when they had to speak to guys like me.

"What's the matter with Teddy?" I asked innocently. "He seemed all right when I saw him less than an hour ago."

"Well, I don't know, Harry. He told me to— Well, told me to come in and talk to you."

Now I was beginning to get it. I didn't understand at first. Teddy had told him to come in and talk to me! See?

"What about?" I said, leaning over to drop my ash carefully into the huge jade ash tray on my desk.

Babushkin stopped rubbing his nose and began to pick it, scowling at the floor as he worked.

"Use your thumb, Meyer," I said. "You'll get more."

"What?" he said, looking up suddenly.

"Nothing."

"Yeah, Harry, he told me to come in and see you."

"Well, here I am," I said, spreading my arms wide. "Take a good look at me."

"He said I should come in and talk to you," he said again.

"What about?" I repeated.

I knew what was coming. I figured I might as well be calm about it.

He took a deep breath and swallowed hard.

"About the money we're spending," he said quickly. "He said you're spending too much money."

"He did?" I said, throwing my eyebrows up to the ceiling. "Teddy said that?"

"Yeah. He said I should come in and talk to you. He said he spoke to you already a few times, but it didn't do any good. He said I should come in and talk to you."

I *knew* I was on the right track. Teddy had told him to come in and talk to me!

"Well, Meyer," I said, "I'm sure Teddy wouldn't say a thing like that if he couldn't back it up, would he? He must've been more specific, wasn't he, Meyer?"

"Yeah, well, yeah, he was."

"That's fine," I said, leaning back and lighting another cigarette. I do an awful lot of leaning back and lighting of cigarettes. "Let's hear what he had to say. Where am I spending too much money? Be specific. Where am I throwing money around like water? He said that, didn't he? That I was throwing money around like water? Or maybe he said I was spending it like a drunken sailor? Which? But let it go. Let's skip that. Just tell me where he said I was spending too much money."

I was handling him delicately. No loud-mouthed denials or objections. With morons like Meyer Babushkin you always take it easy, draw them out, reason with them, try to make what you say sound logical. The mailed fist in the velvet glove.

"Well, he said you were, well, you were spending too much money."

"Maybe you better turn that record over, Meyer," I said.

"What?"

"I said in what ways did Teddy tell you to tell me I was spending too much money?" Fooled him that time. I didn't lean back nor did I light a fresh cigarette. I still had the one I lit before.

"We-ell, he said you were spending too much on presents for buyers."

"Aw, come now, Meyer. You don't believe that, do you?"

"Well, he showed me bills. He showed me bills from that French place, I don't know the name, you know the one I mean, he showed me the bills for the boxes of candy and honest, Harry, gee whiz, that's a lot of money for candy. Honest, Harry, it's a *lot*."

"But that's nothing new in the dress business, is it, Meyer? Why, even Teddy himself sends presents to the buyers. You have to. They expect it."

"Yeah, but he sends them flowers and little things like that. Flowers don't cost so much."

"That's where you're wrong, Meyer," I said earnestly, leaning across the desk to make it sound convincing. "Flowers cost less, but you don't get anything for your money. Flowers die. And then what've the buyers got? Nothing. And when the flowers are dead, they don't remember you. You send them something substantial, like a box of candy, something practical, something they can at least eat, and they appreciate it. At least it lasts longer. And the longer it lasts, the longer they remember you. See what I mean?"

"Yeah, well, I know, Harry. But he said other things, too."

"Yeah, what? Tell me what?"

He scratched his head. I debated with myself whether I should warn him against splinters, but I decided against it. After all, it was his head.

"We-ell," he said, "the pocketbooks, the theatre tickets, the—oh, you know, Harry, all those things."

"Oh, well, *that*," I said, leaning back and waving my hand. "That's only more of the same thing. I'm telling you, Meyer, this business of sending flowers and things like that is the bull. Just because that's what most every salesman in the business does, doesn't mean it's the best, does it? I mean, I leave it to you as an intelligent person, Meyer." That was one hell of a place to leave it. "You've got to do these things right or don't do them at all. All the money spent on things like flowers is just so much money wasted. These buyers aren't any of these dainty dames, you know. For these horse-faced pots, you should excuse the expression, Meyer, for these tough broads, flowers is like—like—I don't know, like sending a machine-gun to a baby. You have to give them something practical, something they can use. Then they remember you, and they come up and buy your dresses. See what I mean?"

He nodded and squirmed around in his seat and sucked his lower lip. I tell you, he had a regular bag of tricks.

"Well, it's not that so much, either, Harry. It's—it's—"

"It's what, Meyer?"

"It's this business of, well, *you* know, this charge account you got with that, you know what Teddy calls it, the call joint. The charge account you got there. That costs a fortune, doesn't it?"

What the hell was he blushing about? Didn't he know the facts of life? He was married, but with guys like him that didn't mean a thing.

"Oh, well," I said, smiling at him. "That's just a little of my own ideas."

"Yeah, but the way Teddy says, it costs a lot of money, doesn't it?"

"So what?" I shoved some papers around on my desk, picked one out, and wagged it in front of his nose. "Here's an order we got this morning from Bentcher of Finck and Swathmore. How do we come to sell Finck and Swathmore? Bentcher's had his steady houses for years, hasn't he, and a new firm never even had a smell in for an order from him. So how come all of a sudden he throws business like this to Apex Modes?" I slapped the order a few times. "Because our line is hot, which it is? Or because Teddy Ast, our star salesman, wears Pat Caruso clothes? Oh, no, Meyer. We got this order because last night I got Mr. Bentcher of Finck and Swathmore fixed up with one of the neatest numbers in that call joint of mine. That's why we got an order from Finck and Swathmore, and as long as we got our account with that call joint, you can bet your boots Bentcher will be buying from us."

Babushkin was blushing like a schoolgirl. I reached over and patted his hand.

"Don't worry, Meyer. I know what I'm doing. Maybe I haven't been in the dress business as long as you or Teddy. But I know a couple of things about selling. With men buyers, you get them put and you can sell them the Brooklyn Bridge. And with woman buyers—" I rolled my eyes like Groucho Marx and lit a cigarette—"With women buyers, Meyer, *I* do all the yentzing. At least *there* you can't say it's too expensive. That's one thing about me, Meyer, I never yet sent a buyer a bill for slipping her the business."

I figured he was through, but I always like to do these things right. I like to add the parsley to the fish and the paper ruffles to the drumstick.

"Is there anything else Teddy told you to tell me was too expensive?" I asked gently.

He was so flustered he could hardly talk. Christ, maybe *he* was hard up and I ought to take *him* out and get him laid? But no, I wanted him to keep his mind in the factory.

"Anything else, Meyer?" I asked again.

"Well, he, Teddy, he said something about the, about the models. He said—"

"Yeah? What about the models?"

"He said all the other houses they pay fifteen a week for models, and we, we pay thirty. Thirty dollars, Harry, you know, that's a lot of money for a model."

"Oh, I don't know," I said. "It all depends how you look at those things and what you expect from them. There are models and models, you know, Meyer. Me, I like the kind that if you put it up to them, they don't drop dead from the shock. You know what I mean, Meyer? And that kind you don't get for fifteen bucks a week. They could make that by themselves, free-lancing, just working a couple of nights a week. See what I mean, Meyer?"

Meyer saw all right, but he didn't say so. He was still too flustered to pick his words right.

"There's another thing yet, too, Harry," he said finally, examining the grain of the desk. Well, it would stand inspection. The furnishings of that little private office cost plenty.

"Yeah, what?"

"The new line. Teddy says you're—I mean, he said you were a little, well, you know, maybe a little foolish about going into that expensive stuff. He said we're a lower-priced house, and to go into that expensive stuff is—."

"Listen, Meyer," I said confidentially, "you want me to tell you a little secret?"

He just looked at me.

"This is between me and you, Meyer," I said, leaning toward him and smiling. "You want to know what?"

"What?"

"Just between me and you, Meyer," I said, "I think Teddy Ast is a big *schvantz.*"

His eyes blinked a little.

"That's just between the two of us," I said, then more briskly, "I don't know what he's hollering about. We're each of us, all three of us, we're making more money than we ever made before. Isn't that so?" He nodded. "And besides that, we've each got a cut-in on the profits. So what the hell is he hollering about, will you tell me?"

He didn't answer. I got up and walked over to his chair and put my arm on his shoulder.

"You just listen to me, Meyer," I said, "and we'll be all right. You just take care of the styling and see that the contractors don't walk away with the place. Leave the rest to me. You're making more money than you ever made and you're your own boss. So stop hollering and stop listening to Teddy Ast and his squawking. Just get going on that fall line, and if Teddy shoots off his mouth, just send him to me. By the way, how *is* the line coming along?"

For once his face took on a little life.

"It's great, Harry," he said. "Just wait till you see it."

"That's fine," I said, patting his shoulder to end the interview, or monologue, or whatever you want to call it.

He hesitated a moment, and the smile on his face faded into a worried frown. Or rather, excuse me, he began to look normal again.

"There's only one thing, Harry," he said.

"Yeah, what?"

"We're a, well, you know, we're a lower-priced house," he said. "How're we gonna get the buyers, the market, you know, how're we gonna get them to know we're switching to the higher—?"

"My dear Meyer," I said, grinning at him. I'd better watch out. Here I was in the dress business only a couple of months and already I was beginning to talk like Phil the Fag. "Don't you bother that cute little head of yours about *that*."

"Yeah, Harry, but how—?"

"Just leave that to me," I said, patting myself on the chest. "The scheme I got for presenting our new line, Meyer, is gonna knock Seventh Avenue's eye out."

"But what—?"

"You just wait and see," I said, holding the door open for him.

23

I would have liked to keep the box behind my back until I came in the door, to make it a surprise. But the package was too large. And besides, as soon as I turned into Honeywell Avenue I could see her leaning out the window, with a small pillow under her elbows, watching the street for me.

Her face lit up as soon as she saw me, and then, when she saw the box I was carrying, she pinched up her lips and began to shake her head disapprovingly.

I waved to her and quickened my pace.

She opened the door for me and said, "Well, what kind

of crazy presents have you been spending your money on now?"

I looked blank.

"Presents?" I said. "What presents?"

"Never mind, never mind," she said, pointing to the box in my hands. "What are you got in there?"

"Oh, this!" I said, carelessly. "Oh, this is nothing. This is just some cheese I brought home so you should be able to make me some blintzes, that's all."

"Again with the blintzes!" she cried, striking her forehead with her hand. "Don't you ever think of anything else besides those blintzes?"

Sure, but I couldn't tell *her* about it.

"What else is there to think about?" I said.

She made a threatening gesture, playfully.

"Go 'way," she said. "So let's see already what kind of cheese you brought, it should be so big that it has to be packed in a box like an elephant."

"First let's get out of the doorway," I said. "All I need is to get a draft on me and I should catch a cold, and then I'll be all set good for to-morrow."

"So come on."

She led the way to the kitchen, quickly, and I put the box on the porcelain-topped table.

"Go ahead," I said. "Open it."

She opened the box and stopped for a moment with her mouth open, staring at the rich-looking mound of black fur, with the sprinkling of grayish-white hairs shot through it, surrounded by the bed of crumpled tissue paper.

"Heshie!" she cried, and turned to put her arms around me and kiss me.

"Go ahead, Ma," I said, patting her shoulder and smiling, "try it on."

She dried her hands quickly and picked up the fur piece out of the box. She stroked it gently for a moment, smiling happily, and then put it across her shoulders. She buried her cheek in the soft thick end that hung down her arm and said, "This is wonderful, Heshie."

"I'm glad you like it, Ma," I said. "Next time I'll get you a whole coat made of the same thing. How'll that be?"

"Heshie!" she said severely. "Don't talk like a baby. You shouldn't even've spent so much money on this."

"Why not?"

"Because," she said, "first of all I have plenty things. And second, you should put your money better in the bank. And anyway, what kind of picnic is it all of a sudden, from a clear sky, in the middle of the week, you should go around buying fur collars?"

"Don't worry so much about my bank account, Ma," I said. "And anyway, I get it wholesale."

"Who's worrying about your bank account, who?" she said indignantly.

"All right, all right," I said, stroking her shoulder with the fur piece on it, "so you're *not* worrying about it."

"I only mean," she said, "I hate you should throw around money like it was water."

"You talk just like one of my partners," I said.

"Then thank God you got at least *one* of them he should be a little smart," she said.

We both laughed.

"No, I'll tell you, Ma," I said. "The real reason why I got you this thing is because to-morrow we—the firm, I mean —we're going into the high-priced dresses, you know. We're going after the real money, now, and this is sort of, well, sort of a celebration. See what I mean, Ma? After all, who then am I going to spend my money on, if not on you?"

She smiled and pinched my cheek.

"Mama's boy, hah?" she said.

"Sure, why not?" I said. "And then," I added, "there's still another reason why I bought it for you. You know why?"

"Why."

"The other things I got you, well, maybe they just made Mrs. Heimowitz eat her heart out. But this," I said, "when you walk down the street wearing *this*—I figure she'll just about drop dead."

"Don't talk like that," she said, but the smile on her face said she was pleased.

I took off my coat and began to roll up my sleeves.

"Well, now that that's over Ma," I said, "how's chances on getting something to eat?"

"All right," she said, putting the collar back into the box carefully, "but no blintzes."

"Why not?"

"You think I'm a dope?" she said. "I should make them for you every time you want them—three times a day, seven days a week, yet—and it'll come a time you'll be so tired of them, you won't even want to *look* at them. And then, when that time comes, how do you think I'll get all those fancy presents, hah?"

I laughed.

"You're pretty good, Ma, you are," I said. "But don't worry. Blintzes or no blintzes, you know I wouldn't stop buying you things, Ma."

"Sure I know," she said, smiling. "But why should I take chances?"

"If I ever need another partner, Ma," I said, "I think I'll take you."

"Don't do me any favors," she said, shaking her head wisely. "To be your partner, Heshalle, I think a person needs an iron heart."

"Now, that certainly is a nice way to talk about your own son, isn't it?"

"Never mind," she said, waving her hand at me. "Whether it's nice or not, I don't care. But it's true just the same, no?"

I shrugged. But I was pleased. The old girl knew her onions, all right.

"Maybe," I said. "But that's the way you have to be in business. If *you* haven't got the iron heart, it's the next guy. And that means the *next* guy'll be building up the bank balance. What the hell, Ma, that's the way things are. In business you got to be that way."

"I suppose you're right," she said. "But I don't know, Heshie. I don't know if it's such a—well, such a good thing."

"Why not?"

"It does to a person something, Heshie. It makes him—I don't know. It changes him."

I waved my hand at her.

"Aah, don't be a baby, Ma. What's the matter, do I look changed to you? Sure I'm changed. Now, instead of bringing you fifteen dollars a week we should try to pay the rent and the butcher and the grocer and the laundry, so now, now I'm bringing you silver fox collars. If you call that being changed, so all right, so I'm changed."

She sighed and picked up the box.

"Well, maybe *I'm* wrong," she said. "Wait here, I'll just put this away in the bedroom. I'll come back and give you something to eat."

"Sure you're wrong, Ma," I said, stroking her cheek. "Just don't worry about your little Heshie. He knows how to take care of himself. And he knows how to take care of his mother, too, don't worry."

"Sure, don't worry," she said, and left the room, shaking her head a little.

Well, I guess it all evened out in the end. I had to worry about business, and she had to worry about me.

I went into the bathroom to wash. When I came out the kitchen table was set for supper. I picked up my spoon and began to eat my soup. Mother turned down the flame on the gas range, poured a plate of soup for herself, and sat down across the table from me. We ate in silence for a few minutes.

"Well, what's the matter, Ma?" I said finally. "I'm not using my spoon right, or something like that?"

She looked surprised.

"Why, I said something maybe?"

"You don't *have* to say anything," I said. "I can tell by the way you're looking at me, that's all."

"Heshie, do me a favor," she said. "Don't think all the time you're smarter than the whole world."

"All right. So I'm not smarter than the whole world. But what's on your mind?"

She shrugged.

"Well, if you ask me, so I'll tell you."

"That's what I'm waiting for."

"What's the matter between you and Ruthie Rivkin?" she asked quietly.

Boy, some day I'd really learn to keep my trap shut.

"Nothing," I said carelessly. Why the hell hadn't I croaked that dame when I had her in the woods? "There's nothing the matter between us. Who ever said there *was* anything between us, anyway?"

"Never mind," she said, "I know."

"Well, if you're so smart," I said, "then maybe you know what's the matter. So what's the idea asking me?"

"I went to see Mrs. Rivkin yesterday," she said. "And—"

"Why don't you hire a squad of private detectives?" I said. "Maybe you can't keep tabs on everything I do. I mean, after all, Ma, you're only one person, you know. A couple of dicks helping you out would bring in more information for you than you could get by yourself. Just tell me, and I'll write you a check to cover it, so you won't have to take it out of the house money—"

"Heshie!" she said sharply.

"All right, Ma, all right," I said. "Forget it. I'm sorry. I didn't mean anything."

"I don't care if you meant anything or not," she said, glaring at me. "I don't care if you're making a lot of money or not. By me you're still the same smart one you were when you were going to school. By your dopes, those partners of yours, you can talk. But don't come by me here with the nose in the air."

"Okay, Ma. Okay." I reached my plate toward her. "How about some more soup?"

She filled my plate and set it before me. As she straightened up to return to her chair, she gave my head a push.

"All of a sudden, my smart one!" she said.

I grinned embarrassedly and began to dip up the soup.

"I went to see Mrs. Rivkin yesterday," she began again.

"Don't make the trip too often," I muttered. "You'll get corns."

"What?" she said, leaning forward across the table. "You said something maybe?"

"No," I said.

"Well, if you wanna talk, so talk a person should be able to hear you. Don't talk in your nose."

"*You* talk," I said, lifting my spoon high. "I'll eat."

Me and Tootsie Maltz.

"*Tokke* that way it'll be better," she said. "So you hear, I went to see Mrs. Rivkin yesterday. I asked her about Ruthie, I asked her about the grocery, I asked her—"

"About me," I said.

"And why not?" she demanded.

"I don't know," I said, motioning with the spoon again. "I'm eating. You talk."

"If you'll only keep that big mouth of yours—it goes all the time like on wheels—if you'll only keep that closed for a few minutes, so maybe I'll be *able* to talk a little."

"You're doing all right now," I said.

"If you keep a little quiet," she said, "so I'll do better."

"Go ahead," I said. *"Try."*

She grinned a little in spite of herself.

"So I asked about you, too. She said you and Ruthie, you went out a couple times together, you even took her up to the mountains for one day on a Sunday—you didn't tell me nothing about that—"

"Do I have to tell you *every*thing?"

She shrugged.

"It's easier," she said. "But if you don't tell me, so I'll find out anyway."

Now *I* grinned in spite of myself.

"You're telling me!"

"And that, Mrs. Rivkin said, was the last. Since that day, she said it must be a few weeks ago already, since that day, you didn't call her up, you didn't go up to see her, nothing. What's the matter? A person could think yet God alone knows what happened."

"Nothing's the matter," I said.

Go tell you own mother you tried to lay a broad, but you couldn't do it because she looked like your mother.

"So if nothing's the matter," she said calmly, "so why don't you go up there to see her any more?"

"Because I'm too busy," I said.

"Is that so? What are you doing all of a sudden, saving the whole world? Even the president, he takes off a night or two in the week he should take out his girl——"

"The president is married, Ma. And he's got about four sons——"

"Shut up!" she said. "So he takes a night or two during the week and he takes his *wife* to the movies."

"For the president, Ma, they bring the movies to *him*."

She seized her spoon and waved it at me threateningly.

"If you don't hold a little that long tongue of yours, and let me speak, I'll give you a smack over the head, you'll have to go picking your teeth all over the house. You hear me?"

I leaned back in my chair and roared.

"Say when, Ma," I said.

She choked back a smile and folded her arms on the table elaborately.

"I'm asking you once more," she said. "Why you didn't go up to see her any more?"

"Aah, hell, Ma, what did I do, sign a contract that I have to go up to take out Ruthie Rivkin every night in the week?"

"Mustn't be every night," she said coolly.

"Yeah, and it mustn't be *any* night, either," I said. "If I don't want to."

"So why don't you want to, why?"

"Listen, Ma," I said. "You brought that dame around here a couple of weeks ago——"

"In this house don't call nice girls a 'dame!' "

"All right, all right, all right. So she's a nice girl." That was the trouble with her. "So you brought this nice girl Ruthie around here, and you said you wanted me to take her out. So I said all right, for you I'd do it. And I did. I took her out a couple of times, I spent my good money on her, and that's all."

"Maybe by *you* that's all," she said. "But not by me."

"No?"

"No."

"Well, I don't care what you say, Ma. You can't force me to go out with a girl if I don't want to, and that's all."

"It's not all, Heshie," she said. She began to speak gently. "I don't want you should think I'm trying to force you into something, Heshie. I'm an old woman. Maybe I don't see things the same way a young boy like you does. And so long you stay honest, you don't become a crook or a murderer or anything like that, so long you can do what you want. I won't say a word."

"Well, you keep quiet pretty loud," I said.

"Because this is different," she said.

"How is this different? Because I don't want to take out Ruthie Rivkin, that means I'm a crook or a murderer?"

"No, dope!"

"Don't call me dope."

"Hold your tongue," she said. "I'll call you what I want. When you're smart I'll call you smart. When you're a dope I'll call you a dope. Right now you're a dope."

That's what *she* thought.

"All right, so tell me how this is different."

"Because this isn't a little thing. To find the right girl is by a person the most important thing in his whole life. There's plenty of them, they spend their whole lives, God forbid, without finding. And you, you got a chance while you're still young, you shouldn't have to become an old bachelor and people should laugh at you, you got a chance like that, a fine girl, with a nice family, who'd make you a good wife, and you don't want her!"

"Well, maybe *you* think she's the right girl," I said, "but *I* don't. And I'm the guy that's doing the marrying, not you."

"What's the idea lying to me?" she said quietly.

I looked at her quickly.

"What?"

"You heard me," she said. "I said what's the idea lying to me?"

"Who's lying?"

"*You* are."

"About what?"

"About Ruthie."

"Why, what's the matter with you, Ma? What did I say?"

"You said you don't like Ruthie, didn't you?"

"Well, I didn't exactly *say* it," I said, "but yeah, now that you put it that way, yeah, I don't."

"Then you're not a dope," she said, sitting back. "You're just a big liar, that's all."

I tried to laugh good and loud. But it didn't come out right.

"You know you like her, Heshie," she said quietly. "What are you afraid of? What are you running away from?"

Look what *I* had to get myself into!

"I don't know where you got all those ideas from, Ma," I said. "It seems to me I ought to know myself whether I like a girl or not without somebody else giving me any advice about it."

"That's right," she said. "You *should* know. And you do. So why do you say you don't?"

"If this isn't the craziest thing yet, Ma," I said. "How do *you* know I like her? How can you—?"

"Don't worry," she said, looking me in the eye. "I know. I could tell from that first night she was here. It's true, isn't it?"

I dropped my eyes from hers and began to play with the spoon.

"Stop bending my spoons," she said, and I put it down. "It's true, isn't it?" she said.

I didn't say anything.

"It's true, isn't it?" she repeated.

"No," I said, without looking at her.

"Well, we'll soon see," she said. "I don't know what's the matter with you or what's in the back there of that pudding of a head of yours. But I know you like her and I know she's a fine girl. Before one of those big tramps of yours gets you, I'd rather a fine girl like Ruthie should get you. And if you're too much of a dope to know when you're well off, so I'll just have to see to it myself."

"Yeah?" I said sullenly.

"Yeah," she said. "When you finish eating you just pick yourself up and go into the living room. It's now,"—she looked at the clock on the ice box—"it's now a little before eight. I told her she should be here by half-past eight, maybe a few minutes earlier."

For a moment I just looked at her. Then I stood up and smacked the table with my fist.

"That's what *you* think," I yelled. "What the hell do you think this is, anyway? What do you think I am, a baby? You can't pull any of that fancy stuff around here, Ma. If I don't want to see her, I won't. And nothing you can say or do can make me. Understand? Where the hell do you get that—?"

"What's the matter, Heshie?" she said quietly, looking up at me from the other side of the table. "What are you afraid of?"

She had the word all right.

"Who's afraid?" I said.

"*You* are," she said.

It looked like I was the answer to everything.

"Don't make me laugh," I said. "Afraid!"

But I sat down again.

"Now look, Heshie," she said, leaning forward. "Maybe I'm wrong. I don't think so. I think I'm right, Heshie. I think you like her and I know she likes you and I'm positive she'll make you a wife like you won't find again if you spend the whole rest of your life looking. But anyway, maybe I'm wrong. Let's say for a minute, I'm wrong. Let's say you don't like her. But why, Heshie? Why? Tell me, tell your mother, why? Give me one good reason."

"Aah, Ma," I said, "you can't give reasons about things like that. You either like a person or you don't. That's all."

"Maybe," she said. "But then you're not so positive. But you, you're so positive you don't like her, you must at least have *one* reason. At least *one* reason let me hear!"

"Aah, Ma," I began, squirming a little, and then I blurted,

"she's so damn *Jew*ish-looking! You take one look at her, you see right away she's a kike from the Bronx. For crying out loud, what do you want me to do, walk down the street and have everybody giving me the horse laugh because—?"

She flared up so suddenly that for a moment I almost couldn't catch my breath.

"You crazy dumbbell without shame!" she cried. "So *that's* what's eating you! You're a Jew yourself, aren't you? Haven't you got a little feeling in you? What are you, ashamed of what you are? What are you going to do, go around hiding from people what you are? Don't think you're so smart, Heshie. The world is smarter," she almost screamed. "They only have to look at you to know. You can try all you want, you stupid dope, you, but it won't help. I'm glad for once that your father is dead. He shouldn't have lived to hear a son of his talk like that, I'm glad." Her voice shifted to a sarcastic note. "So that's why you don't like Ruthie Rivkin! She's too Jewish-looking for you, hah? And maybe *I* look like a *shickseh* to you? Well, let me tell you something, Mr. Dope. That girl is got more fineness in her one little finger than all the rest of those tramps you're all the time running around with. She's got more—"

"I didn't say she didn't have," I yelled.

"Hold your tongue, my fine one," she cried. "Who do you think you're yelling at, those dopes that you got for partners?"

"Keep them out of this," I cried, and was surprised for a second to find myself in a position where I was defending those two klucks. "I only said I didn't—"

"Never mind what you said," she shouted. "I heard what you said. You said enough for one day."

Suddenly she dropped into her seat and was silent. I sat down, too, and tried to reach across the table to take her hand, but she snatched it away. She sat there, staring at her hands.

Finally she said, "Why do you bother coming home altogether, Heshie, if we're going to fight like this?"

"I don't want to fight with you, Ma," I said. "I don't want to stay away from home, Ma."

"If this is what happens when you come home," she said dully, "maybe it would be better—"

"Don't say that, Ma," I said, reaching across for her hand. She let me take it. "I'm sorry if I said anything, Ma. I didn't really mean it."

"That you're sorry, I can believe," she said quietly. "But don't say you didn't mean it, Heshie." She shook her head. "When a person says what you said, it's only because he *does* mean it. It's a terrible thing, Heshie."

"I guess it is, Ma," I said, scowling. "But I can't help feeling the way I do, can I?"

"No," she said. "But me—I don't feel like that."

"But don't ever say you don't want me to come home," I said. "I like to come home here. I *have* to come home, Ma."

"What for? We should fight? You should say things you don't want to say? We should holler at each other like two crazy ones? *That's* what you like to come home for?"

"No," I said. "And that isn't exactly fair, either, Ma. This is the first time we ever even raised our voices to each other, isn't it?"

"That's all those things need," she said slowly. "A beginning."

"That's not true, Ma. Don't feel that way about it. I don't want you to say those things. It means too much to me to come home here for you to say those things."

"When a person begins to think and talk the way you do, Heshie, home doesn't mean anything to him any more," she said.

"Yes, it does, Ma," I said.

"No," she said. "You're a businessman now. You're a big businessman. You don't think any more the way a son should think. You think the way a businessman thinks. What's a home to a businessman?"

"I don't care about what it means to businessmen, Ma," I said. "All I care about is what it means to me. For crying out loud, Ma, this is the only place where I can sit down

and take a rest without feeling that somebody is going to
jump on me from behind. This is the only place where it
isn't dog eat dog. Don't you understand that, Ma? You think
I enjoy all this fighting, fighting, fighting all the time, trying to show people you're smarter than they are? All right,
maybe I *do* enjoy it. I don't know for sure. Maybe I think
I enjoy it because I know it's the only way to *get* any place
in this world, it's the only way to make money and buy the
things you want and really live like a person, not a dog. But
whether I enjoy it or not, that's not the point. The point is
you can't stand a thing like that forever. You have to have
a place where you can sit down and take a deep breath and
know you're with a friend, you're with a person that really
cares for you. That's what coming home here at night means
to me, Ma. It makes me feel like a human being for a change.
I can sit back and stick my legs under the table and eat your
blintzes, without thinking about whether somebody is trying
to put one over on me or not. Aah, hell, Ma," I said, "don't
you see what I mean?"

"Sure I see what you mean," she said, nodding. "You
think you're saying something new? Maybe I never said it
in the words the same like you use, maybe I never even
thought of it that way. I suppose maybe I didn't. But *I* know
that. You aren't telling me something I never heard. What
do you think I want you should go with a nice girl like Ruthie
Rivkin? Because she'll be able to wear the diamond rings
and the fur coats you'll be able to buy for her? Of course
not. Because a wife is to a man what you just said. How
long do you think I'll be here for you to come and sit and
eat blintzes and talk? I'm not a chicken, Heshie. I'm an old
woman already. Never mind," she said when I tried to protest. "What's true is true. I'm getting older, Heshie. What are
you gonna do when I'm not here? You've got to have a wife.
You've got to have the right kind of a wife. I don't say you
must marry Ruthie Rivkin. Maybe you know another nice
girl, a girl you didn't tell me about yet. If you have, so all
right. But that's the only reason I talk all the time about
Ruthie Rivkin. Because about *her* I'm sure. A mother can

tell those things, Heshie. A young boy, sometimes he can't."

The hell he can't.

"All right, Ma," I said. "Let's forget the whole thing. Let's not fight or argue."

"When are you giving the party in the showroom for the buyers?" she asked. "To-morrow?"

I nodded.

"So why don't you invite Ruthie she should come down to the party, she'll have a nice time, you can—"

"I don't think she can make it, Ma," I said. "You know she works during the day, and this is for the afternoon."

"Don't worry," she said. "For a thing like this she can get off a half a day. You just tell her she should ask her boss, that's all."

"Nah, Ma," I said, "she wouldn't enjoy it. These people are, well, they're tough, Ma. They're hard drinkers and things like that, Ma. A nice girl like Ruthie, she wouldn't enjoy herself at all."

She dropped her eyes from my face and withdrew her hand from mine.

"It's up to you, Heshie," she said quietly.

That was the trouble with hanging around with guys like Babushkin and Ast. I'd been softened by poor competition.

"But I'll tell you what I'll do, Ma," I said with a smile. "When she gets here to-night—" I looked at the clock— "she's due here any minute, now, I guess. When she gets here, I'll take her out and show her a good time. All right? For you, Ma, for you I'll do it."

Yeah, for *her* I was doing it!

24

"You stay put here," I said to the men behind the counter that the caterer had rigged up in one corner of the showroom. "All you do is keep mixing drinks and making sandwiches and whatever else you got there. That's all. You just keep mixing them. Understand?"

"Yes, sir," he said, and nodded.

I turned to the three others.

"And you three, you keep loading up your trays here with drinks and stuff and keep on circulating around. Keep moving all the time and keep your trays filled. Make sure everybody's got enough to drink and eat. There's gonna be a big gang here, maybe a hundred, and I don't want anybody to be thirsty. Understand?"

"Yes, sir," they said, and nodded.

I looked at my watch.

"They ought to begin arriving pretty soon now. So all right, then, you fellows, you know what I want. Go to it, and if everything's all right, there'll be a nice little something extra for each one of you when it's all over. Okay?"

"Yes, sir," they said, and nodded.

It wasn't really as monotonous as it sounds. I even liked it a little, the way no matter what I said they yessed me and nodded.

I turned to the long, low platform the carpenters had built along the wall opposite the windows. It stretched, like a stage, for about twenty feet down the showroom, beginning at the curtained doorway that led into the models' room. I climbed the three low steps at the far end and walked along its length, dropping my feet heavily, to test its strength. It was good and solid. At the end I stepped down, parted the curtains, and walked into the models' room.

There was so much noise and smoke in the room that nobody noticed me. About twenty girls were jammed into the small space, dressing, undressing, smoking, and all the time jawing away at each other. In the middle, fitting a dress on a platinum blonde with a cute little fanny, was Meyer Babushkin. He had a tape measure around his neck, a mouthful of pins, and from the frown on his face you would think he was measuring his closest friend for a wooden overcoat.

I rapped on the wall with a hanger until they heard me

and began to quiet down a little. Then I held up my hand and said, "Can I have your attention for a minute, girls?"

I heard a few "Who's that"s and "Who's he"s and I heard my own models say, "That's Mr. Bogen. That's the boss."

In a few seconds they were quiet.

"You all know what we want, girls," I said, smiling pleasantly. "But just a quick summary before we begin. The guests'll be arriving soon, and when they're all here, say in about, oh, I don't know, say a half hour or so, I'll come to the doorway here and give you the word. Then you begin to file out slowly, in the order Mr. Babushkin told you about. After the show, when I give the word, you come down off the platform and mingle with the guests. Okay?"

"Yes, Mr. Bogen," they said.

"Fine," I said. "And if everything goes all right, when it's all over there'll be a nice little something extra for every one of you."

They began to giggle and chatter, but I held up my hand for silence.

"Everything okay, Meyer?" I asked.

He nodded. That was the big trouble with him. He was always shooting off his mouth.

"That's fine," I said, and went out. So far it looked like I was the only one who thought so.

The first thing I ran into was Teddy Ast, standing in the middle of the showroom, watching the caterer's men and the platform and the decorations in the showroom with a face that looked like it could reach from here to Kocktebel, Russia.

"Hello, Teddy," I said cheerfully.

"Boy," he said, shaking his head, "what this thing cost!"

"So what?" I said.

He just looked around the large room again and shook his head.

"Boy, oh, boy!"

"Ah, nuts," I said. "Got a cigarette on you?"

He gave me one and held the match for me.

"Boy," he said again, "what this thing cost!"

"Pipe down, will you?" I said. "The war's over. This is the way to sell dresses and make dough these days. Don't worry so much about what this cost. We'll get it all back spades doubled."

"Yeah," he said, "we'll get it back. In the pig's eye."

The only reason I didn't say what I wanted to say or do what I wanted to do was that the front door opened and the first gang of buyers came in.

"See if you can look alive there a little," I said out of the corner of my mouth, and then we both went forward to meet them.

Soon they were arriving so fast that one of us had to keep standing near the door to greet them. Teddy seemed to like the idea, so I said, "You better circulate around a little and see that everybody's got enough to drink." This was my show and the buyers were going to remember *me,* not Teddy.

By four o'clock most of them had arrived and had a couple of drinks. So I climbed up onto the platform and rapped for silence. They turned to face me, holding drinks and cigarettes.

"Ladies and gentlemen," I said, flashing my best smile from one end of the room to the other, "may I have your attention?"

The large room became quiet.

"Thank you, ladies and gentlemen, thank you, thank you, thank you. I want you all to know that I really and sincerely appreciate your all showing up like this, and if there's anything I've forgotten, and it's something anybody here thinks will in any way make this a bigger and better party, why, then, folks, let him speak up now and I, as the management, will do my little bit to see that he or she is taken care of properly. What say?"

I looked around the room, smiling, and they smiled back. But nobody spoke.

"All right, then," I said, "let's get on with the christening. The firm," I said, "is Apex Modes. The president"—I pointed to myself—"is Harry Bogen. We are the proud parents, ladies and gentlemen, who present, for your approval, the apple of our eye—our new fall line."

There was a little applause, not much, because most of them were holding glasses or sandwiches, but a little. I ran down the three steps of the platform, stuck my head into the models' room, and said, "Okay, Meyer."

"Okay," he replied, and I stepped back, holding the curtain away from the doorway.

The first girl was a blonde. She stepped through the doorway, climbed the steps of the platform, turned slowly to show the lines of the dress, and moved down the platform. She was followed by a brunette. Then came a redhead and then a platinum. They followed each other like that slowly, a blonde, a brunette, a redhead, a platinum, until the platform was jammed with a long line of them, some twenty strong. They stood like that for a few moments, posing with their hands on their hips or clasped in front of them. Then the whole group turned slowly and came to rest again, like a line of statues.

This time the applause was louder and longer. When I saw some of those boozehounds actually set their glasses down so they could clap their hands, I knew the line was a hit.

"Okay, girls," I said, and they walked off the platform and began to mix with the crowd.

A half dozen buyers, men and women, crowded around me.

"Where did you get the models, Bogen? They're a knockout!"

"Say, that's some bunch of babies. Where'd you get them?"

"Hey, Bogen! I don't see models like that around the other houses. How come?"

"That's easy," I said, laughing. "They're not regular models."

"Who are they?"

"That's the chorus of *Smile Out Loud*," I said.

"You *mean* that?"

"Sure," I said.

"Oh, boy, oh, boy, oh, *boy!* Pick me that little redhead with the you know whats. Gangway, boys, here I go!"

Five minutes after the girls joined the crowd on the floor, the place was in an uproar. People kept slapping my back and spilling their drinks over me, but I didn't mind. The opening was a success. Not only were the dresses pips, but the idea of getting the chorus of a musical comedy to wear them had caught on.

One of my regular models came up to me.

"Mr. Bogen," she said. "What's the matter with Mr. Ast?" She pointed to Teddy sulking in a corner. "What is he, drunk?"

He wasn't, but it was as good an explanation as any.

"Drunk?" I said. "Why, for Christ's sakes, he's potted. Just let him alone and don't worry about him."

The hell with him, I figured. Let him sulk. After all, he was the only one there that didn't seem to be having a good time.

I poked my nose into the little group around Boonton of Arnolds-Tepperman. She bought the highest-priced stuff in the market, and the mere fact that she was present was something of a triumph. I knew the others, but I had never met her.

"Everybody happy?" I said, putting my arms around two of them.

"Oh, *Harry*. It's *you*."

"Harry Bogen, I want to congratulate you. You little louse, you've got the hottest line on the Avenue, do you know that?"

"Thank you, my dear," I said, bowing from the waist and grinning. "But that's the general idea I had."

"You can take it from me, it is— Oh, by the way, Harry. Do you know Miss Boonton?"

"Why, no," I said, bowing again. It's easy, once you get used to it. "I've never had the pleasure."

If meeting Miss Boonton was a pleasure, then so is a case of piles. She had a figure like a subway kiosk and a face like the state of Texas done in three shades of pink.

"All right, then, here goes. Miss Boonton, Mr. Bogen. Mr. Bogen, Miss Boonton."

"How do you do?" I said.

"Lousy," she said in a voice that started somewhere about eighteen inches below her feet. "But seeing a line like that makes me feel better already. Who's your designer?"

"Meyer Babushkin."

"Of Pulbetkal?" she said, surprised.

"Right."

"How in the God damned hell did you ever get the little kike away from Pulvermacher?"

I tapped my nose and winked.

"My hidden charms," I said.

"So *that's* the kind of guy you are, eh?" she said, and we all burst out laughing. "Seriously, though, how come I haven't seen any of your stuff before?"

"We were making sixteen-seventy-fives up to now."

"I get it," she said, giving me a shove. "Getting high hat, eh?"

I grinned. I couldn't talk. That gentle shove of hers had knocked the wind out of me. It looked like I'd have to join a gym if I wanted to sell the higher-priced trade.

"Well, just watch out you don't get so high class you don't know the difference between a good dress and a lousy one."

"Not me," I said, waving my hand from side to side. "I wrote a poem to remind myself."

"A *what?*"

"A poem."

"Listen, brother," she said, grinning, "Maybe that's the way you got Babushkin, after all. A poem!"

"Sure," I said, grinning back at her. "I always write poems in my spare time. In fact, I'm just about the world's champion lavatory poet. Most of my stuff is unpublished, but if you've ever seen the walls of a men's toilet, you've seen—"

"Jesus Christ," she said, "you got me all excited. How does it go?"

So I had her all excited.

"Like this," I said, and swung into something real dirty.

All of a sudden she broke into a squeal and collapsed into my arms. Now I know how it must feel to support the Woolworth Building when it begins to lean over too far. She shook up and down for a while until she recovered her breath. Sometimes I wished I could get as much pleasure out of my own jokes as the dopes I told them to did. It looked like I was the only one who knew they were lousy. Well, at least there was some little kick in knowing that I could adopt the right tone in a conversation, even down to the crummy jokes.

"Mr. Bogen," she said finally, "or maybe I better call you Harry. Yeah, Harry. Harry old kid," she said slapping me on the shoulder, and drying her eyes with her sleeve, "do I get a poem like that with every order I place with you?"

"You bet," I said.

——And more.

"Shake, kid," she said.

We shook, and she slapped me on the back once more. I didn't wince, though. I was getting used to it.

"Hey, Molly," she yelled suddenly at a woman across the room. "You wanna hear something?" And she went charging across the crowded showroom, shoving people out of her way like a cowcatcher going through a snowdrift. She left just in time. My constitution isn't what it used to be.

I turned toward the rest of the room, and stopped with my mouth open. Standing near the platform, talking to two men, was the neatest-looking brunette I'd ever seen. She stood so that I saw her in profile, and for a moment I couldn't catch my breath. She had the kind of tits you could see coming around a corner ten minutes before the rest of her body followed. Ma-*ma!*

I walked over to Teddy and pointed her out to him.

"Who's the dame?"

He looked at me in surprise. "What are you, screwy?" he said.

"Why?"

"You don't know who she is?"

I looked again. She wasn't a buyer, she wasn't one of my models, and she wasn't wearing one of our dresses.

I shook my head.

"That's a hot one all right," he said, screwing up his lips. "You're paying her, and you don't know who she is."

"You mean she's from *Smile Out Loud?*"

"Sure she is."

"Well, how come she isn't modeling one of our dresses, then?"

"Aw, she's not just in the chorus. She does a specialty number. She sings or something."

"Oh, yeah? You know so much about her, how about a knockdown?"

He looked disgusted.

"Aw, Christ! Why don't you keep your mind on your work for a change, Harry? What do you want to bother with those pots for?"

Get an earful of *that! He* was giving me advice!

"Listen," I said, "I'm paying her, ain't I? All right, then. Come on." I took his arm. "By the way, what's her name?"

"Martha Mills," he said.

25

There are two kinds of dames. The kind you want to put, but with whom you wouldn't be found dead. And the kind you not only want to put, but with whom you get a kick out of being seen walking down the street. All the others don't count.

This dame was in class two.

For three weeks in a row I took her out every night. We had dinner and talked until it was time for her to go to the theatre. After the show I called for her and we made the rounds. Always, when the time came to take her home, I thought maybe to-night. But always that's as far as I got, her front door.

Sometimes, after I'd had a chance to cool off a little and I wasn't sore any more, I'd stand there on the sidewalk in front of her apartment house for a while and ask myself was I crazy or wasn't I. If somebody would've told me that I'd be spending the time and money on any dame that I was spending on her, and not even getting to first base, I would've told him to go get his head examined. I would've told it to myself, too. Yet there I'd be, out on the sidewalk, with my hot pants to remind me that I wasn't dreaming. Then I'd get sore and say the hell with her and go home.

Then, the next morning, sorting out the checks in my private office, going over the mail, I'd remember the way we'd looked the night before. I'd remember the jealous looks of the heels around the stage door when I called for her. Or the way all eyes turned to look at us when we walked into a restaurant or a night club. Or the line in Winchell's column, "Martha Mills, the baby-voiced warbler of *Smile Out Loud* is doing the hot spots with what prominent young manufacturer of feminine haberdashery?" I'd think of how swell it made me feel just to be seen walking down the street with her, and how people looked after her, and then at me, and wondered who I was and wished they were me. I'd think of all that, and I'd reach for the telephone.

"Get me Riverside 9-0437."

In a few seconds the girl at the switchboard would ring me.

"Here's your Riverside number, Mr. Bogen."

"Okay." Then, "Hello, Martha?"

"Hello, Harry."

"How do you feel?"

"Sleepy. What's the big idea waking me up so early in the morning?"

"Sorry," I laughed. "I just wanted to make sure I was filing my application for to-night before the rest of the city. Anybody ahead of me yet, Martha?"

"You know there's nobody ahead of you, Harry."

Crap me easy, kid, I thought. You've played mumblety

peg as much as I have. But I said, "Then how about to-night?"

"All right."

"Same time?"

"Same time."

" 'Bye, Martha."

" 'Bye."

This was the part I didn't like. As soon as I'd hang up I'd begin remembering all the nights that had gone before, and I'd begin thinking of the one that was coming, and wondering if it would be the same. Then I'd begin thinking what a holy *schmuck* I was making of myself, and I'd get so sore at myself I felt like calling her back and telling her to drop dead.

But this time I didn't get a chance to get sore. Because before I could put the receiver back on the hook the door opened and Teddy Ast came in.

"Hello, Theodore," I said, "how's the world treating you?"

He slapped a thin packet of blue-covered papers on my desk.

"I just been looking through the accountant's report," he said.

"Why, Teddy!" I said, surprised. "You didn't tell me you knew how to read!"

"Never mind," he said grimly. "I just been looking through it."

"So've I," I said, picking up my copy. "Looks pretty good, doesn't it?" I leafed through it to the operating statement. "Eight thousand net for the month. Not bad. Not bad at all."

His face squeezed up a little tighter and he turned to the schedule of expenses.

"Traveling and entertaining," he read, "twenty-two hundred dollars."

I picked my teeth with my tongue but didn't say anything.

"Well," he said, "what've you got to say to that?"

"You really want to know?" I said.

"Yeah," he said.

"All I have to say is: in your hat and over your ears; you look good in brown."

He snatched the report off the desk and rolled it into a thin line.

"Can that wise-guy stuff, Harry," he said. "This is serious. I'm not kidding now."

"My error," I said. "I thought you were."

He was so sore that his hand shook when he lit a cigarette. But I didn't say a word. He was dumb enough to dig his own grave. He didn't need any help from me.

"What are you gonna do about it?" he said.

"About what?"

He hit the desk with the rolled up report. "Don't give me any of that, Harry. You know what. What about those entertaining expenses?"

"Well, what about them?"

"You gonna cut them out?"

"No," I said. "I'm having a lot of fun spending that money, and it's good for the business. If you got any objections, spit them out."

"Listen, Harry."

"What do you *think* I'm doing?"

He shook off the interruption.

"From the first minute we opened up here, you've been throwing money around like water. I didn't like the idea, but I didn't say anything." No, not much. "But this is different."

I picked up a sheaf of orders from my desk and waved them under his nose.

"Where the hell do you think *these* came from? How the hell do you think we got these? Just by showing your phiz around to the buyers? Don't kid yourself, Teddy," I said, "you're not that good-looking."

"Don't try to hide things. What do you think I am, a dope?"

"Sure," I said, grinning.

He glared at me.

"Well, I'm not as dumb as you think. When you spent all that dough, I figured all right, it was on buyers, it was for the business. But you can't keep pulling that crap on me. The whole damn market knows what you're doing. When you start pissing away the firm dough on a pot like that, on an actress, where we don't stand to make anything, then I got a right to object."

"You all finished?" I said calmly.

He didn't answer.

"Now you listen to me for a change," I said. "First of all you're such a dumb bastard you don't even know what you're talking about. And secondly, where did you ever get this 'I got a right' business? If I want to spend money endowing a hospital for *cats,* I'll do it, and I won't ask for any advice from you, either."

"I don't care what the hell you do with your own money," he said, "but when you start spending firm money, then I got a right—"

"Yeah? Who ever told you that?"

"I'm a partner, ain't I?"

"But I happen to own sixty per cent of the stock," I said, grinning at him, "and maybe I'll endow that hospital for cats after all."

"Not with *my* money," he said, breathing quickly. "I don't care what you say, I'm still a partner here, and—"

"Then maybe you and I better just stop being partners," I said.

"That suits me," he said, slapping the report onto the desk and turning on his heel.

"It can't suit you any more than it suits me," I said. "We'll go down to Golig to-morrow."

"The quicker the better," he said, and slammed the door.

With the door closed behind him I couldn't hold it any longer. I just had to laugh out loud. It couldn't have worked out any better if he'd've been killed in a railroad wreck. He had taught me all he knew a long time ago. As far as I was concerned he'd shot his load.

I picked up the receiver and spoke to the girl at the switchboard.

"Tell Mr. Babushkin I want to see him right away," I said.

26

After the waiter pushed the chair under her and she had done things to her lips and hair she looked up at me with a smile and said, "Now go on with your story, Harry."

"Where was I?" I asked, sweeping my eyes from her thick black hair, that looked like a greased helmet, down her tiny button nose and thick red lips to her chest. From there I couldn't go any further. That chest, with the dress bunched up and drawn tightly across it, had never failed to stop me yet.

"I don't know exactly," she said, shaking herself a little and clearing my mind of any doubts as to whether she was wearing a brassiere, "but when you decided in such a hurry that we had enough of Seventy-Seven— By the way, why do you always want to go from one place to another? We're no sooner settled in one place, than you want to get out and go some place else."

"You want to know the reason?" I said, smiling at her, and watching out of the corner of my eye the way the people at the next table kept staring at us.

"Oh, so you *have* a reason. Well, what is it?"

"I get a kick out of walking in and out of places with you," I said.

"Oh, *Harry!*" she squealed, covering her mouth to stop the laugh, and sending her chest shivering all over the lot in a way that made me grip the edge of the table to keep my hands from running away with themselves.

"That's the truth, Martha," I said. "Honest."

"Oh, Harry, cut it out."

"I mean it, Martha," I said. "You're not like other girls." Which was the bull. Upside down they all look alike. "You ought to see the way people look at us, at you, rather, when we come into a place. And they look at us the same way when we go out. So I leave it to you. The more times we get up and go out, the more times we walk in, which means the more times people look at us, and the more kick I get. See?"

"Oh, Harry, you're funny."

"Well, I can't help it," I said. "So far, that's the only real pleasure I've had from going with you."

She looked at me quickly and then down at the tablecloth. Bull's eye! Score one for the old marksman! For the time being this dame had me stopped. But I wasn't quitting yet. I had too much of an investment in her already. And besides, to be honest about it, I couldn't have quit if I'd wanted to. Not while she was built the way she was. And not while she was an actress. And not while every guy on Broadway that saw us together wished he was in my shoes.

"What about the rest of your story?" she said.

"Oh, yes," I said, putting my thumb in my vest, "my story. Now, ah, where, ah, was I?"

"Mr. Ast," she said, mimicking my voice, and grinning, "had just told you he didn't like the way you were running the business and he wanted you to—"

"Oh, yes," I said. "So I said, Teddy, I said, my hearing isn't so good these last few days, so maybe I didn't get you right the first time. But did I understand you to say, I said, did I understand you to say that you didn't *like* the way I was running the business? And he said yes. So I sort of leaned back in my chair and shook my head like I'd just gotten the news my mother died or something, you know, and I said, gee, Teddy, that's too bad. That certainly is too bad, I said, because you know, Teddy, I'm a funny guy, and I wouldn't be able to sleep well at night if I knew a partner of mine didn't like the way I was running things."

"What did he say to that?" she said, laughing.

"What *could* he say? Nothing. So I continued, and I said in that case, Teddy, seeing as how you and I don't sort of, well, you know, sort of agree on things, then maybe it wouldn't be a half bad idea if you and I, we *stopped* being partners from now on. Well, Martha, as soon as I said that, you should've seen the look on his face. He started to cry and this and that and the other, you know, and tried to talk me out of it, but I just shook my head like a pallbearer, you

know, and I said sorry, Teddy, you and I, we couldn't continue being partners if I felt that you didn't like the way I was
running things. He tried a little more crying, you know, because he knew what a dope he was for letting himself out of
one of the most profitable businesses in the city." If she
couldn't take that hint, she was blind. "So the only thing left
for him to do was to get tough. Well, Martha," I said, paus-
ing to light a cigarette, "I'm not saying I'm the bravest guy
in the world. If Jack Dempsey would get tough with me, then
maybe I'd just say yes, sir. But when a baloney like Teddy
Ast gets tough with me, then Martha, old kid, I get so tough
myself that you'd think I chewed battleships and spit rust."

"Well, what happened?"

"Nothing," I said, waving my hand. "Nothing much, I
just picked up the little heeb"—what the hell, Mama wasn't
listening—"I took him by his collar and kicked him out of
my office. And that was the end of my partner Teddy Ast."

"You mean just like *that* you got rid of him?"

"Oh, well," I said, dusting my ashes elaborately, "just like
I get rid of anything else I can't use." Hm. "There were a
couple of minor details, of course, but I'd taken care of all
that in advance. I knew he'd run to Babushkin, so I'd spoken
to Babushkin in advance. I knew he'd run to the lawyer, so
I'd fixed it with Golig in advance. In fact, before Teddy Ast
knew what hit him, he was out on his ear with nothing but
his original investment and his share of the profits to date,
which, compared to what that business is capable of earning,
is the equivalent of not only taking his shirt, but his pants
too."

"You mean that from now on the whole business is
yours, Harry?" she said, leaning toward me across the table.

The light began to dawn so suddenly, that for a moment
I almost forgot to look down into the front of her dress. But
you don't get as far as I've come if you haven't got a halfway decent portion of self-control. So I managed to keep my
face straight and at the same time get my look in, too. Hell,
I was paying for it.

"Practically," I said. "I've still got Babushkin, but I really *need* him. He's my designer. But I'm not worrying about him. There's one thing you can be sure *he'll* never die from, and that's brains."

"Gosh, Harry," she said, shaking her head at me admiringly. "A young man like you, with a business like that!"

Well, anyway, it *looked* admiringly. But whether it was or wasn't, there was one guy she wasn't kidding. And that was the president of Apex Modes, Inc., Harry Bogen, to you.

"This is only the beginning," I said. "You just watch my smoke."

Smoke was right. I was hot enough to burn.

"How about another drink?" I said. "Waiter!"

"Oh, no, Harry, please! I've had enough."

"Let's get something to eat, then."

"Gosh," she laughed, "don't you ever want to do anything but eat?"

"Sure," I said quickly, "but this is about as good a substitute as I know."

Am I subtle! Boy, like an after-dinner speaker.

"Yes, sir?" the waiter said at my elbow.

I looked at her. "No, nothing, Harry."

"Check, please," I said to the waiter.

In the cab going uptown I put my arm around her, but when we came to her door and she said, "Good night, Harry, call me in the morning," I wasn't surprised. I was disappointed, but not surprised.

And even though I was in the same place I'd been every night at the same time for almost a month, out on the sidewalk, this time I wasn't sore.

The first time she'd stopped me at the door, I admit I was surprised. Maybe, I thought, maybe, Mama knows best. Teddy had said she had some kind of a heel of a husband floating around somewhere, but I didn't attach much importance to that. I didn't even ask too much about it. It was enough for me that they didn't live together. That's all I ever want to know about husbands. So at first I figured maybe I'd picked a foul ball. But then I remembered how attractive she was, and all the guys hanging around her in

the showroom. There was no sense in kidding myself. She
had dates and she went out with married men, too. And
when a dame like that goes out with a married guy, it's not
so he can read poetry to her, either. So why should it be any
different for me? If she wouldn't have been married, I'd have
thought well, maybe. But she was married, or she'd been
married. So what was one more slice off a cut loaf? The first
time I figured all right, maybe the flag was up. But I'd seen
her every night for almost a month. So *that* was out, too.
Which left what? Until to-night the answer was search me.
But now the answer was different.

And that's why, even though I was still standing out on
the sidewalk, this time I wasn't sore, the way I'd been every
other night. Because this time I had the combination. Now,
at last, I had the formula. From now on at least I knew
where I was going. I was going to play *her* way. It was going
to be expensive, but what the hell did I care about that? She
was an actress, wasn't she? Actresses weren't like book-
keepers or stenographers or models. You had to play them
differently. But that was all. Once you got the hang of the
game, the rest was the same. And whether dear old Martha
knew it or not, she was going to come through with a bang.

The best part of all, though, was that I had a hunch she
knew it all right.

27

Mother pretended to be surprised when she saw me.

"Oh," she said, "look who we have to-night! A guest in
the town!"

That was a nice way to start off an evening that I knew in
advance was going to be lousy.

"What's the matter, Ma?"

"Nothing," she said, setting the table as she talked. "Only
it's getting already a surprise to see you when it's still light
enough so we shouldn't have to turn on the electric."

I reached for a piece of bread, but she pushed my hand away.

"Here's the point," she said, giving me the hard brown end of the loaf. "I saved it for you."

"Thanks, Ma," I said.

I bit into the rubbery chunk and chewed slowly.

"What time did you get home last night?"

"Oh, it wasn't late," I said.

I was thinking fast, trying to shift the conversation to another subject—it would get back to this soon enough—but I couldn't.

"Sure it wasn't late," she said. "He comes home God knows when—fourteen, fifteen o'clock—so by him it's not late. Sure not. It's already early in the morning."

"Aah, Ma."

She screwed up her face and twisted her lips in an exaggerated imitation of my expression and said, "Aah, Ma! Aah, Ma! Everything I say, all the time I talk, it's by him always 'Aah, Ma!' "

She made a motion of disgust with the ladle she was holding and turned back to the pots on the gas range.

After a few moments I said, "Well, Ma, what do you know that's new? Anything happen during the day?"

"What do you want should happen? The skies should fall? The ocean should dry up? What do you want should—?"

"No," I said, "I was just asking, that's all. Can't I ask a simple little question like that, without you getting all excited?"

"Who's excited?" she demanded. "You see maybe I'm excited? You ask questions like a donkey, so I answer them you should understand. That means I'm excited? Go, go, eat better. Talk a little less and eat a little more. The talking isn't worth by you anything, anyway, so at least do a little eating."

I began to eat slowly, still thinking of the best way to begin. But I knew it was useless. There wasn't even one good way. So how could there be a *best* way?

"Oh, yeah," Mother said suddenly, turning from the gas

range with a plate in her hands. "I forgot to tell you. Ruthie called you up."

"I guess it just accidentally slipped your mind, didn't it?" I said.

"Yeah," she said, "I forgot all about it."

Yeah! Like she forgot to collect from me when the end of the week came around.

I continued to eat in silence.

"About seven o'clock, she called. Maybe a few minutes after."

"That's not a bad time to call," I said, still eating.

She set the plate down before me and took up the one I had been using.

"I told her you weren't home," she said.

"Since I wasn't," I said, "that was the best thing you could do. After all, there's no sense in lying about it."

"Don't you wanna know what she said?"

"No," I said. "I can guess."

She set down the pot she was holding with a bang and turned to face me, her hands on her hips.

"Listen, Heshie," she began.

"Please, Ma," I said. "Let's not get into an argument over Ruthie Rivkin. I didn't come home for *that* to-night."

"No?"

"No."

"Then maybe you'll do me a big favor and tell me why you all of a sudden became—God forbid!—so *kind* to me that you come home for a change to-night? Maybe you'll tell me that?"

Well, there was the opening. What the hell was I afraid of?

"Nothing," I said. "What ever gave you the idea I came home for any special reason?"

"Nothing," she said sarcastically. "Except only for God knows how many weeks already you've been coming home with the chickens, three, four o'clock in the morning, ruining your health—"

"I am not," I said angrily. "I feel all right. So what if I

do come home a little late? I don't get up till late the next morning, do I?"

"In my house," she said, "you'll do your sleeping at night, like regular people, not during the day."

"All right, all right," I said, mumbling in a low voice to make her forget the long speech she had been starting out on.

"So," she continued, "after so many weeks of showing your face for a couple of minutes in the morning, before you grab your behind in your hands and run like a crazy one downtown, now, to-night you all of a sudden come home half-past seven, like a real person for a change, and you sit down with a face long like a horse, and then you ask me how I know you came home for a special reason? What am I all of a sudden, a dope?"

"Aah, hell, Ma, that's—"

"Never mind with the 'Aah, hell, Ma' business. I know you a little longer than you know yourself, my Heshalle. You became all of a sudden smart since you became a business-man. But I was smart yet when you were peeing in the diapers, Heshalle. You can be smart with those dumbbells you got for partners. But don't think you can be smart with me."

I figured there was no sense in trying to put one over on *her*.

"All right, Ma," I said quietly, "I did come home early for a special purpose."

"For what?"

"I wanted to tell you something," I said, smiling suddenly and talking lightly. "I'm taking a little place downtown, near my business. I'm going to be living away from home for a while, Ma."

I should have known better than to try to treat it humorously. Her own manner changed abruptly. The anger went out of her face and she dropped into her chair at the table, facing me across the dishes.

"You're not going to live home," she said quietly.

"It's only for a little while, Ma," I said. "Maybe a couple of weeks or so. Till we get the new line going good."

She stared at me without speaking for a few moments. Then she said, "You know, Heshie, sometimes I wish you were back again working for fifteen dollars a week."

"Aah, Ma, that's no way to talk. This won't be for long. It's only on account of business that I'm doing it."

"Business!" she said bitterly.

"It *is* business, Ma," I said quickly. "You know I wouldn't lie to you. It's on account of business I'm doing it."

She shook her head.

"I don't say you're lying to me, Heshie. I don't say it's not business," she said.

"Then what's the sense of feeling that way about it?" I said. "The way you act, Ma, somebody would think I was dying or something."

"It's the same thing," she said. "Since you started with that business of yours, you're not the same. The business sees you more than I do."

"Don't say that, Ma. It's not true."

"I don't have to say it," she said. "Other people say it. The neighbors they say it. I get all dressed up. I put on the fancy clothes you bought me. I put on the fur collar. I walk in the street. The neighbors they stop me, they tell me how nice I look, they ask me where I get the nice things. I tell them I have a son and how good he is to me. And they look at me like I was a little crazy. You have a son, they say? They never see you. You're all the time buried in that business of yours."

"What do you care what the neighbors say?" I said. "Does it matter to you what *they* say? You still have me, haven't you? It's not like I'm going away to Europe or something. I'll still be here in the city. And it'll only be for a couple of weeks or so. I'll send you all the money you need. I'll send you dresses and things like that. I'll even bring them up to you when I'm not busy. You know that, Ma."

"What's the good of having fine clothes, of having a fur collar, if when you walk in the street the people think you went and bought it for yourself? How do people know I have a son if they never see you?"

Well, I could see where she'd be working *that* line to death for a while. I swear, if I had the guts, I'd handle these things by mail.

"I think you pay too much attention to what the neighbors say. If they want to talk, let them talk. I can't run my business to suit the neighbors, Ma."

"There's other people in business, Heshie. Not only you. Why is it other people, they run their business, they make a living, they come home at night to their wives, to their children, to their mothers. Why should it be different for you?"

"Because I'm in business differently from them. They work like niggers, they make a little profit, they come home, and they're satisfied. They might just as well be working for somebody else for a salary. I don't want that. You never get rich *that* way. If you want to get rich in business, Ma, there's no time for coming home at night and sitting down and wasting time. You've got to work at it twenty-four hours a day. When I'm through at the place, I have to take buyers out, I have to entertain, I have to do a thousand things, Ma. I can't be satisfied with just a little bit. I can't sit back and say all right, I'm getting by, I'll take a rest. I can't do that, Ma."

"But why?" she cried. "Why should it be different for you? Why shouldn't you be satisfied with a little, like everybody else? What do you need the whole world money for?"

"I don't know, Ma," I said, shaking my head. "It's hard to explain those things. I could do things the way the others do. But it wouldn't be me. I got my own rules. With me it's a question of giving as much as I'm taking. If I wanted to be satisfied with a *little* money, so I'd spend a *little* time in my business. But I want a lot of it, so I have to spend a lot of time at it, that's all. But what's the sense of talking," I said, "you don't understand, Ma."

"Don't worry, Heshie," she said. "I understand only too well."

First she said she didn't understand. Then she said she did. Well, that's the Bogens. We learn fast.

"I'll be living downtown for a while, Ma," I said. "And that's all. It's not going to kill anybody."

She looked at me without blinking, as though she hadn't heard my last words.

"You know what I sit here and try to figure out, Heshie?" she said finally.

"What?"

"How a thing like a few months in business could change a person so. What," she asked, "what can your business give you that your own mother can't?"

Martha Mills instead of Ruthie Rivkin, for one thing, if she really wanted to know.

"I swear, Ma," I said, shaking my head and smiling at her, "you ought to be an actress. All I keep hearing is how I'm changing. What kind of silly talk is that? I'm changing! What am I, getting taller? My nose is getting shorter? My hair is changing from black to red?"

"I wish it only *was* that," she said.

So did I.

"Then let's forget the whole thing," I said, starting to get up. "I don't know how the hell we ever get *into* these long-winded arguments—"

She continued to stare at me, without moving, and I dropped back into my chair.

"I think I know what it is," she said.

"Yeah? What?"

"You don't need me any more," she said slowly. "You got something you want better."

"Aah, Ma," I said sharply, "you know that's not true." It makes me sore as hell to have to go around insisting I'm honest. "Just because I don't go around like a damn fool saying I love you and all that, that doesn't mean anything. I don't like that kind of silly talk, Ma, that's all. It sounds fake. I like people should have, well, they should have dignity, they should act like grown-up human beings. The way *you* act, Ma. I don't like to talk like a baby. But hell," I said, "if you want me to do that, all right, I will."

I reached across the table and took her hand in mine, but there was no answering pressure when I squeezed it.

"That's it," she said again, "you don't need me any more.

You're not soft like you were when you were a boy, a year ago. You don't need a rest any more. You're hard now. That's what business did for you. That's what those rules of yours, that's what *your* way of doing business, did for you."

"That's not true, Ma," I said. "I feel the same as I always did. I'm not different."

She nodded and smiled a little. But it wasn't funny to see.

"Yes you are, Heshie," she said. "You said it yourself. There used to be a time when you had to come home at night. You said you had to come home and sit by the table and eat blintzes and stretch your legs out and get a rest where nobody is going to jump on you from the back, like you said. You said—I remember even the words—you said you had to come home because here it's not—you said it yourself—here it's not dog eat dog." She shook her head. "But it's not like that any more. You're hard now. You don't need a rest any more. Now it's all right by you if it's dog eat dog all the time."

"I don't know what wound you up to-day, Ma," I said, shaking my head. "I come home and tell you a simple little thing like that I have to sleep downtown for a couple of weeks because of business, and you give me a long speech about I don't like you any more, I don't have to come home any more, I don't have to do this, I don't need that, I'm changed—for *crying* out loud, Ma, what's going on here?"

"Maybe a year ago you would have understood me," she said, getting up and beginning to collect the dishes. "But now—" She shrugged. "Maybe it's my fault, too," she said. "Maybe I should have talked to you before. But now, now I'm afraid it's too late. You're changed, Heshie, you're changed."

A guy can stand just so much, even from his own mother.

"But what the hell kind of talk is that?" I cried, raising my voice to a shout suddenly, and jumping out of my chair. "What kind of 'changed'? I *feel* the same way I ever felt. I *act* the same way I ever acted. Where do you get this 'changed' stuff? Maybe I have a little more money. Maybe I'm a little smarter. But what—?"

She turned the hot water tap on full, and the sudden rush of water against the dirty dishes almost drowned me out. She shut it off again, quickly.

"*You* say you're not changed," she said over her shoulder. "But in the old country, Heshie, we have a saying. We say, what you *do,* you *are.*"

Twisting her wrist, with a gesture of finality, she sent the hot water thudding down noisily on the dirty plates in the sink.

28

One of the girls from the office stuck her head into my room.

"Miss Olincy of Butler Barnwell is in the showroom, Mr. Bogen," she said.

"Ah, hell," I said. "Did you tell her I was in?"

"No, not yet."

"Good," I said. "Don't. She's a pain in the rear end and she's not important enough, anyway. Say, what the hell have I got a squad of salesmen for, anyway? What do you think I'm paying them for, they should play mumblety-peg while I have to take care of every two-by-nothing buyer? Tell Schwartz to take care of her, or Niederman, or any one of them. You got a half dozen out there, what do you have to come bothering me for?"

"Yes, Mr. Bogen."

"Oh, Miss K."

Her head came around the door again.

"Yes, Mr. Bogen?"

"Get me the garage on the phone right away, will you?"

"Yes, Mr. Bogen."

Yes, Mr. Bogen. No, Mr. Bogen. Yes, Mr. Bogen. It sounded like a musical comedy sketch, but boy, did I love it!

When the phone rang I picked it up and said, "Hello, West Side Garage? This is Mr. Bogen of Apex. Bring my car around right away, will you? Yeah, on the Thirty-Eighth Street side. I'll be down in ten minutes. All right?"

"Yes, sir."

What, no Mr. Bogen?

I jiggled the hook until the girl in the office got on.

"Yes, Mr. Bogen?"

Ah, that was better.

"Riverside 9-0437. Get it right away."

"Yes, Mr. Bogen."

It wasn't as bad as it sounds. I only dropped in a few hours a day, now, to see the important buyers and give everything the once-over, so I only had to listen to it for a small part of each day. Not that I objected, really. I was paying them, wasn't I? So I figured along with the work I got out of them, I might just as well get the trimmings, too.

"Hello, Martha?"

"Yes, Harry. How are you, dear?"

The little bitch. From the way she deared me all over the lot, you'd think we'd been sleeping together since the Armistice.

"I'm great," I said. "And you?"

"All right."

"How about a little lunch?"

"So *early?*"

"Well, I want to do a couple of things before we eat. I want to show you something. What do you say?"

"All right."

"I'll be up in a half hour, then."

"Harry dear, give a girl a chance to dress!"

"You don't have to work too hard at it," I said. "You look good to me as is."

"Oh, Harry!"

Oh, Harry, my ass.

"So what do you say, will you be ready when I get there?"

"I'll try, dear."

"Okay, then, 'bye."

" 'Bye, dear."

On my way through the office the bookkeeper stopped me.

"Will you be back, Mr. Bogen?"

"I don't know. I might. What's the matter?"

She waved her desk diary at me.

"We've got to make some payments to-day, Mr. Bogen, and if—"

"Put the checks on my desk," I said. "I'll sign them when I get back. And if I don't get back, it won't kill them if they get their checks a day later."

The car was waiting for me at the curb. I'd had it for three days already, but it was such a beauty, that every time I saw it I had to stop for a few seconds and just look at it.

"There she is, Mr. Bogen," the man from the garage said.

"Thanks."

I got in and drove uptown.

I didn't say anything to her until we got out of the elevator and into the street. Then, instead of hailing a cab, the way I usually did, I walked her over to the car and reached for the yellow door.

"Why, *Harry,* don't tell me this is *yours!*"

All right, so I won't tell you.

"Like it?"

She clasped her hands and said, "It's a *beauty,* Harry. When did you get it?"

"A couple of days ago. But a couple of things on it had to be adjusted."

She walked around it and ran her hand along the edge of the door and said again, "It's a beauty, Harry."

"Hop in," I said, "and we'll see how she runs."

I drove down to Seventy-Second, turned right, and brought the car to a stop in front of the Montevideo.

"Where are we going?"

I grinned at her and said, "I want to show you something."

The doorman opened the car and I helped her out. She held back a little as we walked into the large foyer, but I patted her shoulder and said, still grinning, "Don't you be afraid, little girl. You're safe. There's a carpenter and a plumber and a couple of painters upstairs that'll act as chaperons."

The elevator stopped at twenty-one without my saying a word. There's some difference between the elevator operators in a loft building and the elevator operators in a classy apartment house like the Montevideo.

I walked to the door at the end of the small hallway and threw the door open. I didn't see a carpenter, but the two painters who were working in the large living room looked up at us and I could hear the plumber in the bathroom.

"There're your chaperons," I said.

She looked at me sideways, smiling a little, and walked in. We paraded through the living room, into the bedroom, out into the living room again, into the kitchen, peeked into the bathroom, came back into the living room and parked ourselves in front of the wide windows that looked out onto the park.

"Well," I said, "what do you think of it?"

"What am I supposed to say, Harry?"

"Oh, there's no script," I said, waving my hand at her. "You can ad lib."

She looked around the large room again, then out the window, and then at me.

"Who's it for, the Salvation Army or something?"

"No," I said, laughing, "it's all for a very close friend of yours. A gent by the name of Harry Bogen. Remember him?"

"I've got a faint recollection," she said, looking around the room once more, then at me, with her tongue in her cheek a little and the kind of a look in her eye that is sometimes referred to as calculating. "What's the big idea?"

"Oh, I don't know. I just got tired of the old dump, that's all. And now, of course," I added, "now that I'm traveling around in such high-class company, you know"—she bowed a little and I bowed back—"why, I figured it was time I moved into a decent place. See what I mean?"

She said she saw.

"Now tell the truth, Martha, what do you think of it?"

"Well," she said, laughing, "all I know so far is that it's one of the nicer apartments at the Montevideo. Which is enough, believe me. But to tell you the truth, Harry"—she waved her hands to take in the room—"it's still kind of empty, isn't it?"

"That," I said, "is where *you* come in."

She looked at me quickly, and I realized suddenly what I'd said. But I didn't bother to correct the impression.

"We're going out this afternoon to buy me some furniture," I said. I patted my breast pocket. "I got the old checkbook with me, and anything you pick out, that's what I buy." Almost anything, anyway. "What do you say?"

"I say okay."

"Great," I said, putting my arm around her and walking her to the door. "Let's eat first."

With her around, it was almost a pleasure to sign checks. She had so much class, that when we walked into a store, the salesmen fell all over themselves for the chance to wait on us. And she had taste, too. None of this fancy crap for her. Personally, I didn't much care what she bought. As long as the furniture included a double bed, I was satisfied. But she was particular. And so long as her being particular didn't mean more money out of my pocket, she could be particular until the salesmen passed out.

After three hours I said, "All right for to-day. We'll get the rest to-morrow. You tired?"

"No," she said; then, "well, maybe a little."

"Come on," I said, "we'll get a hot drink of something and then go for a drive in the park. All right?"

"All right, Harry."

I was a little tired myself, so I drove back to the garage, left the car, and took a cab.

I put my arm around her and held her hand in my lap. After the cab entered the park, I didn't speak for a while. Then, still holding her close, and looking out the window, I said, "What have you got against me, Martha?"

"Nothing," she said, "I've got nothing against you, Harry."

The fact that she wasn't surprised showed she knew what I was talking about.

"Don't you like me?"

"Sure I like you, Harry," she said. Then, as though she

were afraid she hadn't made herself clear, she added, "I like you a lot, Harry." Boy, she was smooth.

I figured the time was ripe for a straight shot, right through the middle.

"Why do you turn me down, Martha?" I said, still looking out of the window.

She stiffened a little in the bend of my arm.

"I'm not turning you down, Harry," she said. "I like you a lot and all that, but, well—I'm just not that kind of a girl, Harry."

And I was Little Lord Fauntleroy.

I didn't say anything. I could feel her head turn a little as she tried to get a look at me to see if it had registered. But I continued to look out of the window, without speaking.

"I like you, Harry," she said again, to drive the point home, "but it's just that I don't know you well enough." She began to talk more quickly, as though she'd been struck by a better idea. "That's the trouble with you: you're so sure right away that you're in love, that you want the woman to be the same. But a woman has to take time, Harry, and be really sure. She has too much to lose." What the hell did *she* have to lose? "A woman can't rush into those things."

All right. Call it love. I had my *own* word for it. We'd soon see which of the two was more accurate. I still had a couple of blank checks on me.

I leaned forward and tapped on the glass.

"Driver," I said, "take us to Tiffany's. Thirty-seventh and Fifth." And, to drive *my* point home, I repeated, "Tiffany's."

29

If it was any other guy I would have said he was a horse's ass and she was taking him over. But I didn't say it for two reasons. Nobody calls me a horse's ass, and nobody takes me over. I knew she thought I was a big sucker. But she wasn't putting anything over on me. I knew what I was doing.

I picked up the receiver and spoke to the girl at the switchboard.

"Send in one of the boys from the back," I said.

Then I wrote two checks. One to Mama for thirty and the other to cash for five hundred. I put the first one in an envelope, addressed it, sealed it, and sat back to wait for the boy.

What if the wrist watch *had* cost four hundred bucks? So what? First of all, half of that was really coming out of Babushkin's pocket, although he didn't know it, which made *that* all right. And secondly, I wasn't even thinking about the price. Some dames are worth ten times that amount. Maybe not to other guys. But what the hell did I care about other guys? I figured like this: when I took, I took hard. And when I gave, I gave hard. If I took more than my share— well, there were some things you had to *give* more for than they were worth. Like Martha Mills. What if she *did* cost a lot? To *me* she was worth it. And until I got what I wanted I'd keep on giving, just as I'd keep on taking.

The boy came in.

"Yes, Mr. Bogen?"

"Take this down to the bank right away and bring back the cash," I said, holding out the check to him. "Get three hundred in twenties and the rest in tens." He took the check and I picked up the envelope. "And drop this down the chute on your way out. Step on it."

"All right, Mr. Bogen."

He went out and I lit a cigarette.

Love? Love my eye! Every one of these guys that goes around looking like he ate something bad and telling you how much he's in love with some tomato is either just shooting you a line of bull, or he's kidding himself. I don't mind when they shovel it at me, but when they throw the shovel at me, too, that's where I draw the line.

I thought of Ruthie Rivkin and I knew that something was cockeyed with my figuring. I got up and walked to the window. But watching the people and the cars passing in the street below didn't help. I knew I was right. I was positive about that. Then how about Ruthie Rivkin? It didn't add up. Where was the mistake?

I threw the cigarette out and lit another one.

"The hell with it," I said. "If I begin to think too much about it, I'll begin to think maybe I'm wrong."

And I knew I wasn't.

I went back to my desk and propped my feet up on the pulled-out top drawer. If it didn't add up, then the hell with arithmetic, that's all. I knew I was right.

Love? I knew what I wanted, and Martha Mills had it. And I was going to get it if it cost me ten times what I'd spent already. And it was going to be good, too. Because I could have gone through the whole chorus of *Smile Out Loud* and half of Broadway besides, for what she was costing me. But I didn't want the chorus of *Smile Out Loud*. I wanted Martha Mills. Do me something.

There was a knock on the door and the kid came in holding the check.

"What's the matter?" I said. "Where's the cash?"

"They wouldn't cash it, Mr. Bogen. The guy at the bank said—"

"They wouldn't *cash* it?"

"That's right, Mr. Bogen. The man said—"

"Why the hell not? Why wouldn't they—?"

"No funds, the man said. He said there wasn't enough in the—"

"Okay. Okay. Gimme the check." I grabbed it out of his hand. "Okay. You can go back to work."

The kid went out and I picked up the receiver.

"Send Miss A in here right away," I said. "Tell her to bring in the cash book and the checkbook."

She came in carrying the books.

"What the hell is this, Miss A?" I said, waving the check at her. "I tried to cash this thing and the bank tells me no funds. What the hell is this?"

"Well, I don't know, Mr. Bogen," she said, screwing up her lips. "My cash book shows a balance of—of"—she looked into the book—"of a little over eighteen hundred."

"So *little?* Eighteen hundred?"

"Well, it's the tenth of the month, Mr. Bogen." She didn't have to use that tone of voice. I wasn't as dumb as all that. I'd managed to graduate from kindergarten on my own brains. "We're always low at the tenth, because we pay all our bills then. In a couple of days, when the customers' checks start coming in, our balance is back to normal, that's all. It's always that way, Mr. Bogen, every month."

"Yeah? Then how about this?" I held up the check. "The bank said no funds."

"Well, I can't help *that,* Mr. Bogen," she said, screwing up her lips again. She was a whiz at it. "As far as I know I keep my books accurately and that balance is correct. If you keep on drawing checks on the outside, Mr. Bogen"— she shrugged—"without telling me about it, so I can enter it in my cash payments book and deduct it from my balance, *well,* Mr. Bogen." She shrugged again. That made two things she was good at. "In that case, Mr. Bogen, there's just nothing I can do about it, that's all."

"Oh. Yeah. Well, I did draw a couple of checks. All right, Miss A," I said. "You can go back."

"Will you give me a list of those checks you drew, Mr. Bogen, so I can adjust my books?"

"Oh, uh. I'll tell you what," I said. "I'll give you a total figure a little later in the day. I'll figure it up and give it to you later."

Before she went out she gave a last quick exhibition of all her talents. She screwed up her face *and* she shrugged. Well, I wasn't interested in her accomplishments. She was hired to be my bookkeeper, and if she displayed any more interest in appointing herself guardian of my private affairs, I'd get myself a new bookkeeper. Because I needed a bookkeeper, but I was perfectly capable of handling my private affairs.

I only hesitated a moment or so before I picked up the receiver.

"Miss K," I said, "remember that Mr. Maltz that used to call me up pretty regularly and I told you always to tell him I was out?"

"Yes, Mr. Bogen. He—"

"Well, let me ask you. Has he called me recently?"

"Yes, Mr. Bogen. He called you only last week."

"He did? All right, then, Miss K. I'll tell you what. See if you can get him for me, will you?"

"Yes, Mr. Bogen."

I hung up and lit a cigarette. It was a good thing I hadn't told him to go to hell. But it wasn't an accident. I don't get into fights unless it's to my advantage.

The phone rang.

"Hello?"

"Here's Mr. Maltz, Mr. Bogen."

"Put him on. Hello? Hello, Tootsie?"

"Yeah. Who's this, Harry?"

"Yeah."

"How are you, Harry?"

"Swell," I said. "And you?"

"I'm all right. Gee, I'm glad to hear from you, Harry. I been calling you for weeks and weeks, I guess. I didn't know—"

"I been out on the road a lot, Tootsie," I said. "I don't get much of a chance to stick around the city, you know."

"Yeah, I know," he said. "Well, gee, it sure is good to speak to you again, Harry." There was no mistaking the pleasure in his voice. I guess he was a nicer guy than I'd given him credit for being. "You all cured now?"

"Cured?" I said. "Oh, yeah, sure. I'm swell, now, Tootsie. Everything one hundred per cent, now. Believe it or not, the doctors gave me the old okay."

"Gee, that's swell, Harry. I mean it. I sure am glad to hear that. Let me ask you, how's business? I hear you're a big dress manufacturer now."

"Yeah," I said. "When I got back, after I was sick, a copla guys I knew, they sorta asked me to go in with them."

"You like it?"

"It's all right," I said.

There was a pause. I could feel that he wanted to say something, but that, of course, was his worry.

"I'll tell you why I called you, Tootsie," I said. I laughed
a little. "All of a sudden, from a clear sky, the bank tells me
I'm temporarily overdrawn. Can you beat that? Just for a
coupla days, till my collections come in, I'm short. And
I'll tell you, Tootsie, I was just wondering if you could sort
of, well, just for a coupla days, you know, if you could sort
of let me have a coupla thousand? You'd get it right back on
the thirteenth, the minute my collections come in. If you
want, I'll even—"

"Jesus, Harry," he said in a low voice, "you know I'd
gladly let you have it if I could. But hell, Harry, the delivery
business isn't what it used to be. I don't even know where the
hell I'm gonna get the money together for my payroll this
week, unless I get some of my accounts to anticipate their
bills."

I opened my mouth to begin to coax him, but I stopped.
I knew Tootsie Maltz. He wouldn't lie to me.

"That's too bad, Tootsie," I said. "Well, thanks anyway.
And call me up sometime, will you?"

His voice became excited.

"Harry!" he said. "Wait a minute, will you? Harry!"

"Yeah?"

"I don't like to bother you, Harry," he said slowly. "I
know you got your own troubles and all. But hell, I don't
know, Harry. Things've been pretty lousy around here for a
long time now. That's why I been calling you, Harry. I
guess I haven't got the head for these things that you have,
Harry."

"Look, Tootsie," I began. "I'm in a—"

This was no time to stop to gather compliments.

"Harry," he said, "Please. Couldn't you come up just
for a few minutes some day? I just want to ask you a coupla
questions and show you my books and all. You know. I
just want your advice, Harry. It wouldn't take you long.
Just for a few minutes, Harry. What do you say?"

"Well, gee whiz, Tootsie, I couldn't do it now. I've got to
straighten this thing out at the bank, you know."

"It doesn't have to be to-day, Harry," he said quickly.

"Any time'll be all right. I just want to ask you a few things. There's a lot of other guys in the business, now, and they're cutting prices and going in for new kinds of services and all —and gee, Harry, I just can't keep up with them." His voice became desperate. "I know you can straighten me out, Harry. You started this business. You know it from A to Z. It wouldn't take you long. A few minutes, Harry, that's all. You don't have to do anything. Just tell me what—"

"Listen, Tootsie. I can't do it now. I'm in a hurry."

"It doesn't have to be to-day, Harry. Any time is all right. Please, Harry."

"All right, Tootsie, all right. Some other time. I'll call you up."

"You won't forget, Harry, will you? It's important, Harry."

"No, no, I won't forget, Tootsie. Stop worrying about it."

"Gee, thanks, Harry. It won't take you long. You can just—"

"All right, all right," I said. "I'll call you next week."

"Thanks, Harry."

"It's all right, Tootsie. Forget it."

I jiggled the receiver. The switchboard operator got on.

"Yes, Mr. Bogen?"

"Get me Mr. Barnes at the bank," I said into the receiver and slammed it down. I wasn't worried. I was just sore. I knew we were in good shape. Our outstandings alone were four times our liabilities. And we had a good inventory, too. And we didn't owe the bank a nickel. And we had more orders on hand than we could fill. So I wasn't worried. But I was sore. Being temporarily short at the bank knocked my plans screwy for a couple of days. Well, I'd have to see to it that it didn't happen again.

The phone rang.

"Yes?"

"Mr. Barnes on the wire, Mr. Bogen."

"Put him on. Hello, Barnes?"

"Yes, Bogen, how are you?"

"Fine, thanks, and you?"

"I'm all right, thanks, Bogen. What's on your mind?"

"I'll tell you, Barnes," I said, "I sent my boy down to cash a check this morning and, heh, heh, believe it or not, we'd accidentally overdrawn our account."

"We-ell, Bogen, don't worry too much about it. That happens every once in a while to the best of us."

"Thanks, Barnes. I just wanted you to know about it and to tell you—"

"Oh, I knew about it, Bogen. In fact, I was just sending you a little note reminding you about it."

No wonder he hadn't acted surprised or worried. Judging from the tone of his voice, it couldn't be overdrawn such a hell of a lot.

"Well, what I wanted to say, Barnes, was that the reason we're overdrawn is that it's the tenth of the month and we paid our bills. But our receivables pay us at the same time, Barnes. In fact, those checks are in the mail to us right now. To-day is the tenth? To-morrow, the eleventh, or the day after, we'll have a big deposit down there, Barnes."

"That's quite all right, Bogen. We're not worrying."

I had to laugh at these *goyim* and their politeness. They aren't born smart, like Jews. And they know it and it scares them. So they figure out a substitute. They act like gentlemen to each other. They're polite all the time, so they can be sure one won't screw the other. Well, thank God I didn't need any substitutes for smartness. I didn't have to be polite, except for pleasure.

"Thanks, Barnes," I said.

"Nothing at all, Bogen. We know you're good."

That made two of us.

"Thanks, Barnes. 'Bye."

"Good-bye, Bogen."

I did some quick mental arithmetic before I picked up the receiver again.

"Get me Riverside 9-0437."

"Here's your number, Mr. Bogen."

"Hello, Martha?"

"Yes, dear?"

"Listen, kid. I've got to run out of town for a couple of days to see some buyers, and—"

"Oh, Harry!"

"Now, Martha, please. Don't take it that way. This can't be helped. But it's only for a couple of days. To-day is the tenth. I'll be back by the twelfth or the thirteenth at the latest. I'll call you up as soon as I get back, all right?"

"Oh, gee, Harry, and I was—"

She was really wasting her breath and that baby voice of hers, because I knew just exactly what she'd been thinking.

"Now don't you worry, Martha. This is just one of those things. And when I get back, we'll take a look at that roadster then. Okay, kid?"

"Okay, dear," she said.

30

For the first time in weeks I had nothing to do. I got up and walked around my private office for a few minutes. I punched the sofa pillows into shape and straightened a couple of pictures on the wall. I shifted the papers on my desk, but there was nothing there that needed my immediate attention. I started to walk out to the showroom, but stopped at the door and came back. There were more than enough salesmen out there already. I looked through my address book, but there was nothing in it I could use. Broadway was out for the next day or so. All I'd need, at this stage of the game, was to have her see me with somebody else. With me supposed to be out of town, yet, too. I stood at the window, smoking a cigarette, and tried to figure out what you *could* do while you were waiting for your collections to come in. Finally I fired the cigarette out of the window. Whatever happened, I wasn't going to spend my time sitting there, doing nothing.

I went into the back to find Babushkin.

"Meyer," I said, "you know those two dresses I asked you to make up for me a couple of days ago?"

"Dresses?"

Yeah, dope, the things we manufacture in our business.

"You know," I said. "Numbers 790 and 890. The two I wanted you to make up in an extra large size."

"Oh," he said. "The forty-fours."

"Yeah, that's right. You got them ready yet?"

"Wait a minute, I'll see."

He disappeared into the cutting room and after a few moments returned.

"They're all finished except for the slips. Why, you wanted them now?"

"Yeah, Meyer, I wanted them for to-night. Could you have them made up by about five-thirty or six to-night?"

"Sure, Harry. I'll tell one of the operators."

"Thanks, Meyer," I said. "And when they're finished, have them wrapped and put the box in my private office. Okay?"

"Sure," he said.

I stopped at the switchboard on my way back and said to the girl, "Get my home."

She hesitated a moment.

"Uptown?" she said. "Or—?"

"My mother," I said and went into my office.

When the phone rang I said, "Hello, Ma?"

But the girl at the switchboard answered.

"I'm sorry, Mr. Bogen," she said, "but there's no answer."

"All right," I said. "Keep trying it at regular five-minute intervals until you get it. I'll be in my office all afternoon. Send in the *News Record* and *Women's Wear,* will you?"

"Yes, Mr. Bogen."

"And while you're at it, send a boy out for the afternoon papers, too, will you?"

"Yes, Mr. Bogen."

I wondered what I'd do if one of them ever said, "No, Mr. Bogen."

When the papers came I didn't touch them. I let them lie on the desk while I sat with my legs propped up on the opened top drawer and smoked.

After a half hour I picked up the receiver again.

"How about that Intervale number?" I asked.

"I'm sorry, Mr. Bogen," she said. "I've been trying it right along, like you said, Mr. Bogen, but there's no answer."

"All right," I said. "Keep trying. And by the way."

"Yes, Mr. Bogen?"

"Send a boy out for a carton of cigarettes, will you? Take it out of the petty cash."

"Yes, Mr. Bogen."

I guess it was a reflex.

"Hello?" I said.

"Yes, Mr. Bogen?"

"*Yes,* Mr. Bogen," I said sharply.

"What?" she gasped.

"Nuts," I said, and hung up.

I figured I could smoke one cigarette every five minutes. That made twelve an hour. Therefore, when the phone rang, it must have been ten after five. Because I'd opened a pack at a quarter to four, and now there were three cigarettes left in the wrapper. I lit a fresh one and picked up the receiver.

"Hello," I said.

"Hello, Heshie?"

"Yeah, Ma." I flicked the freshly lighted cigarette out the window and sat up in my chair. "How are you?"

"All right," she said. "And you?"

"I'm okay, Ma."

She cleared her throat.

"Did you get my check, Ma?"

"Yeah, Heshie. I got it. Thanks."

"Everything is all right, Ma?"

"Everything is all right, Heshie."

"Anything you want, Ma?"

"No," she said, "nothing."

"Don't be bashful, now, Ma," I said. "And don't worry about my spending money. Anything I buy for you, I can get it for you wholesale, so don't worry."

"Thanks, Heshie," she said. "I don't need anything. If you want, if it's not too much trouble, you could send me

two or three small checks, instead of one big one. It's easier
that way for the grocery man to cash. But that's all. Only if
it's not too much trouble—"

"No trouble at all, Ma," I said. "I'll do that."

We were both quiet for a time.

"Where were you all afternoon, Ma?" I said. "I been trying to ring you since two o'clock."

"Couldn't be, Heshie," she said. "I only went out a little
after half-past two."

"Maybe I got the time wrong, Ma," I said.

"Must be."

"Where were you?"

"Where should I be? I went out in the park a little, to
sit in the sun."

"That's fine, Ma. I want you should take care of yourself."

"All right," she said.

"Keeping you busy these days, Ma?"

"With what? What should I be busy with? I don't even
have to cook any more."

"You want to cook, Ma?"

"What?"

"I mean, you'd like to cook to-night, Ma?"

She didn't say anything.

"Hello?" I said. "Hello, hello?"

"Hello."

"I said, Ma, would you want to cook to-night?"

"Sure," she said. "What's the matter?"

"I'm getting lonesome for a good meal," I said.

"You mean you'll—?"

"That's right, Ma," I said. "You cook me a meal to-night,
and I'll come home. And I'll sleep over, too. What do you
think of that?"

Damned if I wasn't working up an appetite already.

"You mean it, Heshie?"

"You bet," I said. "And not only that. You be a good
girl, Ma, and I'll bring you home—"

"Don't bring me no presents, Heshie," she said quickly. "I
don't want you should spend—"

"Who said I'm going to spend? You let me handle this, will you? You just do the cooking. Okay?"

"Okay," she said, and laughed at how funny the word sounded when she said it. I laughed, too.

"Say, Ma?"

"Yeah?"

"You know what I'd like to eat to-night?"

"Blintzes," she said.

"Right," I said. "Do I get them?"

"What a question! Of course!"

She sounded lonesome.

"Fine," I said. "I'll be right home."

"All right," she said.

"Good-bye, Ma."

"Good-bye, Heshalle."

I walked into the back, whistling, to look for Meyer.

"Those dresses ready yet, Meyer?"

"A few minutes, Harry. The boy is wrapping them," he said.

I waited until they were folded into the box and tied and took them. I went into my office for my hat and stopped at the switchboard on my way out.

"I'm leaving for the day," I said to the girl.

She looked at me, a bit frightened, and said, "Yes, Mr. Bo—"

I put my hand on her lips quickly and grinned.

"Save it for to-morrow," I said, and went out.

I got a seat in the subway, but I gave it to a woman at Ninety-Sixth Street. I like to do things once, just to see how they make you feel.

One mistake I almost made, though. I was a good block past the bakery on the corner of Daly Avenue and 180th Street before I remembered about the cheese cake and the *Stollen*. I went back and bought them.

When I turned into Honeywell Avenue I saw her leaning out of the window, watching for me. I shifted the packages to one arm and waved to her with my free one. She waved back and I quickened my step.

She opened the door and threw her arms around me without a word. I kissed her several times and then lifted her bodily, packages and all, and carried her into the kitchen.

"Heshie!" she said, when I set her down.

"In person, Ma," I said. "How's the girl?"

"Fine," she said, "and you?"

"I didn't feel so good in the morning, but I feel okay now."

"What's the matter?"

"I was hungry for blintzes."

She laughed and took the boxes out of my hands.

"Let me see what kind of foolishness you went and spent your money on now."

The first package she opened was from the bakery. She broke off a corner of the cheese cake, the way she always did, and nibbled at it while she smiled happily.

"You never forget your mother, hah, Heshie?"

"You bet, Mom," I said. "Just take a look in the other box."

She dusted the crumbs of cheese cake from her fingers and opened the second box.

"I've got so *many* dresses already, Heshie," she said, "I don't know when to wear them all. You didn't have to spend money—"

"I didn't spend any," I said. "I had these made up for you in the place."

"Yeah, sure," she said derisively. "You had them made up in the place! Since when such a high-class firm like yours, they make dresses this size, big like elephants?"

"We don't," I said. "But for you, Mom, we make anything. I wanted you to wear the same kind of dresses the young girls wear, and they should still be built for you, not for somebody thinner, so they don't fit."

For a moment her face took on a serious look.

"Dresses don't help, Heshie," she said quietly.

"Yes, they do, Ma," I said. "Everything helps."

She folded them back into the box and said, "Thanks, Heshie."

"That's all right, Ma," I said. "Forget it."

She went out of the room to put the dresses away, and I went to the gas range. Nothing was on the fire.

"Nothing cooking yet, Ma?" I asked when she came back into the room. "I'm starved."

"Don't worry," she said, glancing at the clock. "You won't die from hunger. It's not even seven yet. So we'll eat a little later to-night, so what'll be?"

"Nothing," I said with a laugh. "I was just hungry, that's all."

"So all right," she said. "Come on, you'll help me."

I rolled up my sleeves and she tied an apron around me.

"Boy," I said, "if some of those buyers could see me now!"

"So what do you think would be? Such a terrible thing it isn't."

"Who said it's terrible? I even like it, for crying out loud."

"Yeah, you like it. Well, for being such a big liar," she said, "here, you can peel the potatoes."

We worked in silence for almost a half hour, but it wasn't as much fun as I'd expected it to be. After a while my thumb began to hurt from pushing the back of the knife across the potatoes. And I was getting hungrier by the minute. But I didn't say anything. She seemed happy and contented, smiling to herself as she worked, and once in a while at me. But she didn't work fast and I didn't want to rush her. She looked at the clock two or three times, and by the time the blintzes were almost ready, she began to look a little worried.

Promptly at eight the doorbell rang, and her face cleared. Even before she answered it, I understood why she had been stalling the meal, and I knew who it was. And I decided, in those few seconds between the ringing of the bell and the sound of voices out in the foyer, that I wasn't going to make a scene, either. Because it didn't matter any more. The old magic no longer worked. I wasn't worried. I knew I could handle myself.

Mother led me into the kitchen, smiling.

"Look who I invited to supper, Heshie."

"Hello, Ruthie," I said, taking her hand, and smiling.

"Mom didn't tell me you were coming. If I'd known, I'd've kept my coat on."

"That's all right," she said, smiling back. "You don't have to stand on ceremony for *me,* Harry."

I let the smile on my face freeze into a slightly sarcastic grin. Then, slowly, I lit a cigarette, holding her eyes with mine through my cupped hands and the faint haze of smoke and flame from the match. She dropped her eyes and blushed. I wiped the grin off as I turned toward Mother to drop the match into the sink.

"Come on, Ruthie," Mother said, putting her arm around her. "Come and take your things off."

While they were out of the room I got an idea. I knew that unless I did something, this thing would drag on forever. Since mother, apparently, didn't believe me when I said no, the trick was to scare the pants off her candidate. Knocking her off would have done the trick, but since, for reasons that I *still* couldn't figure out completely, that had been a flop, there had to be another answer. And I thought at that moment that I had it.

"You know, Ma," I said when they came back into the room, "if we don't get something to eat pretty soon, not only will I starve, but the whole damn evening'll be killed, too."

"A guarantee that you won't starve," she said, "I can give you. And for the other, tell me, you got something better to do to-night than to sit here at home with us?"

"That's not the idea, Ma. Maybe Ruthie and I want to go out some place, or something like that? When are we going to go, eleven o'clock?"

Mother's face brightened at once.

"Oh," she said, "why didn't you *tell* me you and Ruthie had a date?"

"Did you ask me?" I said, winking broadly at Ruthie.

She blushed and said, "Oh, Harry, I don't know if we should leave your mother all alone like this—?"

Mother pushed her into a chair playfully.

"Don't be a dope," she said. "An old woman like me, I got something better to do than to sit listening to the radio—

you saw the new radio, Ruthie, that Heshie bought me?—
and read the *Forward?*"

"Well, you could start dishing out blintzes," I said. "That
would be better than reading the *Forward.*"

"We'll see how hungry you are when the food is on the
table," she said, and began to serve.

Mother did most of the talking during the meal, and
Ruthie did most of the listening. I had plenty of time to
observe her. This time it was curiosity. After to-night I'd
probably never see her again. So I thought I might just as
well try to see if I could figure her out. Because while I
knew, now, that I was safe from whatever it was about her
that had made me forget temporarily what my eyesight and
my intelligence told me, still, I had to admit, she was an
unknown quantity. It was one thing to get wise to the fact
that a soft face and a gentle smile were making a sucker out
of you. It was another thing to look beneath the skin and
the smile to figure out why you knew they weren't fake.

And looking at her as she smiled and nodded at Mother, I
had it. Aside from that warmth and gentleness that drew you,
there was nothing. She had no more personality than Babushkin, maybe less. At least he stood out in your mind as a
dope. But when you thought of Ruthie Rivkin you thought
of a gentle, warm smile. You didn't think of a person. She
was a lump of meat with an attractive cover.

Coming to that conclusion made me feel a little better
about what I was going to do. And it made it easier to face
the job. But it was worth spending one lousy evening to get
rid of her for good and all.

"You sure there's nothing I can get you, Ma?" I said as
we stood in the doorway, ready to leave.

"Positive," she said. "Only remember, Heshie, don't forget
the address here where you live."

"Don't worry, Ma," I said. "I'm coming home to-night.
And if you're a good girl, I'll stay home all day to-morrow,
too. What do you think of that?"

"*Hoo-hah!*" she said, shaking her head. "You sure you
feel all right?"

"Of course I feel all right."

I pinched her cheek.

"Have a nice time," she said.

I was glad that wasn't an order.

"We will," I said.

"Good night, Mrs. Bogen," Ruthie said.

"Good night, Ruthalle," Mother said, touching her arm for a few seconds.

In the street Ruthie said, "Maybe we shouldn't have left your mother alone like that."

"Don't be silly," I said. "She likes it."

We walked toward 180th Street and turned right, going toward the subway.

"Where would you like to go?" I said.

"Oh, I don't care," she said slowly. "Any place you want to go."

Some day she'd actually prod that brain of hers into a suggestion, and I'd drop dead from the shock.

"Well, I'll tell you," I said. "I haven't been to Coney Island for a long time, now. What do you say we take the subway out there and give the place a whirl?"

She looked startled, but didn't say anything. I grinned to myself.

"That okay with you?" I asked.

She nodded.

"Let's go, then," I said.

I took her arm to help her cross the gutter, and then released it. At the foot of the subway station I bought two papers and we climbed the stairs.

"You want one of these?" I said, offering her one of the papers when we were settled in our seats.

"No, thanks," she said.

I shrugged and turned to my paper. All the way downtown I read. Once or twice I glanced at her out of the corner of my eye. She was sitting quietly, staring straight ahead of her, her eyes unblinking. Good, I said to myself. Maybe she was getting wise, finally.

At Forty-Second Street we got out and changed to the

B.M.T. I offered the paper to her again, but she shook her head slightly and smiled. I guess I should have got her a picture book. I folded the paper and put it under the seat. Then I opened the second paper and read that clear out to Stillwell Avenue.

"Well," I said, "here we are. Any particular thing you want to do first?"

"It doesn't matter," she said.

"Suppose we get over to the boardwalk, then," I said.

We crossed Surf Avenue, went past the concessions, and climbed the incline to the boardwalk. It was a comfortably cool night, with a light, steady wind blowing in from the ocean. The boardwalk was crowded, but not badly. We edged into the stream of people moving up the boardwalk slowly, and walked along, listening to the barkers roaring their spiels into microphones that sent them out so loud that they didn't make sense.

Aside from the job I had to do, I was glad I'd come. There was something about the craziness of the place that got me.

"How about a drink of something?" I said.

"All right," she said.

We stood in front of a stand and drank root beer. A custard-making machine caught my eye. I bought two cones and gave her one.

"The idea is to suck it around the sides, near the cracker," I said, "so it shouldn't run over on your hands and clothes."

She laughed a little.

"I'm afraid I won't—" she began.

"Oops," I said, grabbing it out of her hand quickly. "Watch it. You almost had it all over your dress, there."

She took out a handkerchief and brushed away a small spot that had landed on her hem.

"Weren't you ever out to Coney Island before?" I asked.

She shook her head.

"What?"

"That's right," she said. "I was born in the Bronx."

"Oh, well, that accounts for it," I said.

Hell, that could account for anything.

"Me," I said, "I was born on the East Side. Coney Island? This used to be heaven to me."

"I guess that's why I don't know how to eat custard," she said with a laugh.

Look at her! She learned how to talk!

"Here's how," I said, holding the cone far out toward her. "I'll hold it and you lick at it till you had enough. All right?"

She nodded quickly and leaned forward to peck at the mound of loose ice cream that kept melting and running down the sides.

"Enough?" I said.

"Enough," she said, wiping her mouth delicately with her handkerchief.

I threw the rest of the cone away and took her arm.

"Let's go."

We walked for a few minutes until a shooting gallery struck my eye.

"Uh-oh," I said. "Here's where we're stopping for a while."

I paid for two clips and leaned my elbow on the counter. I'd pumped out a dozen shots before I noticed that she hadn't touched her gun.

"Say, aren't you shooting?"

She laughed and showed the white teeth that always looked so startlingly hard between her full lips.

"I'm afraid I don't know how, Harry," she said.

"C'mere," I said, taking her arm and pulling her toward me. "You hold the gun like this, and rest your elbow here."

I got behind her and put one arm around her left side, to help her support the gun, and my other arm around her right side, to help her with the trigger.

"Now you look through this little dingus here, this V. That's right. Till you see that little raised point, that little dot at the end of the gun—that's it—till you see that dot right smack in the center of the notch in the V. Get it?"

She nodded, her eyes squinting and her lips parted.

"Then you hold it that way, the raised dot in the middle of the V, and point it, without letting that dot get out of the

V, at anything you want to hit. How about that bell there? No, take something easy. Take one of those ducks, the white ones. That's it. Now you keep that dot in the middle of the V pointed right at that duck and then you pull the trigger—like this."

The slight recoil of the gun threw her back against me, gently, and her cheek brushed mine. I didn't want to believe it, but right then I wouldn't have taken the short end of any bet, no matter what the odds, that I wasn't *blushing!*

"Now try it yourself," I said.

"Did we hit it?" she asked.

"I—uh—hell," I said, laughing, "I forgot to look."

I picked up the gun and said, "We better try it again, then. And this time, *you* sight it and pull the trigger. I'll just help you hold it."

I put my arms around her again, steadying the gun, and feeling her warm body against me. Just before she pulled the trigger her body tensed up and the shot went cockeyed.

"Here," I said, "you better try it all by yourself. You certainly can't do any worse than with me helping you."

I dropped another quarter on the counter and the man handed me another loaded gun.

"Now just do as I told you," I said, "and shoot for the same things I do. I'll call them out to you."

We stood at the counter together for a half hour, side by side, pumping away at swinging targets, bells, candles, moving ducks, clay pipes, until she could actually hit something once out of five or six tries. I waited until she knocked down one of the ducks moving across a small pond in the middle of the gallery, and put my hand on her gun.

"This is a good place to quit," I said, "on a hit. My back aches already. How about yours?"

She stood up and placed both hands far back on her hips and stretched, with a pained smile on her face.

"Oh, my!" she said. "That *hurts.*"

"I know just the thing for that," I said, winking.

"Yeah, what?"

"A hot dog."

"For a *back*ache?"

"Sure," I said. "The idea is to eat enough of them till you get a bellyache, and then you don't feel the backache."

"Oh, Harry!" she laughed.

I laughed, too. But I couldn't help wondering what the hell I was finding so funny in a joke as lousy as that one.

We had some hot dogs and potato chips and grape juice before she cried quits.

"Why, this is only the beginning," I said. "Come on, have some more."

"I can't," she said. "Honest, I'm full."

"Well, then," I said, "you'll just have to sit and watch me. And take my word for it, Ruthie, it's no fun watching me eat. You better get something, too."

She put her hand to her mouth and shook her head.

"Oh, I can't, Harry," she said. "I couldn't eat another thing."

"Well, don't say I didn't warn you," I said.

She began to laugh as I downed a hamburger and an ice cream sandwich on waffles.

"Goodness," she said, "what a combination! And it's not kosher, either, you know, Harry. Ice cream and meat."

I pretended to be shocked.

"You mean it? Gee, that's terrible. Well, I'll just have to cut out the ice cream, then."

After a few more items, she began to look worried.

"Harry," she said, "I really think you ought to stop. You'll ruin your stomach."

"I know it," I said, "but do I love this junk!"

"But Harry—"

"All right," I said, "no more. Come on."

"Where to?"

"Steeplechase, the funny place, where, if I remember correctly, my dear Ruthie, for a fifty-cent combination ticket, you can ride on fifty—yes, sir, no less than fifty—fifty separate and distinct rides. You can try the—"

"Oh, Harry, I don't know if—"

"What's the matter, little girl? You aren't scared, are you?"

She nodded quickly, looking up at me from under lowered brows.

"Holy smoke," I said, and let out a loud laugh. I slapped my thigh and put my arm around her, squeezing her to me gently. "Come on. Now we're first going to have fun."

She held back a little, but I pulled her along, laughing and kidding her.

The next hour was so fast and giddy I couldn't keep track of it. We tried everything on the combination tickets, and some we paid to try again. At first she was scared stiff, holding my arm tightly and screaming in a low voice when we hit the turns or the dips. But gradually she got used to it and even went down the biggest drop on the Sky Ride with a happy laugh.

When we got out on the boardwalk again it was almost midnight. We stood there, catching our breath, and laughing at each other for no good reason.

"I must look a sight," she said, trying to straighten her hair.

"Here's a mirror," I said.

We stood in front of a chewing-gum vending machine and I held her hat and purse while she combed her hair and straightened her dress.

"My," she said when she finished. "That feels better."

I put my arm through hers and we walked back toward Stillwell Avenue. But this time we were on the outside of the boardwalk, the side near the water, and the crowd, moving at the other side near the concessions, a mere thirty or so feet from us, seemed far enough away to be almost out of sight. We could hear the barkers and the music and the moving people, but the low rolling of the waves on the beach seemed louder.

"Let's rest for a few minutes," I said.

We sat down on one of the benches that faced the water and I lit a cigarette.

"Tired?" I said.

"A little," she said.

"We'll just sit for a while," I said, "and then we'll go home. This place isn't so bad at night. But it's terrible during the day. At night you can't see the dirt."

She didn't say anything.

"Maybe you want a drink or something?"

She shook her head.

"Sure you don't want anything?"

"Well—" she said.

"Well what? Come on. Just say it and I'll get it for you."

"I guess it's silly in a way," she said slowly, looking out at the ocean carefully. "But I just thought I'd like to—"

She stopped.

"You'd like to what, Ruthie?"

"When you go out with other girls," she said, still looking ahead of her carefully, "do you—I mean, Harry, do you take them here, to Coney Island?"

I dropped my cigarette and ground it out carefully.

"Why, I guess so," I said. "Once in a while, I suppose. I mean, not lately. I've been too busy in my business. But I guess once in a while—I mean, it's— Say," I said, turning to face her, "what's on your mind, anyway?"

"Nothing," she said; then, quickly, "maybe I'm a fool, Harry, but you know what I wanted to do? Once, just to see, well, just to see what it's like, I'd like to go to a night club."

"A night club?"

"Yes."

"What does a nice girl like you want to do in one of those joints?" I said. "There's nothing to see. You just sit around and drink and maybe watch some dumb toma—some dumb dames without much clothes on dance and sing and maybe —well, that's about all. What do you want to go to one of those places for?"

"I've never been, that's all," she said. "I suppose you're right, though, Harry. Forget it. I just thought—"

Forget it was right. But like a damn fool I was already checking my list mentally, trying to remember one that wasn't

too conspicuous. And on top of that an idea about Babushkin, something that I'd been trying to puzzle out for days,
suddenly came to me. One moment I was trying to think of
how I could avoid taking Ruthie Rivkin to a night club. The
next moment a knotty problem about the office came to me,
all solved, on a silver platter. Hell, I had to be grateful,
didn't I?

"If you really *want* to," I said.

She shrugged, slightly embarrassed.

"I was just wondering," she said. "Other girls, they seem
to get—"

"All right," I said suddenly, "come on. I'll take you."

We walked off the boardwalk at the next street and got
into a taxi. I gave the driver the Fifty-Second Street address.
We sat together quietly during the long ride, but I didn't
touch her. When we drew up in front of the place I paid
the driver and prayed like hell that nobody I knew would
recognize me.

We went in and I asked the waiter for a small table at
one side.

"What'll you have, Ruthie?"

"I don't want anything," she said, looking about her.

I ordered steak sandwiches and beer, but she didn't touch
hers. I watched her as I ate.

"Not much to see, is there?" I said.

She shook her head, still staring about her with a puzzled
expression on her face.

I glanced around quickly myself. The place was crowded,
but I didn't recognize anybody. A Cuban band in long-
sleeved shirts began to play. Some of the musicians stood
up, shaking gourds and rattles and showing their white teeth
as they grinned. A thin, dark-haired girl in a low-cut dress
came out from somewhere and stood in front of them, singing
in a language I didn't understand, and wiggling her hips and
her tits in a way that nobody could fail to understand.

"That's all there is to these places?" Ruthie said.

"That's all," I said. "Just what you see. Some of them

are bigger, of course, and more expensive. But that's all. When you've seen one, you've seen them all."

She still had the puzzled frown on her face.

"Then what is it, Harry, that these other girls—when they get taken out by a fellow—he takes them to—?"

She stopped and took a sip of water.

"What is it what?" I said.

"Oh, nothing," she said. "I guess I *was* being silly, asking you to take me to a place like this."

"Why, there's nothing wrong, Ruthie. I could take you any place you want. You want to go to another night club? Come on, I'll show you another one."

"No, that's all right, Harry," she said quickly. "I don't want to go to any more. If you don't mind, Harry, I'd like to go home now."

"Sure," I said, "come on."

In the taxi I put my arm across the back of her seat and let my hand stroke the soft warm flesh of her cheek. But that's as far as I went. At her door we both got out.

"Wait for you, bud?" the taxi driver said.

"No," I said, and paid him.

We stood on the doorstep for a few moments, without speaking.

"Well," she said, finally, "I had a lovely time. Thanks, Harry."

"I'm glad you did," I said, taking her hand.

"Well—" she said awkwardly.

I dropped her hand. I felt scared as hell.

"I'll tell you what I'll do," I said suddenly. "Suppose I call you up in a day or so? All right?"

That's how you scare the pants off a girl!

"All right," she said, smiling quickly.

"Good night, Ruthie," I said.

"Good night, Harry," she said, and ran up the steps lightly.

I walked up the block slowly. When I reached the first lamp-post I stopped and said, "Jesus Christ!"

What the hell was the matter with me? With a dame like that I'd actually had a good time!

31

On my way to my private office I stopped at the bookkeeper's desk.

"Good morning, Mr. Bogen."

"Morning, Miss A. How are the collections?"

"Fine, Mr. Bogen. Look."

She held up a batch of checks. I took them and leafed through for a glimpse of the larger amounts. They were there.

"Anybody slow with us?"

"Just a couple, Mr. Bogen, but they're small ones."

"Well, get after them. What's to-day, the thirteenth?" I looked behind me at the calendar.

"That's right, Mr. Bogen, the thirteenth."

"Well, even if the mails are slow, their checks should've been in by now. Send them a letter or two, and if they don't come through with them, turn them over to Golig for collection. He knows what to do with those birds."

"Yes, Mr. Bogen."

I slapped the checks down on the desk and said, "How much are we depositing, roughly?"

She twisted her lips and said, "Oh, I don't know, Mr. Bogen, I haven't figured it yet, but about nine, ten thousand, maybe a little more."

"Well, all right, Miss A, get busy on that deposit, will you? I want that money in the bank in twenty minutes."

"In twenty *minutes,* Mr. Bogen?" She looked at me with her mouth open and her hands spread out. "Why, I got all my posting and—"

"That stuff can wait," I said. "Or you can put one of the other girls on it. What have we got four girls in the office for?"

"But Mr. Bogen—!"

"Get that deposit down to the bank in twenty minutes," I said. Who did she think she was talking to, Babushkin? "I told Barnes I'd have a deposit in before ten in the morning, and I want it there. Understand?"

"Yes, Mr. Bogen."

"All right," I said. Then, "Is Mr. Babushkin in the back?"

"Yes."

"Tell him I want to see him in my private office right away."

"All right, Mr. Bogen."

I went into my room, hung up my hat and coat, and sat down at the desk. There was a knock on the door and Babushkin came in.

"Hello, Meyer," I said. "How are they hanging?"

"What?"

"Nothing. How are you?"

"I'm all right," he said. "You wanted me, Harry?"

"Yeah," I said, lighting a cigarette and waving him to a chair. "Sit down. How are things coming in the back?"

"All right, Harry. Things are all right."

"Everything under control, eh? The orders being filled on time?"

"Oh, sure, Harry. Everything's fine."

Ah, hell, I figured. What was the sense of wasting time? Being subtle with him was like giving J. P. Morgan a tip on the stock market.

"I'll tell you why I called you in, Meyer," I said. "I been looking over the accountant's reports, you know, and I'm afraid, Meyer, I'm afraid we're making too much money."

He squinted his eyes at me a little more.

"We're making too much money?"

"Sounds crazy, doesn't it?" I said with a laugh. "But it's true just the same, Meyer. I don't mean we're making too much for ourselves. Hell, we can *never* make too much for ourselves. But I just mean we're making too much money for the government."

"For the government?"

"Sure," I said, "for the government. You've heard of the income tax, haven't you, Meyer? Well, if they ever get a squint at the money we're making, it'll just be good-bye Charlie. What we'll have to pay them in taxes, don't ask!"

He rubbed his hand over his mouth and stared at me. "So what'll we do?"

"I'll tell you," I said. "I've figured out a plan to beat the government. Have you got a personal bank account, Meyer?"

"Yeah, I got in the savings bank a—"

"I don't mean that, Meyer. I mean a regular checking account. You got one of those?"

He shook his head. What I would've liked to have seen was this baby and Coolidge in a gab fest.

"That's fine," I said. "Now here's my plan, Meyer. You open up a personal bank account in your name in the Manufacturers. We're in the National, the firm I mean, so to keep things straight, you open up this personal account in the Manufacturers. Now here's how we work it. The corporation, Apex Modes, Inc., the corporation draws checks to your order. You take those checks, endorse them, and deposit them in your personal account in the Manufacturers. Then you draw checks on your personal account, you draw them to the order of cash, endorse them, get the cash for them in the bank, and you and I, we take that money for ourselves. See what I mean, Meyer? In that way we'll be drawing money out of the business, and nobody'll know how or why or what. If the tax men ever ask us where the money from the corporation checks went, we just tell them we used it to buy goods, to pay labor, or any one of those things, and we say we paid cash for it. See?"

He stared at me without blinking for a few moments, and then started on his favorite indoor sport, picking his nose.

"Do you get what I mean, Meyer?"

He nodded slowly, but that part of his face that wasn't hidden by the hand he was using on his nose still looked worried.

"Let me repeat it again, Meyer," I said. "Here it is, in a nutshell. You open personal account. Corporation draws checks to you. You deposit checks. You draw checks to cash

on your personal account. You endorse checks. Get cash.
You and I, we split the cash. Government gets a royal screwing. Understand?"

"Yeah, Harry," he said slowly. "I understand all that all
right, but how—?"

Wouldn't that jar you? For a week he'll act like a mummy,
then when he does open up, the first word out of his mouth
is the wrong one. I wasn't answering any questions beginning
with the word how.

"That's fine," I said, breaking in on him. "So suppose we
get started. I'll have Miss A draw a check to you for a thousand dollars and you can go right down to the Manufacturers
and start your personal account."

He continued to stare at me without moving.

"What's the matter, Meyer? Don't you understand how
it's gonna work out? You want me to explain it again?"

"I understand all right, Harry," he said. "But what I don't
see is how—"

"Listen, Meyer," I said sharply, "you're not trying to pull
any of this Teddy Ast stuff on me, are you?"

"Why, no, Harry. What's the matter you're—?"

Boy, did I know my customers! All I had to do was raise
my voice to him and he started crapping green.

"Well, gee whiz," I said, raising my voice and slapping my
desk. "You'd think I was asking you to go jump off the roof
or something. For crying out loud, Meyer, all I'm asking you
is to start a personal bank account with firm money, that's
all. Is that something to make speeches about? Do I have to
write you a whole *megilla* about a little thing like that? I
haven't got all day, Meyer. I've got buyers to see and dresses
to sell. We can't sit around all day talking. Do you understand what I was talking about, or don't you? If you want me
to explain it again, I'll do it. But for God's sakes, don't—"

"All right, Harry, all right. Don't get excited. Couldn't you
just wait a day or so? I mean, I'd like to have a chance to—"

I wondered if he even asked his wife which side of the bed
to get out on in the morning.

"For crying out loud, Meyer," I said angrily. "Don't you understand plain ordinary English? If I didn't make myself clear before, I'll try again. I've got buyers to see. And I've got dresses to sell. I can't sit around all day on my ass waiting for you to make up your mind, Meyer."

Nor could I wait for him to go home and ask his wife about it. She'd probably have sense enough to tell him what to do.

"All right, Harry," he said. "I just didn't—"

"Okay," I said.

I picked up the receiver and spoke into it.

"Send Miss A in here with the checkbook," I said.

Maybe I didn't get boffed when I went out with Ruthie Rivkin, but I certainly got some swell ideas.

When Miss A came in I said, "Did that deposit go down all right?"

"Yes, Mr. Bogen," she said. "I sent one of the boys down with it only five minutes ago."

"All right," I said. "Now draw a check to the order of Mr. Babushkin for a thousand dollars."

"A thousand?"

"Yes, a thousand."

She leaned the book on the desk and wrote the check. Then she tore it out of the book and handed it to me.

"All right," I said to her, "you can go."

When she left, I turned to Meyer.

"Endorse this on the back," I said, "and go right down to the Manufacturers and start an account. Remember, start it in your name, personally, Meyer Babushkin. Get it?"

He nodded and took the check.

"I'll tell you what," I said. "I've got some work here, so I'll be sticking around for about an hour or so. Go right down and when you come back, drop in here for a minute and tell me about it. Okay?"

"Okay," he said, and went out.

Boy, oh, boy, oh, boy, I said to myself, did I have a partner!

32

Miss A stopped me on my way through the office.

"Oh, Mr. Bogen."

"Yes?"

I was at the other end of the office, and she was at her desk. But I didn't walk over. I was paying her, and if she wanted to speak to me, she'd come over to me, not me to her. Besides, I was still tired and sleepy.

"Well, well, what is it, Miss A, what is it?"

She came over with her desk diary.

"We've got some very big piece-goods bills due to-day, Mr. Bogen."

"So what? Pay 'em, that's all."

I turned to go.

"But Mr. Bogen—"

I turned back.

"How much do they amount to? Who are they?"

She read from the diary.

"D. G. Dommelick fifteen hundred, Commercial Textile Factors eight hundred, Mandel Laces twelve hundred, Sanson and Huber—"

"What's the cash balance?"

"Twenty-five hundred."

"What?" I looked at her quickly. "Twenty-five hundred? That's all?"

She squeezed up her mouth and said, "That's all, Mr. Bogen. Twenty-five hundred."

"Why, we deposited over twelve thousand on the thirteenth and fourteenth, didn't we? And we had more collections later, didn't we?"

She screwed her squeezed up mouth all the way around to one side and picked up the checkbook. Then she read from the stubs, as though she enjoyed it. "Well, last week Mr.

Babushkin drew two thousand dollars, and two days ago he took another fifteen hundred and then the week before that there were, let's see, there were—"

The girl at the switchboard looked up and interrupted. "Miss Mills on the wire, Mr. Bogen," she said.

"I'll take it inside," I said, then, "No, wait, give it to me here."

I picked up the phone on Miss A's desk and said, "Hello, Martha. All right. Yeah, sure. Any time you say. What? It did? I'll tell you what. Don't you worry about it, Martha. I'll call my own garage and have them send a man over to look at it for you. Okay? That's all right. What? Sure. You bet. Any time you say. You know me. Fine. Okay, then, kid. I'll pick you up right after rehearsal. About two, two-thirty. 'Bye. *What?* What was that?"

"I said," she said sweetly, "I hope you won't stand me up for any Bronx housewives."

"Where did you—? What the devil are you talking about, anyway?"

"Nothing," she said. "Only a couple of nights ago, in Dumb Dick's, I saw you—"

"You didn't see *me,* Martha," I said with a laugh. "Not me, kid. Because I was out of town, see?"

"I guess it was somebody else, then," she said slowly.

"It *was,*" I said emphatically. "You made a mistake, see?"

"I suppose so," she said quickly. "But anyway, Harry, dear, you wouldn't stand me up for a Palestine import, would you?"

"Not for the whole country, kid," I said. "You know that."

"Then it's a date," she said.

"Right," I said, and hung up.

The little sharp-eyed bitch!

I turned back to Miss A.

"Where's Mr. Babushkin?"

"Somewhere in the back, I guess."

I turned to the door that led to the factory.

"What about these bills, Mr. Bogen?" Miss A said, holding up the diary. "Mr. McKee of Dommelick called you twice about them."

"Ah, the hell with them," I said, waving my hand at her. Then I stopped and turned back. "No, wait, Miss A, I'll tell you what. Send them each a couple of hundred dollars on account. Send D. G. Dommelick five hundred and the rest three."

"All right, Mr. Bogen," she said, "but what about the others?"

"What others?"

"We've got some smaller bills that are due."

"Let them go to hell," I said, putting my hand on the doorknob. "They can wait."

Before I could pull the door open, it moved in toward me and Babushkin came into the office, carrying some papers.

"Hello, Meyer," I said, "I was just going to look for you," I said.

"Good morning, Harry," he said. "Just a second."

He walked over to one of the other girls, dropped the papers on her desk, and said, "Call the express company and tell them to put a tracer on this charge." Then he turned to me. "You want me, Harry?"

"Yeah, Meyer," I said, "I've got an appointment with some buyers and I'll need some cash."

I sat down at Miss A's desk, opened the checkbook, and wrote a check for five hundred dollars. She watched me over my shoulder.

I stood up and said, "Come on down to the bank with me, Meyer, will you? I've got an appointment with some buyers this afternoon and I want to get this cashed."

"All right, Harry," he said, "I'll go get my coat."

"But Mr. Bogen," Miss A said, "you just made an appointment with Miss Mills. You just spoke—"

"Just don't worry too much about it, Miss A," I said, shaking my hand at her. "You just make those payments like I told you."

"Yes, Mr. Bogen," she said.

"All right, Meyer," I said, turning back to him, "step on it, will you?"

"Sure, Harry, I'm just going in for my coat."

"All right, Meyer, but put a little jism into it, will you? Let's get down to the bank. I've got to see some buyers."

33

I woke up with a headache, and the first thing I thought of didn't help it any. The little bitch. What did she think I was buying her wrist watches and automobiles for, so I could practice penmanship in my checkbook?

I went into the bathroom for an aspirin. The bottle was empty. Just a well-ordered household. "That's for you, you little whore," I said, and fired the bottle into a corner of the room. One of the splinters backfired and nicked my leg. The iodine burned like hell, and the tape wouldn't stay put. I ripped it off and yelled, "Ouch." Two inches of skin and a fistful of hair came off with it.

Halfway into my pants I decided I wanted to wear my cordovan shoes. They weren't in the shoe cabinet and they weren't in the closet. I bit my lip and said, "All right, Mr. Bogen, you're going to wear cordovan shoes to-day if you have to rip the leather off the window seats and make yourself a pair." I started in one corner of the bedroom and worked my way systematically. Anything I looked into or under, and didn't find them, I kicked over. When my right foot felt sore I started with my left. I found them under the sofa in the living room when I tipped that over. I held them in my hand and looked around the place. The only things left standing were a small vase that had set me back thirty bucks in Ovington's and a framed picture of her on the mantelpiece. I picked up the vase and heaved it. The picture went down with a crash, and I felt a little better. Anyway, my aim was still good.

In the middle of knotting my tie the phone began to ring. I let it ring until I finished with the tie and buttoned on the vest. Then I picked it up, but I didn't speak.

"Hello? Hello? Mr. Bogen?"

It was the girl at the switchboard in the office.

"What do you want?"

"Who's this, Mr. Bogen?"

"Who the hell does it sound like, the King of England?"

"Whuh, whuh—! Mr. Bogen? Is this Mr. Bogen?"

"Yeah, yeah, yeah! This is Mr. Bogen. For Christ's sakes, what do you want?"

"Mr. Babushkin told me to call you at home. He's been looking for you all morning, and when you didn't come in, he said I should call—"

"Tell Mr. Babushkin not to strain his milk."

"What?"

"Ah, nuts! Tell Mr. Babushkin I'll be down a little later," I said, and slammed the receiver onto the hook.

I didn't have enough troubles, I had to have that little pyoick calling me up on the telephone.

On the way out of the building I stopped to talk to the starter.

"Tell the super to send a couple of maids up to straighten out my apartment. I got in too late last night to tell him about it, but the place looks like a cyclone hit it."

"Why, Mr. Bogen—"

"I haven't got time to listen to speeches about it. Just tell him I'd consider it a personal favor if the help used somebody's else's apartment for their crap games while I'm out."

"But, Mr. Bogen—"

"You heard me," I said. "And you can tell him if it happens again I'm moving out, lease or no lease."

I took a cab to the barber and slipped into my regular chair.

"Try to remember my face is covered with skin," I told the ginney, "not asphalt."

"Sure thing, Mr. Boge', I never cut—"

"And save the talk for somebody else," I said. "I got a headache."

"You got a headache, Mr. Boge'? Special for you, Mr. Boge', I give you, my steady customer, I give you free a massage, it'll take away the headache, Mr. Boge', one, two, three."

"Just shut up for a change," I said.

When I got out it was still too early to go down to the office. First of all I was in no mood to face that phiz of Babushkin's, and secondly, I wasn't getting down there so soon after he called me, anyway. I wasn't giving him or anybody else the impression that I was taking orders.

I took a cab to the tailor.

One of the fitters was in the small front room.

"Good morning, Mr. Bogen," he said, looking surprised.

"Where's Caruso?"

"Mr. Caruso is out now, Mr. Bogen."

"What does he think he's running, a night club? Why doesn't he stick around to take care of his customers?"

"Why, he's, he's out taking a fitting, Mr. Bogen. You didn't have an appointment, did you, Mr. Bogen?"

He reached for the appointment book and began to turn the pages.

"Where's my brown herringbone? Is it ready?"

"Ready?" He looked at me with his mouth open. "Why, you only had the measurements taken two weeks ago, Mr. Bogen! It won't be ready for another *week,* Mr. Bogen!"

"Oh, no?" I lit a cigarette, but it tasted lousy. I dropped it on the rug and stepped on it. "I want to wear that suit to-morrow, see?"

"But Mr. Bogen—"

"Never mind," I said. "Never mind. You can tell Caruso from me if that suit isn't delivered at my place to-day he can take it and stick it up his ass and holler fire."

I went out and slammed the door before he could Mr. Bogen me again. Boy, did I feel mean!

I stood on the curb and chewed my lip. I wasn't sore at the dough I'd spent. Not too sore, anyway. Hell, there was acres of it where the rest had come from. What made me sore was that I couldn't figure out what she was driving at. What was she holding for? What did she want me to do, get down on my knees, or send her an engraved invitation—? An engraved invitation? Say! Was *that* what she was holding out for?

The idea hit me so suddenly, and it seemed like such a perfect explanation, that for a minute I didn't know whether to laugh or get more sore than I was. But I didn't spend much time worrying about *that*. Because I knew right then and there just about how far she'd get with *those* ideas. What was she doing, stealing Ruthie Rivkin's stuff?

Maybe I was right, and maybe I was wrong. But one thing was sure, I said to myself. She was going to come through. This just made it a little more interesting, that's all. Whether she had that in her mind or not, she was going to come through, either which way. And it was going to be within the next day or so, too. I was getting a little sick of this stalling and spending three-quarters of my day trying to figure out what was going on in her mind.

Can you imagine the nerve of a little pot like that? Holding out for marriage? Jesus Christ and the gas company!

No wonder she was getting fancy ideas. Instead of concentrating on her, I had to go around wasting my time in the Bronx.

What the hell was the sense of kidding myself? You couldn't blow hot and cold at the same time. You took one or the other. You couldn't have both. It didn't work. You couldn't reach for a Martha Mills and let yourself be distracted by a dumb squash that smiled pleasantly. You couldn't reach for the big dough and listen to your mother's lessons in morals.

All of a sudden I felt sore. What the hell was I going to do, sit on a fence the rest of my life? The hell with Ruthie Rivkin. And Mama? What was *she* doing for a living?— making me blintzes? She could stay up in the Bronx where she belonged.

From now on I was traveling in a straight line. Without

any excess baggage, either. And the first stop was Martha Mills.

Making up my mind like that made me feel better already. I spit into the gutter and yelled, "Taxi!"

One of them swung out of the stream of traffic and stopped in front of me.

"Fourteen Hundred Broadway," I said.

All the girls looked at me as I went through the office, but I didn't say anything. I went into my private office, threw my hat and coat on the couch, and reached for the telephone. Before I could pick it up, Babushkin came in. This time he didn't knock. Maybe I'd been wrong after all. Maybe he wasn't a gentleman.

"Gee whiz, Harry," he said, "I been looking for you all morning. I didn't know where you were. I called your home even."

"What's the matter? What's all the excitement about?"

"I can't get any goods, Harry," he said, spreading his hands. I'd never seen him talk so fast. "Nobody wants to ship. I called up Dommelick, I called up Mandel, they all tell me the same thing. They say Apex is slow. How can we be slow, Harry, with all the business we're doing?" He waved a batch of papers. "Look at these orders, Harry. I got orders to fill, and I can't get goods to cut! What's happening, Harry? I gotta have goods, Harry! I gotta fill the orders! What's this business all of a sudden, we're slow? How can we be slow, Harry, with all the business we're doing, all the money we got coming—?"

"Take it easy, will you, Meyer? Don't get so excited."

"But Harry, we got orders! If I don't get no goods, how can I cut the dresses—?"

"Who'd you speak to? Who said we're slow?"

"All of them, Harry. Dommelick, Mandel—"

"Aah, they're nuts," I said, getting up and patting him on the back. "Stop worrying about it. Let me handle this."

"But Harry, we gotta get the goods or—"

"You'll get the goods, you'll get the goods," I said, guiding him to the door. "Just let me handle this."

As soon as the door closed behind him I went to the phone and called Martha.

"Listen, Martha," I said, "I haven't got much time to talk now. A couple of big buyers are in the showroom waiting for me. I'll pick you up to-night right after the show. I've got something important to talk to you about."

"Important?" she said. "Couldn't you—?"

Sure I could. But not on the phone. Boy, was that baby going to get an earful of straight talk!

"I'll tell you when I see you," I said. "Right after the show. All right?"

"All right, dear," she said.

"So long, kid," I said. "I'm in a hurry."

I jiggled the hook.

"Yes, Mr. Bogen," the girl said.

"Get me Mr. McKee, the credit man of D. G. Dommelick."

"Yes, Mr. Bogen."

Pause.

"Hello? Hello, McKee?"

"Talking."

"This is Bogen, McKee. Bogen of Apex Modes."

"Oh, yes. How are you, Bogen?"

"Fine. Listen, McKee, what's this I hear about you not wanting to ship us? What is it, a gag?"

"No gag, Bogen. I'm sorry, but it's true."

"Why?"

"Your account has been slow for months, Bogen. And we've checked you way above your credit limit. I'm sorry, Bogen, but we can't send you another yard of goods until we get a check."

"Don't be like that, old man. We've got orders to fill. Send us the goods, and you'll get a check on the tenth. What do you say, McKee?"

"Sorry, Bogen, it's no dice."

"Look here, McKee. You can't do a thing like that to us. Why, we've done over seventy-five thousand dollars worth of business with you during the past year, haven't we? After doing business with you like that, don't tell me you're going to cut us out just because we're slow on one bill, are you, McKee?"

"It's not one bill, Bogen, and you know it. You've been slow with us for months. We've carried you, but we can't do it any longer. Your balance is too big right now, as it is."

"Oh, come, now, McKee. Be a sport, will you?"

"Sorry, Bogen. With somebody else, maybe we would. But there's no room for fine feelings in the way *you* do business, Bogen, and you know it."

"Aah, now, McKee, listen. You—"

"No go, Bogen. The way you wrote your contract, there's no room for that. You wrote the rules, Bogen, remember that. We're just playing your way, that's all."

"Oh, come on, McKee. Don't tell me you're still holding against me those allowances we took last year. I'll tell you what. I'll send you a check on account right away. I'll put a check for five hundred in the mail right away. What do you say?"

"Sorry, Bogen. That's all you've been giving us for months, just on-account payments. We want a check in full, to clean up your balance immediately, or we don't ship."

"But McKee—!"

"Sorry, Bogen. Not an inch of goods till we get your check."

All of a sudden, while I was holding the phone in my hands, it occurred to me that here I was, begging, actually *begging,* a thick-headed Irish *putz* like that to sell me goods. The realization that I was crawling in front of anybody made me so sore, that for a few seconds I couldn't talk straight. But when I spoke, it was in a low, clear voice, so he shouldn't miss a word.

"You know what you can do, McKee?" I said.

"What?"

"You can go right straight to hell," I said. "I'll get all the goods I want from some other place."

I wanted to say a lot more, but I didn't have time. I had to beat him to the punch. I slammed the receiver down on the hook. Nobody was going to slam receivers down on *me*.

34

As I got into the elevator, I had to laugh a little to myself. Not that I was in what you could call a happy frame of mind. But it was a little funny, the way the whole thing was working out, just like in a movie. I'd even gotten to the stage where I was buying her a diamond bracelet!

But that's as far as the similarity went. Because while I'd been willing to let her think I was a rummy and she'd been taking me over, I had my limits, too. The bracelet was the last payment. And as a payment it was going to be strictly C.O.D.

I knew that once I got my mind concentrated on this thing it would begin to work out. I should have done it long before, instead of wasting so much time. Now, if she wanted the bracelet, she knew what she had to do. I'd made *that* plain. No tickee, no shirtee.

I had to admit, though, that there was a little pleasure in that laugh, too. There was a certain satisfaction in knowing that you could actually afford to go out and *buy* a diamond bracelet. I liked milestones like that.

But even that little bit of pleasure was knocked out of me when I saw the elevator pass my floor.

"Twenty-nine!" I said sharply.

"Sorry, sir," the operator said, giving me a look out of the corner of his eye. "You have to call your floor, sir."

That was a nice way to start off a morning. You can always count on some eighteen-dollar-a-week punk to put you in a nice cheerful frame of mind. You pay ten thousand dollars a year for a loft, and the elevator operators don't even remember what floor you're on. But when Christmas comes around they're there with the gimme act. Well, wait till Christmas came. I'd get him a gift. A fur-lined jockstrap I'd get him. The little jerk.

"I'll stop on the way down, sir."

"Thanks," I said. "That's goddam nice of you."

I opened the door into the showroom and stopped. Half a dozen credit men were standing around Babushkin, all talking at the same time.

"Well, well, well," I said, grinning at them from the doorway. "Good morning, gentlemen. What is this, a convention?"

They turned around quickly, and looked at me. I recognized McKee of Dommelick and Hazzard of Mandel. Before I could spot the others, Babushkin let out a cry and came toward me.

"Harry!"

In all the time I'd known him, this was the first time I'd ever seen him look happy.

"What's going on here?" I said, coming into the showroom. "What's up?"

He opened his mouth to tell me, but the others beat him to it.

"Gentlemen, *please!*" I said, holding up my hand. "One at a time."

"Look here, Bogen—"

It was McKee talking.

"We-ell! Good morning, Mr. McKee," I said, bowing a little toward him and smiling. "I'm glad to see we're still on speaking terms. No hard feelings, eh?"

He clamped his teeth around his cigar so hard that his face looked like it was made out of little crossword puzzle squares.

"Cut the comedy, Bogen," he said out of the other corner of his mouth.

"Okay," I said, running my hand over my face and wiping off the smile. "Look how serious I am!"

"Harry!" Babushkin cried, "they say—"

"Listen, Bogen," McKee interrupted.

"That's my specialty," I said, turning back to him. "What do you want?"

"We want our money," one of the others said.

"Yeah, we want our dough."

"You're way past due," McKee said. "We want our bills paid."

I looked around at all of them, and then back at McKee.

"You'll get your dough," I said.

"Yeah? When?"

"The same as you always got it. In a couple of days, when my collections come in. What are you guys hollering about? You'll get your dough."

"Yeah? We been hearing that for a long time, Bogen."

"We want it now."

"We want checks, Bogen, and we want them now."

I looked at them quickly, hesitating. But in a moment I had made up my mind. This was no time to crawl. There was only one way to play this.

"That's just too bad about you guys," I said. "You'll get your dough when my collections come in, and not before. How do you like that?"

McKee took the cigar out of his mouth and took a step toward me.

"I'll tell you how we like it," he said. "We're calling a creditors' meeting this afternoon."

"Suits me," I said. "Call a meeting and I'll show you guys that this is a one hundred per cent liquid business. You'll get your dough. What are you guys hollering about? What am I all of a sudden, the first dress manufacturer on Seventh Avenue that was ever slow in his payments? Go ahead, call your meeting. I'll be glad of the chance to show the whole creditor body the kind of a business we got here. Go ahead. Call your meeting for to-morrow morning first thing."

"Nothing doing," McKee said. "This afternoon."

"I can't make it to-day," I said. "Make it to-morrow morning."

Can you beat that? Here I am on the home stretch, I've got an appointment with Martha to go pick out the bracelet, so of all the days in the year, these bastards have to pick this day to get tough!

"No, Bogen," McKee said, "that meeting is for this afternoon."

"Sorry, gentlemen. I've got an appointment with a buyer this afternoon. Make it for to-morrow morning, and I'm with you."

Babushkin put his hand on my arm.

"Go ahead, Harry. Make it for this afternoon. Let's see what's what. Make it for this afternoon, Harry."

"Your partner's right, Bogen. You better be there this afternoon."

If those rummies thought I was going to take the chance of ruining a four months' foundation by letting them throw me off my stride *now,* they were crazy.

"Listen, you guys," I said, talking tough. "We've got thirty thousand dollars' worth of sun tan dresses on the racks. I've got an appointment this afternoon with the buyer for the biggest mail-order house in the country. Just remember that it's getting on toward the end of the summer. If we don't move those dresses off our racks now, they'll never move. And if we get stuck with all those dresses, then you guys'll be up the creek for good. You'll *never* get your dough. This buyer is interested and it looks like she'll take the whole lot. She's making a Chicago train at three o'clock this afternoon. To-morrow is too late. Buyers don't wait, and you guys know it. That's why I can't go to that meeting this afternoon. You guys call that meeting for to-morrow morning, any time to-morrow, I don't care, and I'll be there."

"Nothing doing, Bogen. We're on to your tricks. That meeting is for this afternoon."

"Well," I said with a shrug, "that's just too bad about you guys. Because I'm not gonna be there."

"Oh, no? If you're not there, Bogen, it's going to be just too bad about *you,* not us."

"Yeah?"

"Yeah."

"Don't frighten me, gentlemen. What are you gonna do, kidnap me and carry me there?"

"We don't have to kidnap you, Bogen. If you're not at that meeting this afternoon, we'll put you into bankruptcy."

"Aah, stop the oil, will you? Who do you think you're talking to, a kid?"

"I'm warning you, Bogen. If you're not there, we're going to file a petition against you."

"Go ahead, file!" I said, tipping my hat back on my head and waving my hand at them. "You guys can't bluff me. This business is liquid and we can pay one hundred cents on the dollar. You guys aren't scaring me."

"We're warning you, Bogen."

"Stop the crap, will you?" I said. "You're losing weight."

35

The ringing of the telephone woke me. I looked at my watch. Twenty after seven. Who could be calling me at this hour? I took the receiver off the little table beside the bed.

"Hello?"

"Hello, Harry? Who's this, Harry? Is that you, Harry?" It was Babushkin, his voice full of excitement.

"Yeah, Meyer, it's me. What's the matter?"

"Oh, thank God, Harry. I been trying to get you since last night. Why didn't you come back to the office? Where were you all night? I been ringing you all night till after one. I thought maybe I'd get you in if I called this morning, so I—"

"For God's sakes, Meyer," I cried. "Stop hollering like that. I'm not deaf. What happened? What are you talking about?"

"They filed a petition, Harry. They—"

"They *what?*" I yelled.

"They filed a petition like they said they'd—"

"Why, the dirty son of a bitches!"

"Harry! Harry, what—?"

"Meyer!" I said sharply. *"Meyer!"*

"Yeah, Harry, what—?"

"Shut-*up!*" I barked, "and listen, will you?"

"All right, Harry, what—?"

"Shut-*up!*" I shouted. "And *listen,* will you?"

No answer.

"Hello? Hello, Meyer?"

"Hello," he said in a lower voice.

"Where are you now?" I asked.

"Home."

"When were you in the place last?"

"Yesterday in the afternoon. Right after the meeting. I went back. I thought maybe you'd be there, Harry. I wanted to tell you—"

"What happened at the meeting? They ask you any questions?"

"Yeah, they—"

"What'd they ask? What'd they ask you?"

"All about the business. They asked about the orders, how many we had on hand, how much stock we had, how much was out at contractors, how—"

"Anything else?"

"Yeah, a few other things. Nothing special, just a few things about—"

"They ask anything about withdrawals?"

"Withdrawals?"

"Yeah, yeah, withdrawals. They ask anything about us taking out any money, or anything like that?"

"No, Harry, they didn't—"

Well, that was something.

"All right, Meyer," I said. "You can tell me the rest when I see you. Right now, just listen. You listening?"

"Yeah, Harry, I'm—"

"All right," I said. "You're home now, right?"

"That's right, Harry."

"It's now"—I looked at my watch—"half-past seven. How long does it take you to come down from the Bronx?"

"I don't know, a half hour, maybe a little longer, maybe a little less. Why?"

"Well, say a half hour," I said. "Don't you leave the house until eight or a few minutes after, understand? Then come right down to the place. That means you ought to get there about eight-thirty. Right?"

"Yeah, I suppose so."

"All right," I said. "When you get there, don't speak to anybody. Keep your mouth shut and don't say a word. Just go right into my private office. I'll be waiting there for you. Understand?"

"Yeah."

"So remember, Meyer, before I hang up. Leave your house at about eight, and when you get to the place, don't talk to anybody, *nobody,* understand? Just go right into my private office. I'll be there. Okay?"

"Okay, Harry."

"Now, remember, don't talk to anybody."

"Okay, Harry."

"Okay," I said, "I'll see you at eight-thirty."

I hung up and hopped out of bed. I picked up the house phone and spoke to the doorman. "Get me a cab. I'll be down in ten minutes. Have it waiting for me."

I dressed quickly, but carefully. I don't care what's going on, I still don't like to look like I went to sleep in my clothes.

"Fourteen Hundred Broadway," I told the driver. "Go over to Broadway, and then down. Stop at the first newsstand."

The first two didn't have it. But I knew one of them further downtown would have it.

"Got a *Daily News Record?*" I asked at the next one.

"Yes, *sir.*"

"All right," I told the driver. "Now Fourteen Hundred."

Not that I thought Babushkin was kidding or anything like that. But I just didn't think they'd really do it. I thought they were trying to bluff me. There it was, though, on page six, under Business Troubles.

> APEX MODES, INC. 1400 BROAD-
> WAY. Harry Bogen, Pres. An invol-
> untary petition in bankruptcy was filed
> yesterday against Apex Modes, Inc.,
> manufacturers of women's and misses'

evening wear. The petitioning creditors were D. G. Dommelick & Co.,
$12,039.50, Mandel Laces, Inc., $8,-
422.29, and Commercial Factors Corp.,
$5,500.00. The creditors' committee,
headed by Earle J. McKee of D. G.
Dommelick & Co., has retained the ac-
counting firm of Seidman & Turletzky
to make an audit of the books of the
debtor concern. Liabilities are esti-
mated at $80,000.00.

The showroom door was locked, but I had a key. As I opened it, the Holmes signal went off. A man in a derby, with a cigar in his mouth, jumped up from the couch when I came in.

"Hey, there," he called, "where do you—?"

"It's okay," I said, walking over to the Holmes box and giving the answering signal. "Keep your pants on. My name is Bogen. I'm the president of the firm. Who're you?"

"I'm the custodian. You can't—"

"It's okay," I said, "it's okay. Just don't get excited. I'm not walking out with anything. Here's my card."

While he read it, I went into the office. I sat down at the switchboard and dialed a number. There was no answer. It was still too early. I reached for the telephone book to look up his home number, when the board buzzed. I plugged in.

"Hello," I said.

"Hello? Who's this, Bogen? That you, Bogen?"

"Yeah, Golig. I just called your office. But there was no answer."

"Yeah, well, listen. I was eating breakfast just now, and I was looking through the paper, and I saw it. I called you right away."

That's the kind of a lawyer to have.

"That's fine," I said. "I'm glad you called. Can you come right down here?"

"Sure."

"How soon can you be here, Golig?"

"What time is it now, ten after eight? I'll just call one of my girls at her home and tell her where I'm going, and then I'll come right down. I'll be there about half past, maybe a few minutes later, maybe twenty to nine."

"Okay, Golig," I said. "I'll be here waiting. I'll have Babushkin here, too."

"All right. How does it look, Bogen?"

"I'll tell you when I see you," I said. "But don't worry about a fee, Golig. I've got *that* salted away."

"I wasn't worrying about it, Harry." Maybe he wasn't. "I'll be right down."

For the next call I connected an outside wire to my private phone and went in to make it. I closed the door and sat down at my desk and dialed Riverside 9-0437.

She answered the phone right away. And her voice was wide-awake, too.

"Hello, Martha?"

"Yes, Harry."

Her voice was something else besides wide-awake. It was a perfect ad for an electric refrigerator.

"I'll tell you why I called you, Martha."

"Why?"

"We'll have to postpone that shopping trip for a couple of days," I said. "In fact, I won't be seeing you for a little while."

"I thought that's why you called," she said.

Apparently she read the papers, too.

"Interesting little paper, the *News Record,* isn't it?" I said.

"It's not bad," she said. "It gives you the news. Short and sweet."

"Well, don't believe everything you read, Martha."

"No?"

"No-o-o," I said, spreading the word out. "When I see you in a few days I'll give you the real story." And something else, besides.

"I'll bet it'll be good."

"You can place that bet," I said angrily. "You won't lose any money on it."

Who the hell was she, to start kicking?

"If that's a guarantee," she said, "you'd better put it in writing. According to the *Daily News Record,* your word isn't so good to-day."

"It's good enough for me," I said, and slammed the receiver down.

There was a commotion out in the showroom. I opened the door to take a look. Babushkin was arguing with the custodian.

"It's all right," I said. "He's my partner. Come on in, Meyer."

I closed the door and locked it.

"What are we gonna do, Harry? I don't understand it. How could a thing like this happen, so all of a sudden? Everything looked so all right. What are we gonna do?"

"Don't worry about it," I said, pushing him into a chair. "Everything is gonna be okay. I just spoke to Golig and he's coming right down. Don't worry about it."

"But Harry, what are we gonna do? What'll we say when—?"

"You don't say anything, Meyer. Let me do all the talking. If they ask you any questions, you don't know from nothing. You were the factory man and I handled all the finances. You don't know a thing. These crazy bastards think they got us up against the ropes, but they haven't. Wait'll the accountants finish with the audit. There's a hundred cents on the dollar here and more. We're solvent and the figures'll show it. You take my word for it, Meyer, the first time this thing comes up for hearing, the petition'll be dismissed. So don't worry about it."

"But Harry—"

"Now, Meyer, please. Don't get excited. And just listen to me carefully. They haven't got a thing on us and they won't find anything, either. Because the figures and the books are absolutely one hundred per cent. There's nothing to be afraid of. The only thing they might question you about, is those checks we drew and deposited in your personal account. But don't worry about it. If they ask you any questions, you just say we used it for expenses. For payroll. And for things like that. That's all. If they ask anything else, you just don't know. You were the factory man, that's all. Understand?"

He shook his worried face up and down.

"So don't worry about it so much," I said, patting him on the shoulder. "Just remember those two things. If they ask about the personal account in the Manufacturers, we used the cash to pay bills and payroll. They ask you anything else, you just don't know, that's all. Tell them to ask me. Understand?"

"I understand, Harry."

"All right," I said, "let's go."

I helped him up and unlocked the door. The custodian was standing in the showroom arguing with Golig.

"It's all right, there," I said, walking toward him and moving Babushkin along with me.

"What the hell is *he?*" the custodian said, shaking his head toward Golig, "one of your partners, too?"

"No," I said, "he's my lawyer. He's all right. Let him in."

Golig walked toward me, and I put my hand on Babushkin's shoulder once more.

"So you got that straight, Meyer," I said, "haven't you?"

"Yeah, Harry," he said, shaking his head. "Okay."

"Fine." I turned to Golig. "Come into my private office, Golig," I said.

36

From my seat between Babushkin and Golig at one side of the medium-sized room, I looked around. A long table stretched down the middle, with chairs all around it. And at the far end, at a desk set at right angles to the table, his back to the windows, a heavy-set, good-looking *goy,* with gray-streaked hair, was bent over, writing busily.

"Is that the Referee?" I asked Golig in a whisper.

"That's him," Golig said. "John E. James in person."

"He looks like a *putz* to me."

"Yeah? Well, don't kid yourself, Harry. He's as smart as they come. Just don't get wise. Answer all questions respectfully, understand?"

I nodded and continued my inspection. The man who sat at the end of the table, to the left of the Referee, was a stenographer. I could tell that by the pens and ruled paper and bell-shaped ink bottle he was laying out. But the little guy who sat facing him across the table, the one that looked like Ben Turpin, had me stopped.

"Who's Handsome Dan?" I asked Golig.

"That's Josh Siegel. He's the attorney for the petitioning creditors."

"You mean he's going to examine?"

Golig nodded.

I began to feel a little better. I had expected a courtroom, with a judge and a jury and what not. Instead, we were in this single room, on the eighteenth floor of an ordinary office building on Pine Street, surrounded by as choice an assortment of heels as you could find anywhere. I felt so relieved, that when I caught McKee's eye, where he sat among other creditors across the room from me, I even smiled at him. He didn't smile back.

At about ten o'clock the Referee stopped writing and looked up.

"What matter is this?" he asked.

"Apex Modes, Inc." the stenographer said. "Twenty-one-A examination."

"All right. Go ahead."

Golig picked up his brief case and moved over to the table, facing Siegel. He spread his papers and sat back.

"Mr. Harry Bogen," Siegel called.

I got up and walked to the chair at the head of the table, to the right of the Referee, facing the stenographer.

"Raise your right hand," the Referee said. I did. "Do you

swear to tell the truth in the matter of"—he glanced down at
the papers in front of him—"in the matter of Apex Modes,
Inc.?"

"Yes," I said.

"Proceed," the Referee said.

I sat down.

"What is your full name, Mr. Bogen?" Siegel asked.

I told him. I didn't like his snotty voice right from the
start. But I remembered what Golig had said. I answered
respectfully.

"You are an officer of Apex Modes, Inc.?"

"Yes."

"What office do you hold?"

"President."

"You were in constant touch with all the affairs of the
business, were you not?"

"I don't quite understand what—"

"I mean, Mr. Bogen, you knew just what was going on all
the time, didn't you?"

"I suppose so," I said with a shrug.

"What do you mean, you suppose so? Don't you know?"

"Well, to such a general question, it's a little hard to give a
positive—"

"Well, all right," he said, waving his hand. "Let's put it
this way, Mr. Bogen. What particular functions, I mean, what
were your special duties, Mr. Bogen, in the business?"

"I was the salesman."

"You were the salesman. Were you a salesman exclusively?
Did you have any other duties?"

"Oh, I sort of watched over things generally, you know."

"You mean, Mr. Bogen, do you not, that you were sort of
the financial man, you—"

Golig jumped up.

"I object, Your Honor. The witness has made no such
statement. I object to Mr. Siegel's—"

"Sustained," the Referee said in a bored voice. I looked at
him quickly, but he seemed to have his eyes closed.

"All right," Siegel said, rubbing his mustache. "I'll withdraw that. Mr. Bogen, who took care of the finances of the business?"

"Why, what do you mean?"

"Don't you know what the word finances means?"

I opened my mouth to say something, but I caught Golig's eye, so I shut up.

"Sure," I said, "but if you'll be more specific, I'll—"

"Well, who arranged for loans from the bank? Who arranged for lines of credit with the various silk houses? Who—?"

"Oh, I did all that."

"You did." He turned to his papers and looked at them for a moment. "What was Mr. Babushkin's status in the firm? I mean, what were his duties—?"

"I object, Your Honor," Golig said, getting up. "It is not for this witness to say what Mr. Babushkin—"

"Mr. Referee," Siegel said, interrupting him, "this man was the president of the firm. He ought to know what his partner—"

"Overruled," the Referee said in his slow voice. "The witness will answer the question."

Siegel looked at me and I said, "Will you repeat the question, please?"

He waved at the stenographer.

"Read the question to the witness."

"What was Mr. Babushkin's status in the firm?" the stenographer read. "I mean, what were his duties?"

"Answer the question, Mr. Bogen," Siegel said.

"He was the factory man," I said.

"What does that mean?"

"He was the factory man. He took care of the factory. He did the designing, the styling, he supervised the cutters, the contractors, all that stuff."

"Did he have anything at all to do with the finances of the Company?"

"Not to my knowledge."

"What do you mean, not to your knowledge? Don't you know?"

"Well, I—"

"I object, Your Honor," Golig said.

"All right, all right," Siegel said before the Referee could speak. "I'll withdraw that." He turned back to me. "Then I take it that so far as you know, Mr. Babushkin had nothing whatsoever to do with the finances of the Company?"

"That's right."

He questioned me for an hour, about the business and how it was run. Plenty of times I was taking careful aim to see if I could spit right into his eye from where I was sitting, but I remembered Golig's advice and answered respectfully. In a way, I was even enjoying it a little, the way I could control the whole room by what I said. If I answered in a certain way, I could keep the room quiet, but if I wanted to play a little dumb, or answer in another way, I could get them all excited. I began to understand why lawyers have such big cans. They get flattened out from jumping up and down on them to make objections.

Finally, at about eleven-thirty, Siegel picked up a batch of checks from among his papers on the table, and turned to me.

"Mr. Bogen," he said, "I show you now a series of—" Then he stopped. "Never mind that," he said to the stenographer. "I withdraw the question." He turned back to me. "That's all, Mr. Bogen."

"Any questions?" the Referee said, turning to Golig.

"No questions," Golig said.

I got up and walked back to my seat against the wall.

"Mr. Meyer Babushkin," Siegel called.

Babushkin got up and walked to the witness chair like a guy who has lost a bet and is on his way to kiss somebody's behind in Macy's front window on a busy Saturday at noon.

Siegel put him through the paces, the same as he had done to me. The only difference was that from Babushkin he got more respectful answers. Because Babushkin probably didn't even know how to be disrespectful if he wanted to. And even if he did know, right then he was so scared that he never could have remembered how.

Suddenly Siegel turned back to the table, picked up the same batch of checks he had started to show me, and waved them under Babushkin's nose.

"Did you have a personal bank account, Mr. Babushkin? I mean an account other than the firm bank account?"

"Yes, sir."

"What bank was that account in?"

"The Manufacturers."

"Have you still got that account there?"

"I think so. I don't know."

"What do you mean, you don't know?"

Golig jumped up.

"I object, Your Honor, to Mr. Siegel's browbeating the witness. He has answered the question. He said he didn't know. He's never gone through bankruptcy before, and for all he knows, he thinks his personal bank account was seized along with the other assets of the firm. How should he—?"

"Mr. Referee!" Siegel shouted. "I object to my learned adversary leading the witness and putting words in his mouth. If he has any objections, let him state them in the approved lawyer-like way. I ask Your Honor to instruct Mr. Golig to refrain from cleverly putting answers into the mouth of the witness by means of long-winded objections. Let him—"

"That's enough, gentlemen," the Referee said quietly. "We'll have no colloquy between attorneys. If there are any objections to be made, make them in the customary manner. Proceed."

"Read the last question," Siegel said to the stenographer.

"Question: Have you still got that account there? Answer: I think so. I don't know. Question: What do you mean, you don't know?"

"Well, Mr. Babushkin," Siegel said, "what do you mean, you don't know?"

"I thought maybe, I thought maybe they, they took it away from me, like they took, you know, like they took everything else."

Siegel gave Golig a dirty look. Golig smiled at him.

"When did you start this personal account of yours, Mr. Babushkin?"

"About two, three months ago. I don't know."

"Would it refresh your recollection if I were to show you a transcript of your account with the bank?"

"I—I don't know."

"I am reading, if it please the court, from a transcript of the account of Meyer Babushkin with the Manufacturers Banking Company, furnished by the said Manufacturers Banking Company, and indicating that—"

"I object, Your Honor," Golig cried. "I object to Mr. Siegel's reading from any papers that have not been introduced into evidence."

"All right," Siegel said. "I offer the transcript in evidence."

"And I object on the ground that it is incompetent, irrelevant, immaterial, and not binding on the parties."

"Let me see it," the Referee said. Siegel handed it to him. He looked at it for a moment, then handed it back. "Objection overruled," he said. "Mark it in evidence."

"Exception," Golig said and sat down.

The stenographer marked it and handed it back to Siegel.

"I am reading, Mr. Babushkin, from Trustee's Exhibit One of this date. The first entry on this transcript is a deposit of one thousand dollars and it is dated May fourteenth of this year. Is that the date on which this account was started, Mr. Babushkin?"

"I guess so."

"Don't you know?"

"If it says so, it's so."

Siegel put down the transcript and picked up the batch of checks.

"If Your Honor please," he said, "I have here in my hand, and wish to offer in evidence, a series of thirty-one checks, all drawn by Meyer Babushkin on his account in the Manufacturers Banking Company, to the order of Cash, all endorsed by Mr. Babushkin on the back, all running in consecutive numerical order from number one to number thirty-one, indicating that they were taken from the same checkbook, each check drawn in the round sums of five hundred, one thousand, or fifteen hundred dollars, and the entire group of thirty-one checks aggregating a total of thirty-two thousand five hundred dollars. I offer this group of checks in evidence as one exhibit."

"Same objection," Golig repeated.

"I offer them subject to connection, if Your Honor please," Siegel said.

"Same objection," Golig repeated.

"Same ruling," the Referee said.

"Exception," Golig said.

Besides Siegel there were two other people in that room who knew what his next move was going to be. They were Golig and myself. And I had told Golig.

Siegel picked up a second batch of checks and said, "I now offer in evidence, if Your Honor please, a *second* group of thirty-one checks, drawn on the *corporation* bank account of Apex Modes, Inc. to the order of Meyer Babushkin, each one endorsed by Meyer Babushkin, and deposited by him in his *personal* bank account in the Manufacturers Banking Company. These checks are drawn in identical amounts with those in Trustee's Exhibit Two of this date, and total, similarly, an aggregate of thirty-two thousand five hundred dollars. I offer this *second* group of checks in evidence as one exhibit."

"Same objection," Golig said.

"Same ruling," the Referee said. "I'll take it subject to connection."

"Exception," Golig said.

After the stenographer finished marking the checks in evidence, the Referee stood up.

"We will adjourn until two o'clock," he said, and walked out.

Golig and I grabbed Babushkin and hustled him out to a restaurant. He said he wasn't hungry, but I didn't allow myself to be influenced by that. When I'm hungry, I eat.

"Remember, Meyer," we told him before we went back, "he hasn't got a thing on us. He thinks he has, but he hasn't. He's gonna ask you a lot of questions about what you did

with the cash you got after you deposited the corporation
checks in your personal account, but you just remember
what we told you. You used it to pay bills, to pay labor, and
things like that. Understand?"

He nodded.

We were right. We? Well, *I* was right.

As soon as Babushkin was back in the witness chair, Siegel
picked up the checks.

"Mr. Babushkin," he said. "Trustee's Exhibit Three of
this date represents a series of checks issued by Apex Modes,
Inc. to you and deposited by you in your personal account.
These checks were not your *salary* from the corporation,
were they?"

"No."

"What were they for?" Siegel said; then quickly, to the
stenographer, "No, strike that out. I withdraw the question."
He picked up the second batch of checks. "And Trustee's
Exhibit Two of this date, Mr. Babushkin, represents an almost identical series of checks drawn by you on your personal account, to the order of cash, endorsed by you, and
obviously cashed. In other words, Mr. Babushkin," he said,
choosing his words and wrapping his lips around each one
so carefully that his mustache began to do double loops, "to
put it more clearly, Mr. Babushkin, in the ten weeks preced-
ing the bankruptcy, between the date you opened your personal account and the date of the bankruptcy, some thirty-
two thousand five hundred dollars of corporate funds were
withdrawn by you, deposited in your personal account, and
almost immediately withdrawn from that personal account
practically in the form of cash. Isn't that right?"

"Yes."

Siegel turned away from him for a moment, then, suddenly, he spun around, shot his hand out at him, and barked,
"What did you do with that money?"

Babushkin just stared at him, blinking his eyes a little. He
was so dumb that he was smart. His mind moved so slowly
that tricks like these had no effect on him.

"What did you do with that money, Mr. Babushkin?"

"I—I used it in the business."

"You *what?*"

"I used it in the business."

"How?"

"I used it to pay for labor."

"To pay for *labor?*"

"Yes."

"Why couldn't you pay your labor with corporate checks? Why did it have to be by cash, in this peculiar way?"

"We had trouble with our contractors. The union wanted us to use only union contractors. So we used scab contractors and we had to pay them in cash."

Siegel looked at him with his mouth open. Take my word for it, he wasn't a lovely sight.

"Why couldn't the corporation pay them with cash? Why did it have to go through your personal bank account?"

"We didn't want it to show on the books."

Siegel's mouth dropped another few inches, until I could see what he'd had for lunch. I didn't blame him for looking surprised. The explanation was so cockeyed, that even I, who had invented it, couldn't follow it.

"Do you mean to say, Mr. Babushkin, that you spent thirty-two thousand five hundred dollars on labor in ten weeks?"

"No. We bought goods and things like that, too."

"You bought goods?"

"Yes."

"Why didn't you buy your goods through the regular channels, from your regular creditors, on terms?"

"We made some very high-priced stuff. The ordinary houses, they didn't carry the kind of goods we needed. We needed exclusive imports. We had to go shopping around for them, and pay cash."

Say, he wasn't bad! Or else I was a peach of a coach. Probably the latter.

"Who bought this goods?"

"I did."

Well, *that* was in the record.

Siegel rubbed his mustache, and turned back to the table. He scowled as he shoved his papers around, and for a few moments it was quiet. Then he turned back to Babushkin and asked quietly, with a little smile:

"Would you mind giving us the names of these contractors to whom you say you paid this money?"

"I don't remember."

"You don't remember?"

"No."

"Didn't you keep any kind of a record?"

"We didn't want it should show in the books."

"You mean to say you don't remember the name of a single one?"

"No."

"How did you remember who they were when it came to paying them?"

"I had it written down in a little book."

"Oh, so you *did* have a record."

"Yes."

"Where is that little book now?"

"I lost it."

"You lost it?"

"Yes."

"When?"

"I don't know."

"When did you see this so-called little book last?"

"I don't remember."

Siegel changed the tone of his voice and said, "All right, Mr. Babushkin, now about this goods you say you bought. Give us the names and addresses of some of the people you bought from."

"I don't remember."

"You don't remember a single one?"

"No."

Siegel twisted up his face and said, "It wouldn't be, Mr. Babushkin, that you had their names in this little book of yours, too, would it?"

"That's right."

Siegel smacked his papers down on the table and turned excitedly to the Referee.

"Mr. Referee," he said angrily, "I respectfully submit that this witness is deliberately withholding information. It seems ridiculous that a week or two after the expenditure of such large sums of money the witness should be unable to recall a single name among the many he claims he dealt with. I ask that Your Honor direct the witness to tell the truth or suffer the consequences in a contempt proceeding."

"Just a moment, please," Golig said, hopping up. "Mr. Siegel seems to forget that my client is under oath. I resent Mr. Siegel's innuendo that my client is perjuring himself, and demand an apology on his part. I have refrained from objecting to the unorthodox manner in which Mr. Siegel has been conducting this 21-A examination, Your Honor, but I simply must draw the line when he says in so many words that my client is lying."

Siegel yelled, "I wouldn't apologize to him if—"

"Quiet!" the Referee said suddenly. He didn't say it loud, but they all shut up. "I will thank you gentlemen to remember that you are in a court of law." He turned to Babushkin. "You understand, Mr. Babushkin," he said, "that you are under oath, do you not?"

Meyer nodded.

"And that if you do not tell the truth while you are under oath, you may be punished by the court?"

Meyer nodded again. It was his only talent.

"You may proceed with the examination," the Referee said to Siegel.

Siegel bit his lip, stared at Babushkin, glared at Golig, rubbed his mustache, and said, "No more questions."

"No questions," Golig said.

"That's all," the Referee said to Babushkin, and he got out of the chair.

There was a stir in the room and both lawyers began to put their papers together and a few people began to get up and walk out.

"May it please the court."

It was Siegel's voice. The room quieted down again.

"May I have a word, Your Honor?"

The Referee nodded.

"I respectfully submit," Siegel said, "that it seems perfectly clear from the evidence taken to-day, Your Honor, that this business was shockingly milked with the deliberate intention and purpose of defrauding its creditors. I respectfully call Your Honor's attention to the fact that I intend to bring a turnover motion in this court against Mr. Babushkin for thirty-two thousand five hundred dollars."

"The court," the Referee said, "can take no cognizance of your intentions, Mr. Siegel, until such time as the proper papers are filed with it." He picked up his diary. "Do you want an adjourned date, Mr. Siegel, on this 21-A hearing?"

"No, sir," Siegel said. "I shall file my turnover papers with Your Honor to-morrow."

"Very well," the Referee said. "Hearing adjourned."

37

I didn't know how long I had been walking like that, back and forth, from one end of the living room to the other, telling myself that there was nothing to be nervous about and that if I'd only sit down everything would be all right. But I *did* know that the advice was lousy. Because when I finally did sit down, it didn't help. I jumped up in a minute and began to parade back and forth again.

For once I was almost sorry I didn't drink. I'd heard of enough guys who carried themselves over the rough spots by getting pissed to the ears. But I knew it wasn't worth trying. The most I'd get out of it would be a bellyache.

Suddenly I got an idea. I took my hat and went out quickly, before I could start thinking about something else again and drive it out of my mind. But when I got in front of the joint I didn't go in. I kept on moving down the block. I didn't want to get laid.

I walked to Broadway and looked around. The Paramount was nearest. I went in and got a seat in the orchestra. But then I thought it would be nicer to sit in the balcony. I went up and found a seat. But that wasn't any good, either. I went out of the theater, looking back at the marquee to see what was playing.

When I turned my head again, I saw a United Cigars Store. I fingered a nickel in my pocket, but I didn't go in to make the call. I made up my mind, though. I bought a paper and went into the subway. I began to feel better at once. I actually sat still and read the paper all the way up.

But the moment I came into the house I knew I shouldn't have done it. Mother wasn't alone. I could hear voices in the living room. I walked toward them and stood in the doorway.

"Hello, Ma," I said.

She was in the armchair, her hands folded on the apron in her lap. Across the room, on the sofa, sat a young woman with a baby in her arms. She was plump and had dark hair and was neatly dressed. Before anybody spoke I knew who she was. And I was struck at once by her resemblance to Ruthie Rivkin. There was in her face that same softness, that warmth that was so appealing and that Mother called *chein*.

"Hello, Heshie," Mother said, getting up and coming toward me. "We were just talking about you."

She took my hat and put it on the table.

"This is Mrs. Babushkin," she said.

I bowed and smiled.

"Glad to know you, Mrs. Babushkin," I said. "It's really too bad that we should finally have to meet at a time like this."

She didn't smile.

"Sit down, Heshie," Mother said.

I took one of the straight-backed chairs. I crossed my legs and lit a cigarette.

"Where's Meyer?" I asked.

"He's home," she said, staring at me.

What the hell was she looking at? I had a clean shirt on. And I'd shaved, too. Maybe she was fascinated. It began to look like I had a fatal attraction for the warm Jewish type.

"That's the best place for him," I said. "He should be resting up for to-morrow?"

"He's not resting," she said.

What was I supposed to do, act surprised?

"Well, I guess he doesn't need it, really, Mrs. Babushkin," I said. "There's nothing to what's going to happen to-morrow. A little hearing, a few questions, a few answers, and it's all over."

She shifted the baby into a more comfortable position in her arms.

"I didn't tell him I was coming here to-day," she said quietly.

That was a nice way for a married woman with a baby to talk, wasn't it? It was lucky Mother was there to act as chaperon.

"Why, you could——" I began.

"You see, Mr. Bogen," she said, looking me right in the eye, "my husband *trusts* you."

I dropped my eyes to grind out my cigarette.

"Mrs. Babushkin," Mother said, "let me talk."

I looked at her quickly. And I could tell at a glance that I was in for it. She wasn't on my side, either.

"Mrs. Babushkin has been here for more than an hour, Heshie," she said. "She told me the whole story, the things that happened and the bankruptcy and everything."

It must have been a regular field day.

"Well, I can't help that, Ma," I said irritably. "The creditors just cracked down on us, that's all. But there's nothing to worry about. I told Meyer it was nothing. There's gonna be a little hearing to-morrow, the same as the last one, and everything'll come out the same as the other one did. Two weeks from now our business'll be running again. That's how things happen in business. I can't help those things. It's not *my* fault that those crazy credit men——"

"Nobody says it's your fault, Heshie," Mother said.

They didn't have to say it. I could tell from the way they looked.

I lit another cigarette.

"Then what can I do?" I said.

"Mrs. Babushkin told me," she said, "that her husband trusts you, Heshie."

Why not? Didn't I trust him?

"That's right," Mrs. Babushkin said.

I turned to her with a sarcastic grin.

"But *you* don't, Mrs. Babushkin," I said. "Is that the idea?"

"Yes," she said quietly.

"Well, now look here, Mrs. Babushkin—" I began.

"I don't know what happened downtown, Mr. Bogen," she said, breaking in. "My husband used to talk everything over with me before he did it. This thing he didn't talk over with me. I didn't know what happened until a few days ago. A couple of months ago, he came home and told me about a special bank account you had opened together. I didn't understand it very well from his explanation." I couldn't blame her for that. "But he said it was to cheat the government out of income tax."

"Oh, I wouldn't say 'cheat,' Mrs. Babushkin," I said.

"That's what it was for, though, wasn't it, Mr. Bogen?"

"Well, yes, I suppose so," I said. "If you want to look at it that—"

"I warned him at that time not to do it," she said. "I told him it wasn't right." Her face pinched up around the mouth. "But he said it was too late. He said you had started already. He said there was nothing to worry about," she said slowly. "He said you would take care of everything."

"And I did, Mrs. Babushkin," I said quickly. "That had nothing to do with the bankruptcy. This thing is just—"

"Maybe it didn't," she said in a low voice. "But it was the only time he didn't listen to my advice, Mr. Bogen."

"I'm sorry you feel that way about it, Mrs. Babushkin, but

I assure you that that account had nothing to do with it. That's a separate thing from this bankruptcy entirely. There's nothing—"

"I don't say there is, Mr. Bogen," she said again. "But it was the only time he didn't listen to what I told him."

Go ahead, tell me again!

"I tell you once more, Mrs. Babushkin, that account had absolutely nothing to do with—"

"Never mind, Heshie," Mother said suddenly. "Let me talk."

"Okay," I said, waving my hand. "Go ahead. You're doing most of it anyway."

"When Mrs. Babushkin came to me an hour ago, Heshie," she said, "and she told me what was happening, I asked her what she wanted me to do. She said she wanted me to make you promise that nothing would happen to her husband."

"For crying out loud, Ma," I said. "I told Meyer Babushkin a dozen times if I told him once. Absolutely nothing is going to happen to him. We're both in this thing and it's one hundred per cent. It's all a big misunderstanding. The creditors think that we haven't got enough money to pay our bills, but they're crazy. We've got plenty. What more can I do? You want me to walk around with Meyer Babushkin and hold him by the hand and see that he doesn't get run over or anything like that?"

"When she was here an hour ago," Mother continued calmly, "I told her there was nothing I could do. I didn't know where you were. But now you're here, Heshie. Now you—"

"What difference does it make where I am?" I said. "I can say it just as well in the Bronx as I can say it downtown. Nothing is going to happen to Meyer Babushkin. You satisfied?"

"Is that the truth, Mr. Bogen?" she asked, leaning forward with the baby in her arms.

I looked her right in the eye.

"That's the truth," I said firmly.

"You promise me that, Mr. Bogen?" she said.

I stood up and waved my arms to the ceiling.

"Jesus Christ alive!" I said. "What do you want me to do, put it in an affidavit for you? You want me to run a full-page advertisement in the paper about it? I just *told* you nothing was going to happen to him, didn't I? What do you want me to—?"

"Stop hollering," Mother said, "and sit down."

I sat down.

"Nobody is going around asking you to make out affidavits," she said, "or anything like that. All Mrs. Babushkin means is you should promise her that *you* won't do anything to hurt her husband."

"*I* shouldn't do anything?" I cried. "Why would *I* want to hurt him? What did he ever do to me? He's my partner, isn't he?"

"Then that's all she wants," Mother said. "She just wants you should promise that nothing'll happen to her husband through anything *you* do. Is that right, Mrs. Babushkin?"

"That's right," she said.

They were both looking at me.

"Do you promise, Heshie?" Mother said.

"That's a nice state of affairs," I said sarcastically. "My own mother and my partner's wife, they want me to *promise* that I'm not going to do anything to get my partner in trouble. Boy, that's pretty good, that is!"

"Don't talk so much," Mother said. "Just say one word, yes or no. You promise?"

"Sure I promise," I said. "Of course I promise. What do you think I am, anyway?"

"That's all I was worried about," Mrs. Babushkin said, getting up. "Thank you, Mr. Bogen."

"Don't even mention it," I said.

Mother put her arm around her and guided her to the door, patting her shoulder and tickling the baby's chin.

I stood in the middle of the living room, listening to them saying good-bye to each other outside, and complimented myself on being the biggest sap in four states. With the whole thing practically in the bag, I had to go looking for trouble. I had to come home to make promises. What a grade A *putz I* turned out to be!

38

Golig and I had Babushkin between us in the taxi going down to the Referee's office.

"There's nothing to be afraid of, Meyer," Golig said. "A turnover action is no different from a 21-A. They'll just ask you the same questions, and maybe get a little tough with you. But you just answer the same way you answered at the 21-A hearing and you'll get off the same way. Understand?"

He shook his head up and down a little.

"But suppose the judge grants the turnover against me?" he said, turning his worried face to Golig. "Then what?"

"He can't grant the turnover against you," Golig said, "because the law says they not only have to prove that you *took* the money, but they also have to prove you have the present ability to pay it back. See? And you haven't got thirty-two thousand bucks, have you, Meyer? So you see how that works out? They can't do you a thing."

"Yeah," he said, shaking his head again. Then, in the same worried voice, "But suppose he *does* grant the motion against me? That means I go to jail, doesn't it? I got a wife and kid, Golig, I can't—"

"Aah, stop worrying about it, will you?" Golig said. "I'm telling you they can't hang a thing on you. Just to show you, Meyer, listen to this: in the last ten years there were only two turnover motions granted in this whole district, and both guys got suspended sentences because they showed they didn't have the money to turn over." He was wasting his time in the law business. He should have written fiction. "Yeah," he added, "and the only reason those two motions were granted was because those two guys confessed."

I put my arm on Babushkin's shoulder.

"Listen, Meyer," I said. "You and I are partners, aren't we? And when this thing blows over, we're going back into partnership, aren't we? So what are you afraid of? Would I give you a bum steer, Meyer?"

"It ain't that, Harry," he said. "It's just that—"

"So forget it," I said, patting his shoulder again as the cab pulled up in front of the Pine Street office building. "They ask you questions, you just answer like you did last time. You don't know from nothing. And don't worry about it. If the worst comes to the worst, you just tell them I can explain everything. Let them call me. Okay?"

"Okay, Harry," he said, but the scared look didn't leave his face.

The same gang was assembled in the Referee's room when we got there. I nodded cheerfully to McKee, but he only gave me a dirty look in exchange.

Siegel called Babushkin as his first witness. He opened his mouth to ask a question, then stopped.

He turned to Golig, across the table from him, then to the Referee, and as he spoke, he swung his head from one side to the other, talking to both of them at the same time.

"If it please the court," he said, "it has just occurred to me that we could save a lot of time at this proceeding if my learned adversary, Mr. Golig, would stipulate on the record all the testimony taken at the recent 21-A examination. I intended to base my turnover action on the identical facts adduced at that previous hearing, and it would seem to me, Your Honor, that we could save a lot of time if the defense attorney would stipulate those facts, so that we would not have to merely repeat again what we did at the 21-A hearing."

"Such a stipulation would, of course, expedite matters," the Referee said, "but it is entirely within the discretion of the defense attorney."

He looked at Golig.

"All right, Your Honor," Golig said, "I'll stipulate the evidence taken at the 21-A hearing."

Siegel looked surprised, but said nothing. He waited until the stenographer made a notation on the record, then he turned to Babushkin.

"According to the testimony that has just been stipulated into the record, Mr. Babushkin," he said, "within ten weeks prior to the bankruptcy of your firm, you made withdrawals, in the form of checks drawn to your order, to the extent of thirty-two thousand five hundred dollars. Those checks you deposited in your personal account, and almost immediately after their deposit, you drew checks on your personal account, to the order of cash, endorsed these checks, cashed them at the bank, and took the cash away with you. You have admitted, Mr. Babushkin, that these moneys were not salaries paid to you by the corporation. And you have insisted, Mr. Babushkin, that you have used that money to pay the debts of the corporation, namely, labor and merchandise purchases. Is that right?"

"Yes, sir."

"Is that the only explanation you wish to make, Mr. Babushkin, as to the disposition of that money?"

"Yes, sir."

"You realize, Mr. Babushkin, do you not, that if His Honor grants this turnover motion against you, and you do not turn that money back into the bankrupt estate, that you will be sent to jail?"

Golig jumped up.

"I object to counsel's attempts to intimidate the witness."

"I'm not trying to intim—"

"Counsel will confine his questions to the issues," the Referee said.

Siegel turned back to Babushkin.

"You realize, Mr. Babushkin, do you not, how silly your explanation of the dispos—"

"I object, Your Honor," Golig cried.

"Sustained," the Referee said.

"Do you want us to believe, Mr. Babushkin, that you spent all that money in ten weeks on labor and piece goods, and—"

"I object," Golig cried again.

"Sustained," the Referee said.

"Do you think a normal man, a man like His Honor, for instance, would really believe, Mr. Babushkin, that you forgot every single name in—"

"I object, Your Honor!" Golig shouted, jumping up and pounding on the table. "This is one of the most outrageous attempts at frightening a witness that I have ever seen. Mr. Siegel is well aware of the fact that his questions are unorthodox and beyond the pale ot—"

"Mr. Golig is right," the Referee said. "You will refrain from this line of questioning, Mr. Siegel."

"Very well, Your Honor," Siegel said. But as he turned away I could see him smile.

And all I needed was one look at Babushkin to see why. He was so frightened, that his lips were actually quivering. He kept staring at Siegel as though he had never seen him before, and even from where I was sitting I could see the spit beginning to collect in the corners of his mouth. Boy, but that Siegel was slick. I had to take my hat off to him.

He turned slowly to face Babushkin and asked gently, in a voice so low you could hardly hear him, "Is there any other explanation you *now* want to make as to the disposition of those moneys, Mr. Babushkin?"

Meyer's lips moved, but for a few seconds no words came out. He was the most frightened man I had ever seen. Gradually sounds began to come from his moving lips, but the stenographer could not hear him.

"You'll have to speak a little louder, please."

"M-m-mister B-Bogen can exp-p-plain everything. M-m-mister B-Bogen can exp-p-plain everything."

He said it over and over several times, as though his mind had fastened on it and he couldn't think of anything else.

"Very well," Siegel said, "I'll call Mr. Bogen."

We had to help Babushkin down from the witness chair, and after we'd put him into a seat against the wall, I went back to the chair.

"You haven't yet been sworn in this proceeding, have you, Mr. Bogen?"

"I was sworn last week."

"That was the 21-A hearing. The Referee will swear you in this proceeding."

After he did, Siegel said, "You were present at the 21-A hearing in this matter, were you not, Mr. Bogen?"

"Yes."

"And you heard all the testimony given by Mr. Babushkin at that hearing, did you not?"

"Yes."

This "did you not" business was beginning to get me.

"And you are also aware, are you not, that all the testimony taken at the 21-A hearing has been stipulated into the record of this proceeding?"

"Yes."

"And you have just heard Mr. Babushkin's testimony?"

"I have."

"You have heard him say, with reference to the disposition of the thirty-two thousand five hundred dollars of corporate funds that passed through his personal account that you could explain everything, you heard him say that, did you not?"

"I did."

"Can you make such explanation to us now?"

For a moment I hesitated. I thought of Mother and Mrs. Babushkin holding the baby and the promise I had given them. But I couldn't help myself. I was in too deep. I couldn't stop now. A promise was a promise. It wasn't a contract. I'd been bulldozed into it anyway, hadn't I? Why did he have to send his wife around, crying, with the damn baby in her arms? I never did like kids, anyway. What was I going to do, let them make a sucker out of me by waving a diaper under my nose?

"I repeat, Mr. Bogen, can you make such explanation to us now?"

What the hell was his hurry? Couldn't he see I was thinking?

"I cannot," I said.

I could feel the whole room looking at me, but I kept my eyes fixed on Siegel's face.

"Why not, Mr. Bogen?"

"Because I don't know the first thing about it," I said, talking quickly. I didn't know how groggy Babushkin was, and I had to get it all out before he came to. "This whole thing has been as much of a surprise to me as it has been to everybody else. I was just as astounded at Mr. Babushkin's story at the 21-A hearing as you were. I have always been so busy with the selling end of the business, entertaining buyers, making out-of-town trips, and so on, that I didn't realize until now how I was being victimized by an unscrupulous partner." When it comes to slinging the five-dollar words, I'm as good as any lawyer. "I never did understand how a business as prosperous as ours was could be ruined so quickly. But since I have learned, at these hearings, about Babushkin's personal bank accounts, and the money that has gone through it, the failure of our business is no longer a mystery to me."

"Harry! Harry!"

I could see every eye in the room turn toward Babushkin, where he stood screaming. But I didn't look at him. I looked directly at Siegel.

"What are you saying? What are you telling them? Harry! Harry! What are you saying! Harry!"

He started toward me, but Golig and a couple of others grabbed him. He continued to scream and fight with them, trying to get away from them and at me.

"What are you telling them?" he shouted crazily. "Why don't you tell them the truth? Why don't you—?" Somebody clamped a hand over his mouth, but he bit at it and got his head free. "Harry! What are you saying!" he screamed.

"Why don't you tell them the truth?" His voice stretched so thin that it cracked, but he didn't stop yelling and fighting with the men that held him. "Harry! Harrr—eeee—eeeeee!"

"Get that man out of here," the Referee said, standing up.

Three others joined the ones that were holding him, and between them they dragged him out of the room.

In a few moments the room was quiet again. Slowly I let out the breath I had been unconsciously holding. I patted my forehead gently with my folded handkerchief.

"I'm sorry, Mr. Siegel," I said, "I didn't mean to start anything like this. I mean, I didn't think he'd—"

"That's quite all right, Mr. Bogen," he said. "It's not your fault at all."

He turned to the Referee.

"No more questions, Your Honor," he said. "The trustee rests."

The Referee turned to Golig.

"Any questions?"

Golig shrugged and said, "No questions."

The Referee looked from one to the other.

"Do you gentlemen want time to submit briefs?" he asked.

"*I* don't intend to submit a brief," Siegel said, shrugging toward Golig.

"Neither do I," Golig said.

The Referee reached for his pen.

"Motion granted," he said.

39

As soon as I woke up I reached for the house phone and spoke to the doorman.

"Send a boy out to get a *Daily News Record,* will you?"

"A what?"

"A *Daily News Record.* It's a newspaper.

"All right, Mr. Bogen."

"He may not get it right away. Tell him to try a couple of newsstands. Then send it right up, will you?"

"Right, Mr. Bogen."

As I hung up I wondered how much longer I'd be able to afford having these "Yes, Mr. Bogen" heels all around me. Well, I'd find out. I got out my savings-bankbooks, the last statement on my checking account, my check-stub book, a sheet of paper, a pencil, and went to work.

When I finished, I felt a little better. Even after paying Golig his fee, I still had a good bit more than nineteen thousand left, almost twenty. Not bad. Not bad at all. I thought of all the money I'd pissed away in the past year, and for a moment I felt sad. But only for a moment. What the hell, I'd had a good time. And besides, a lot of that was an investment. What was I crying about? I had twenty thousand in the bank. I had an apartment. I had a car. I had a wardrobe. And best of all, I still had my brains. What was there to be sad about? I'd made it once, and I'd make it again. I wasn't worried. For guys like me the world is wide open.

For what I wanted to do right now, I had more than enough. I even had enough to carry me until I got going again. I'd cut down on expenses, that's all. Mama's weekly check would come down for a while, and I'd reduce expenses all along the line. So what was I hollering about? Who was hollering?

There was a buzz at the door.

"Paper, Mr. Bogen."

"Thanks," I said, and paid for it. But I didn't tip him. I was reducing expenses all along the line, wasn't I?

I didn't have to look very hard. It was right on the front page. "Court Upholds Referee In Babushkin Case. Officer Of Defunct Apex Modes, Inc. To Be Sentenced Friday. Federal Judge Francis J. Guernsey, of the Southern District of New York, yesterday confirmed the turnover motion granted by Referee John E. James against Meyer Babushkin, officer of Apex Modes, Inc."

There was a lot more, but I didn't bother to read it. I knew all about it, anyway.

I sat back in my chair, with the paper in my lap, and tried to figure out how I felt. I waited a few moments, half afraid, but the feeling of worry about Babushkin that I was expecting didn't come. It surprised me a little, how he didn't mean anything to me any more.

Then, to make the test harder, I thought of his wife and kid. But there was no reaction. And why should there be? Come to think of it, it was her own fault in the first place. Was it my place to worry if she was so dumb as to get married to a kluck like Babushkin?

I rattled the paper on my knees. I did it a little proudly. I'd worked the thing out all by myself. And it wasn't a bad job. It gave me confidence for the future. Now there would be no more doubts. Now there would be no more scared moments. Because now, with that paper on my lap, I couldn't go back if I wanted to.

Who the hell wanted to?

Instead of feeling worried or scared, I felt happy. I felt so good that I laughed out loud. I had finally arrived.

I got out the phone book and looked up a number. Then I dialed it.

"Hello? My name is Bogen. I don't know if you remember me, but I was in to look at a diamond bracelet a couple of weeks ago—"

"Oh, yes, Mr. Bogen! I remember you quite well."

Who wouldn't?

"Well, have you still got it in stock?"

"We certainly have, Mr. Bogen."

"Well, then, I'll tell you what. I'm coming down for it this morning, or maybe this afternoon. Anyway, some time to-day. You have it ready for me, will you?"

"We certainly will, Mr. Bogen."

I hung up and whistled to myself as I dialed Riverside 9-0437.

"Hello?"

"Is this Miss Mills' apartment?"

"This is Miss Mills talking. Who is this?"

"Why, ah, my name is Bogen. I don't know if you remember me, but—"

"Why, hello, stranger. Where've you been all these years?"

"Oh, I've been rather busy cleaning up some heavy dough in a little unpleasant thing known as a bankruptcy."

"Oh, *Ha*rry! I'm *so* glad everything turned out all right. I knew it was that crooked partner of yours all the time, Harry. I knew you'd be all right, Harry."

It looked like she still read the papers.

"Thanks," I said. "How are you feeling, Martha?"

"Oh, so-so."

"I see *Smile Out Loud* is still running."

"Yeah."

"By the way, Martha, when did I see you last?"

"Oh, a couple of weeks ago."

"Oh, sure, now I remember. We were looking at something in some sort of a place, weren't we?"

"That's right, Harry, we were—"

"How's your wrist feeling?"

"It's all right. Why?"

"Because if I remember correctly, it was a bracelet we were looking at, wasn't it?"

"That's right, Harry."

"And your wrist feels okay, you say?"

"Uh-huh. Why?"

I love these dames when they try to play dumb.

"You think it's strong enough to hold all the weight of that bracelet?"

"Why, *Ha*rry!"

"Yes, sir, Martha," I said, "I think I'll bring that little trinket up to your place to-night. What do you say?"

"Oh, *Ha*rry, that'll be *won*derful."

That's just what *I* thought, too.

"I'll tell you, though, Martha, you know what?"

"What, Harry?"

"What with all the trouble I've been having these last few weeks, Martha, I don't feel so strong as I used to."

"Oh, that's too bad, Harry."

Maybe it was. But at least there was room for an honest difference of opinion.

"And carrying a heavy bracelet like that all the way up-town to your place is just about going to knock me out, Martha, with me in the weakened condition I'm in. See what I mean, Martha?"

No answer. But I wasn't worried. I knew she was still on the wire. I could hear her breathing.

"In fact, Martha," I continued, "by the time I get up to your place to-night with all that load, I'll be so tired out, I'll never be able to make the trip home again. Why, I'll bet, Martha, I'll even have to spend the night at *your* place."

What the hell, I figured the time had come for me to talk turkey.

"So what do you say, Martha? Do you think you'll be able to put up a worn-out messenger boy like me?"

"I think so, Harry," she said.

I could tell by her voice that she meant it. But I wanted to make sure.

"Can't you be more positive than that, Martha? I mean, here I am, all worn out, and I'm going to make that trip all the way up there, carrying such a heavy load, and all you can say is you *think* so!"

"All right, Harry," she said, laughing, "I *know* I'll be able to put you up."

"Okay, kid," I said, "I'll be up right after the show, say about eleven."

"At *eleven?*"

"Sure," I said, "I like to start early."

"Okay, dear," she said. "Good-bye."

Look, I was a dear again!

"Good-bye," I said.

Now that it was all over, and I was released from the strain, I felt so nervous and excited that the hand in which I held the receiver was shaking. I tried to steady it, but I couldn't. It rattled against the hook a few times before it dropped into its place. It was all I could do to keep myself from jumping up and down and yelling crazily. I looked into the mirror over the telephone table and grinned at myself.

I knew it was true. I knew it all happened to me. But still it was a little hard to believe.

"Boy," I said out loud to the face in the mirror, "is that Harry Bogen, or am I nuts?"

Two years ago I was just another poor slob from the Bronx. And to-night I'm going to sleep with an actress!

Weidman, Jerome
I can get it for you wholesale. N.Y., Modern library [c1937]
309 p.

t

Interior by Melanie Kahane, A. I. D.

No modern library is complete
without THE AMERICAN
COLLEGE DICTIONARY

1472 pages • 7″ x 10″ • large, clear type, Buckram binding, thumb-indexed $6.00
Buckram binding, without index, $5.00 • Special red Fabrikoid binding, in hand-
some gift box, $7.50 • De luxe red leather binding, gold edges, gift box, $15.00